The Prodigal Heart

BY

SUSAN ERTZ

"It is worth the labour"—said Plotinus —"to consider well of Love, whether it be a God, or a Divell, or a passion of the minde, or partly God, partly Divell, partly passion."

RICHARD BURTON,
The Anatomy of Melancholy.

THE BOOK CLUB
121 CHARING CROSS ROAD
LONDON, W.C. 2.

THE CHARACTERS IN THIS BOOK ARE ENTIRELY IMAGINARY AND BEAR NO RELATION TO ANY LIVING PERSON.

First Published November 1950

This edition, by arrangement with
Hodder and Stoughton Ltd.
1951

Printed and Bound in Great Britain
By the Hollen Street Press, Ltd., London, W.1

CHAPTER

1

THE LITTLE RAILWAY STATION LAY IN A DEEP CUTTING between high banks. Steep wooden steps with a hand-rail on either side led down to it from the country road above. The banks had been cut into terraces by the stationmaster, who had planted shrubs and flowers in this hanging garden, and in spring he even put in a few rows of lettuces and french beans, which rainstorms sometimes washed away. He favoured pink rambler roses, which linked terrace to terrace, snapdragons and hollyhocks, and in the summer the place was a blaze of colour. Now, in early February, there was little to show for his labours, and the wind blew keenly through in wild gusts and drove travellers into the tiny waiting rooms which had been built into the high banks. In the one on the up side there were now two people, a young woman who was reading a book, and, as the light was bad, bending her head closely over it, and an old lady who stood at the door looking for the porter. He had crossed the tracks to attend to something on the other side and she feared he might not return in time to help her into the train.

The young woman, Medwin Blair, looked up, saw her anxiety and said, "It's all right. He always does get back in time." The old lady thanked her and said she wished he would hurry, then, as her suitcases were heavy.

It was still some minutes before the train was due, but Medwin slipped the book into her pocket and sat for a few moments with her eyes closed. She might almost have been praying. It all depends, she was thinking, on Louise. As far as I can see I sink or swim according to my ability to make her do what I want. This interview is crucial.

She was waiting here in the draughty little station for the train to Rosehill, where she would change into another train which would take her to Reading. No one knew why Louise, her aunt—but she did not wish to be called Aunt—should have chosen to live in Reading. There was no reason, of course, why she should not, but equally there seemed no good reason why she should. She had no friends there, so far as anyone knew. She went there as a cat might go one day into a strange house and take up its casual abode. Six years before she had suddenly left London, where she had always lived, and taking her few bits of furniture had moved to Reading, had rented an ugly four-roomed house in a street of exactly similar little houses, had acquired a lodger and settled down. It is true that she made this move during the war, but it was not the war which caused it, for she had withstood the blitz, had treated it, in fact, with indifference, and left at a time when London believed that the worst was over. She had for many years worked as a librarian in London, and she found a similar position for herself in Reading as assistant librarian in a near-by branch of the public library.

She seemed to revel in the most complete anonymity. She wished, it appeared, to be outwardly different from no one, to be most like those who are most indistinguishable from their fellows. She was beholden to no one, and wished no one to be beholden to her. Like her sister, Medwin's mother, she had an annuity from their father, Dr. Carmichael, which brought her in about sixty pounds a year, the rest she had to earn. Her lodger, to whom she referred in her dry and infrequent letters, was a middle-aged widower named Mr. Beedle, manager of a hardware shop in a near-by street. "Mr. Beedle keeps well and is no trouble," Louise reported at long intervals. "Mr. Beedle's son was here the other day. He expects to be married in the spring." Her letters were devoid of imagination or humour. "Vegetables are very dear at present. I eat chiefly raw cabbage and raw carrots." "I have found a new bakery where I can buy really good whole-wheat bread." Such were the sparse bits of information her letters yielded. Though she had spent her life dealing with books and with the people who read them, she seemed little interested in either.

Louise had never married, and if she had ever been sought in marriage she had kept the fact to herself. Now she was nearly sixty, and wore and for many years had worn the same brown felt hat winter and summer. She was like a tough little plant growing among bleak and windy rocks. It was not easy to see what nurtured her.

The young porter jumped down from the platform on the other side and crossed the tracks just before the electric train glided out of the tunnel and made its brief, condescending pause at the little station, where a few recently arrived and breathless passengers had now gathered. Medwin got into a third class compartment for non-smokers, as she did not smoke herself, and the old lady, being a nervous traveller, followed her, for she thought there was something protecting about this young woman who told her not to worry. She did not want to talk but she liked to know that there was someone at hand of whom she could ask questions, if the need should arise.

Medwin resumed the thoughts—or allowed them to resume her—that troubled her in the station, and pondered how best she could bend tough, wiry Louise to her wishes. It mattered so much. It mattered intolerably. Why should Louise have, and uninterruptedly enjoy, what she herself so longed for—a life of her own? She did not know what it was to think of others. True she had little, but that little was of her own choosing. She resembled a child, Medwin thought, who was sent out into a world of spring flowers to pick what she would, and who came home with a tight, hard little bunch of dusty dandelions in her hand. "These are my choice." What she had, she had chosen. No doubt, like others, she chose what her nature compelled her to choose, but one cannot, thought Medwin, a little wearily, go into all that. She had a good education, she was taught music and French, she had "advantages," and now she spends her life in that ugly little house in its ugly street with noisy trams passing the door. But she appears to be content. I don't understand her, she thought, not even knowing what I know, and not understanding her, how can I make her do what I want? She has my life in her hands. I cannot go on. I have come to the end. It is time Louise took some responsibility. My mother is her elder sister, I am her niece. Charlotte can do nothing; her hands are full and she has her own trouble. It need only be for four months, three months, and then I will find a way out. She can go back to her house again, to her boarder and the rest.

She peeled the glove off her left hand and felt her wedding ring, moved it up and down. It was loose. She pulled the glove on again, thinking, once this thing is settled I shall have less to worry me; I shall put on weight again. It is not my way to be thin.

She rarely thought of herself as a married woman, though the ring was there to remind her. Her married life was only four months long. It was as a daughter that she thought of herself; a daughter with a daughter, for though Sarah was being taken care of by Charlotte she was very much in her thoughts. She supposed that she had been, on the whole, a good daughter to her parents, if sometimes unwillingly, rebelliously good, for burdens were laid upon her earlier than they should have been.

Oh well, she thought, we are not the first family to have gone through bad times and to have found no way out of them. Who would have thought, all the same, that my father, whom we all thought so clever, so all-powerful and all-knowing—yes, even my mother did—should have failed so utterly? How well I remember standing at the window of our house, pressing my nose against the pane, breathing on it and watching the breath fade, so as to be the first to see him as he came in sight, sometimes, on rainy days, arriving in a taxi, but more often walking from the Underground station. And that walk of his, so characteristic, so supremely confident. Shoulders back, elbows held away from his body, head up. And the way he used to carry his stick or umbrella, over his shoulder, like a gun. What was it he did or failed to do, that brought disaster on him so suddenly? Charlotte and I will never know. It can only have been in the spring and summer that I used to watch for him. Somehow I cannot remember winter evenings at that time, except one. My childhood seemed to have been steeped in summer.

Thinking, remembering, even at moments, daring to plan she was borne along. The way she could think or dream time away amazed her. Time only dragged when she was with those who made demands on her (though silently and wishing not to demand), that she could not satisfy, that she had not the power to satisfy. The needs of others dragged at her, slowed up the wheels of her life.

February this year was like March in other years, she thought. Today the sun burst out, shone palely and then retreated behind vast, piled-up, blue-black clouds with the quickness of thought. The wind tore ragged holes in the clouds and showed a blue that was tender, miraculous, but fugitive. This is the right day for my errand. I shall always remember it. Succeed or fail, I shall remember these threatening blue-black clouds, full of hail, and the brief, white smile of the sun.

Here is Rosehill, and I have fifteen minutes to wait. Gasometers and coal dumps, and all around, pleasant hills. In London one accepts sights like these as part of the great dirty city; here they are as incongruous, she said to herself, as a black thought in a child's heart.

"A cup of tea, please, and a cheese sandwich," she said to the girl behind the refreshment counter. (Heaven knew what Louise would give her for lunch. The time before last it was boiled cod and cabbage.) Now I shall see once again that odd little life she guards so jealously. Am I ruining her afternoon off? If she likes, I will go with her to the Co-operative Stores to do her weekly shopping. It might be better than sitting in that room, talking. She thanked the girl and carried cup and plate to a little marble-topped table, and took sips of steaming tea from the thick, white cup. Yes, she's all right thought the girl, bending to do some hasty washing-up. She'll be from some posh country house; I know the sort. Nice pair of brown wedgies, like I nearly got, only Fred don't like to see me without heels. He's funny that way. Wouldn't look twice at a girl who wasn't wearing high heels.

The train from London to Reading was announced by loud speaker in clear feminine accents, and Medwin took her empty plate and cup back to the counter, smiled at the girl once more and went out. The wind caught her, and her coat billowed out, the loose waves of her hair lifted. Quickly she whisked the grey silk scarf from about her neck and tied it over her head again. She preferred not to wear hats if it could be avoided, but tidy she must be. A cat-like neatness was necessary to her, it was a means of self expression like any other.

The train was crowded and she sat between a husband and wife, who occupied corner seats and occasionally talked across her, a thing no one likes. It's not for long, she thought, it's a fast train. She brought the book out of her pocket and the wife looked to see what it was. She was little the wiser. It was a thin, dark blue book and bore on its spine the one word "Donne" in silver letters. The wife was presently convinced of what she at once suspected—(she should have known by now, but she was always seeking and getting fresh evidence)—that this was the sort of young woman her husband admired. She had more than once caught his dull and drooping eye sullenly devouring that comely profile. That's the way he always looks at the ones he likes, she thought, as if he hated them. Doesn't take me in. No more, I dare say, than it takes her in. She knows he's looking at her as well as I do. Nice-looking gloves. Hand sewn. Married, I wonder? When I was her age, I never kept a glove on my left hand if I could help it. That proud I was. They aren't proud of it nowadays. Just an incident to them, unless there's babies, and she's got no babies I'll warrant. Too clever by half.

And now Reading, Medwin's destination, raced towards them, and she pushed the book into her pocket and was out of the door the instant the train had stopped. The husband and wife and the three women of varying ages opposite, all watched her as she hurried towards the exit. Louise had told her that if she was quick she would catch the tram, Number 998, that would take her past the door. She succeeded in catching it, fighting her way against the wind, which opposed her with all its strength. What a journey, she thought, and all to do again in reverse. Shall I be going back with Louise's consent in my pocket, so to speak? If so, nothing matters. And if not, then equally, in a sense, nothing matters. Oh, which is it to be?

The tram ground along but ground fast, with abrupt stops. She had told the conductor where she wanted to get off, but knowing that he might be on top collecting fares when the right cross-street was reached, she watched for the name. But he remembered, and came half-way down the steps to call out to her. She flashed him a grateful look and got off. Number 97 was almost in the middle of the block, in the middle of the grim little row. How can Louise, she wondered, how can she live out her one life here? I'd rather live in a hut in the woods, with trees and birds, she thought, but I know now what Louise's mind feeds upon. She is both here and not here. Unless one knows, Louise is too much of an enigma. One would go crazy wondering. But I shall never speak of it unless she speaks first.

In the middle of the middle panel of the front door, between sections of red and yellow glass was a bell, and as she pressed it it gave a sharp electric whirr that startled her almost as much as if her hand had been bitten. She did not remember it as being so rudely peremptory. Then Louise could be heard coming along the little hall, and as she opened the door the wind rushed in as if it had been waiting all day for just this moment, and she put a hand up to her wild grey hair. She was wearing a snuff-coloured woollen dress that Medwin remembered, with surprise, as having once belonged to her mother. It was big for Louise and Medwin wondered that she accepted gifts, even of old garments, from a sister she so rarely troubled to see. Louise was not at all concerned with whatever effect the sight of the dress might have had on her niece. "Come in, dear," she said, pushing the unwilling door shut. "You are exactly on time."

Medwin offered her cheek, and after an instant's hesitation, for she was not a woman who kissed, Louise approached hers and the two cheeks, one soft and firm, the other like a dry leaf, met briefly. Medwin said, with a smile,

"Louise, can you realize it's almost a year since I was here last?"

"Yes, my dear, easily. Time passes quickly you know, at my age. Come into the living-room. There is a fire for you."

For me, thought Medwin? Then have you no need of fires?

It was a gas fire in four vertical sections, of which only the centre two were alight. The match, it seemed, had just been applied to it, for the sulphur smell still lingered, and the small room was as cold as a tomb. As it was sitting-room and dining-room combined there was a round table of yellow, varnished oak in the centre of it, surrounded by four chairs of the same wood. On the table was a fern in a pot, but it was an imitation fern, and over it was suspended a naked electric light bulb on a cord. Close to the fire were two small arm chairs in imitation leather, much worn and cracked, and beside the door was a small bare sideboard which matched the table and chairs. The walls were in cream distemper, and two reproductions of oil paintings hung on them which Medwin did not remember having seen there before. One was of a well-known Van Gogh, the other depicted a bowl filled to overflowing with green apples, and bowl and apples were surrounded by thick black lines. Medwin knew the painter's name, but it momentarily escaped her. She thought it began with a B, but hoped it would not nag at her, as she wanted to keep her wits for more important matters. There was nothing else in the room except a small object in the centre of the mantelpiece. It was of white china, and represented a West Highland terrier holding a basket in his mouth, and clearly expecting ashes to be put into it. Medwin wondered if this was a present from Mr. Beedle, who might have hoped to be allowed to smoke his pipe in here. But if Mr. Beedle were a pipe-smoker, or at any rate, an indoor pipe-smoker, would he be living in this house? Medwin imagined not.

"Take off your coat," Louise said, but Medwin answered that for the moment she would only take off her scarf, until she had warmed up a little. "The wind is very cold," she said with a shiver, though in fact she had not felt in the least cold out of doors. "Look at the hail! I got in just in time."

It was indeed hailing. One of those mountainous, blue-black clouds now triumphed, and covered all the sky, nearly extinguishing the day, and hail rattled against the window-pane, bounced off the top of the little gate and leapt whitely up from the pavements, which reflected the sky so that it seemed a dark, slate-coloured world out of which no good could possibly come. A world given over to slate-coloured wind and white driven hail and nothing more.

Oh, God! Melvin's whole being cried out, suffering the brief, unmitigated anguish of the still-young. She was overcome by everything; by the room, by the imitation fern, by the ash-tray as much as by the dark fury out of doors.

"It was nice of you to come," Louise said. She sat in the other arm chair, dry little hands folded in her lap, aware of no lacks, aware of no emotions. It was hailing, that was all, as it often did at this time of year. "Tell me about your mother," she said. "How is her hip?"

Medwin felt but hid some resentment at her aunt's tone. It might, she felt, be anyone's broken hip that Louise was asking about, instead of a bone that was a sister to the bone now sitting in that chair.

"It's going to be a slow business," she said. "You see, it wasn't even a simple fracture. But at least her worst sufferings and her worst humiliations are over. With crutches, she can get up now, though she's only allowed a few steps. But even to get to the bathroom is something. The district nurse, Miss Mayfield, still calls regularly. Poor mother, she so hates having to have everything done for her, and being able to do nothing at all for father. I get breakfast for all three of us and tidy up before I go off to the hospital. Then about eleven, blessed Mrs. Briggs comes in, does some cleaning and gets a bite of lunch for them. I'm usually back soon after five. Father gets tea. It's his one household chore. I get dinner and then I get mother to bed. After that I read or listen to the wireless while father plays patience; and that's my day."

"I suppose it must be a little dull for you," said Louise.

Medwin felt her lips twitching. Really, it would take Louise to say a thing like that. I've never known anyone, she thought, so utterly lacking in humour and a sense of proportion. God forbid that I should hate my only aunt, though at the moment I feel it would be easy enough.

"Well," she said, "that, perhaps, might be called an understatement." She looked into the gas fire, leaving Louise to mend the silence.

"I hope Sarah is well," Louise presently said, and Medwin answered that Sarah was extremely well. She saw her as recently as last Sunday.

"And your father?" Louise asked next. She asked this coldly. She was mistress of many degrees of indifference, it seemed.

"He's much the same," Medwin said. "Mother's accident has worried him dreadfully, of course. But on the whole he's very good and tries not to give any trouble. He's still longing to be back in London again, though I don't know quite what he would do there."

"He should know better at his age," said Louise, "than to want to go back."

Medwin went on, wishing she had not left Louise that opening: "He's still busy with inventions."

"I'm afraid nothing will come of them," said Louise.

"Well, nothing has yet, it's true," Medwin agreed. "Still, it keeps him occupied. That and the hens. The last thing, I thought, was quite ingenious. He says he used to watch the charwomen down on their hands and knees, scrubbing out offices, and he thought their work ought to be made easier. So he devised a combined scrubbing-brush and watering-can, with a handle attached. You push the brush or mop over the floor, standing up, and at the same time you work a little sprinkler which sprays the floor with soapy water. He got two of the things made, and they worked quite well, but no one seems willing to put money into the idea, though he's shown it to a number of people."

"People have other uses for their money," said Louise, but as if her mind were elsewhere. Medwin never felt, when talking to her, that she was really listening. Sounds came from her, little comments, not quite irrelevant, or she said "Really?" now and then, but she could never be sure how much she had really heard with her mind. There was nothing wrong with her ears. It had been said of her that she could hear a fly alight.

"And you, dear?" Louise inquired next. "I suppose you are still at the hospital."

Medwin remembered referring to her work at the hospital a moment ago, which proved that Louise was not interested in anything she had been telling her. She made up her mind, then, to surprise her.

"Yes," she said, "but I've told them I'm leaving. That is one of the things I want to talk to you about today."

Her aunt interrupted her there.

"It is always best to stick to one job. You have been at the hospital for some years now. They must think highly of you. And you can feel that your time there is not wasted. So much so-called work is socially valueless. Tell me about Charlotte and her children. Are they well?"

She's going to make it as hard for me as she can, thought Medwin. But I'll get it out if it takes all day.

"Charlotte's very well," she said, "and the children are too. She's being lent a small house quite near us for two months this summer—not more than five miles away—so she'll be able to see something of mother and father. She still has the old Austin, and a bit of basic petrol. It will cheer mother up to see the children. She sees them so seldom."

It seemed that the subject of Charlotte was now exhausted. Louise appeared to think of Charlotte's children as a group, an inchoate lump of childhood, though one of them was named after her. She next inquired, as though her elbow had been jogged,

"And Harold?"

"I'm afraid I've nothing very good to tell you about Harold," Medwin replied.

"You mean he still—after all this time——?" Louise was now looking directly at her niece with a flicker of curiosity, of interest in her small, faded, dispassionate eyes. Something quite human, though perhaps not altogether nice, was still there, Medwin thought, with amusement.

"That woman, as of course we all call her, won't give him up, or he won't give her up, I'm not sure which it is. Not that it matters. Charlotte's been wonderfully courageous about it all. She keeps on hoping. For the children's sake, she wants to keep him if she can."

"What a creature!" said Louise, turning her head away. She spoke with disdain and resentment; she seemed to know of some ideal world in which such beings as Harold would not be permitted to exist. She added, "She would be far better off without him."

"With four young children to bring up, and very little money? And they adore their father."

"She should never have married him, never," said Louise. "All the women of our family marry foolishly."

Medwin felt like hitting her aunt now. Just one good box on the ear, she thought, would be a joyful thing, and an immense relief to her feelings, which she was so carefully repressing. The element of truth in the statement made it yet more intolerable.

"He was attractive enough, I suppose," she said, admiring her own self-control. "And full of life and good spirits. Not attractive to me, but still I can see why Charlotte——"

"And you, dear," said Louise, brushing aside anything further Medwin might be about to say. She had plainly had enough of Harold. "I hope you have been keeping well."

Medwin had never liked talking about herself. She did not know the truth of herself, wondered if she would ever know it. She could have described herself in ten different ways to ten different people. She lived with a mysterious being; unknown to her. She forced herself to say, "Oh, pretty well, on the whole," and thought she would wait until after lunch to say what she had come for.

There was something about Medwin's detached, independent state—independent, at least, of a husband—that pleased Louise, and Medwin knew this and resented it. She knew that Louise believed, or wished to believe, that every woman had the uninhibited right to her own life, her own career. Children, if any, could be taken care of by others. She would have admired Medwin more—and Medwin was aware that her aunt did admire her—if she had not married at all. She considered, and indeed once said, that it was quite unnecessary for her to have married. If she had felt a sudden desire for this young man—or a young man—better to have satisfied it and sent him about his business than to have tied herself to him for life. (In this case, of course, his life was of unexpectedly short duration.) In her ideal world, women would take men and throw them aside if a permanent relationship should prove of no value. The dry, mousy little creature would have liked women to be Amazons.

Now Medwin got up, went out into the hall and hung her coat on a peg. Under the coat she was wearing a dress of beige coloured wool, full-skirted, widely belted. Louise looked at her with hidden satisfaction. The best of the family, she thought. She had never been to Russia, but so, she imagined, do Russian women look, with firm breasts, neat waists, good shoulders. For an instant she clothed herself in Medwin's flesh, she wore her, and knew, with fleeting, fierce joy, what it was to be Medwin. But, she thought bitterly, she will waste it all. She will waste it, sooner or later, on someone quite unworthy. Oh, the folly of it!

"Now dear," she said, getting up, "I will go and get your lunch. No, you must let me do it myself. You know I have my little rules and my little ways."

Medwin's nose had already told her that her guess was right. Cod and cabbage were both boiling away in their pots, the steam escaping from under the lids, filling the little house unashamedly.

"I made you a trifle," said Louise, at the door. "You used to be so fond of trifle."

I used to be, Medwin almost replied, but stopped herself in time. She only said, "I'm afraid I'm giving you a lot of trouble, Louise."

"No doubt you are hungry," Louise said and added, with her hand on the door, "when I am alone, of course, I have a salad and a bit of cheese. There wouldn't be time to get here from the library, cook a lunch and get back within the hour. As it is I do it nicely, walking both ways. Even on my afternoons off I prefer an uncooked lunch. At night, of course, I have to get a hot meal for Mr. Beedle, so we share it. Now I will leave you for a moment."

Does she ever see her friends in here, Medwin wondered, looking about her? Do they sit and talk, around that table? Angry men with rough hair, indignant women with hair in tight knots? For so she envisaged Louise's visitors.

She would never have guessed but for that visit a year ago. There had been a mistake in the date; Louise's fault. She had said the 16th when she meant the 17th. Medwin would not have got in but for Mr. Beedle who was at home with a cold in his head. Miss Carmichael, he said, handkerchief held in readiness for a sneeze, was not coming home for lunch. She had taken sandwiches to the library. "It's tomorrow she expects you, not today." "But she *said* today," Medwin insisted, "and here I am. What shall I do? Can I telephone her?" He told her the number and where to find a telephone booth. Louise was much upset that a mistake had been made. She said she could be there by three. She could get her friend, Mrs. Prowse, to take her place for the rest of the afternoon. "Make yourself at home, dear," she had said. "You'll find bread, margarine and a tin of sardines in the kitchen if you look for them. And make yourself some tea." After a second's hesitation she had asked, "Did you bring a book to read? If not, you will find plenty of books in my bedroom".

Medwin presently went upstairs to the bathroom and then opened the door of her aunt's bedroom, where she had never been before. There was a couch bed, a dressing-table made out of a packing-case and hung with faded chintz and half a dozen shelves tightly packed with books in worn, dull bindings. She looked at their titles and the truth was made plain to her. Louise was a Communist.

That was her secret, which, for some reason, she had now chosen to reveal. Had she thought: Medwin is almost sure to go into my bedroom to tidy herself. Better be quite open about it and suggest it myself? Or, on the other hand, had she been wanting her to know, and thought this as good a way as any? For Medwin, it was as if she had come upon her aunt standing naked in the room. She felt embarrassed. Then Louise's life, her character, her oddnesses, were lit up for her. Before, there had been no way of explaining her. Now she understood a little.

When her aunt returned she did not find Medwin reading a book from the bedroom shelves, but a biography of Charles Dickens which she had brought with her. They did not speak of the books upstairs, but now there was this knowledge between them which they could plainly read in each other's eyes; Medwin's knowledge of her aunt, and her aunt's awareness of it. At last Medwin knew what nourished Louise. It was as if at least part of a dark landscape had suddenly sprung into vivid light.

In a few minutes Louise brought in knives, forks, spoons, water and some straw mats, which she placed on the table. Then she went back for the lunch, which she had arranged on two plates; boiled cod, boiled cabbage and boiled potatoes. They came in steaming.

"You will find the cod very fresh," said Louise, as they sat down.

"Well, if it isn't," Medwin said in jocular reply, "you'll have me on your hands for a week or more."

Her aunt smiled to show that she was aware of a joke and said,

"I remember that your stomach is your weak point. You were very bilious as a child."

"I'm dreadfully susceptible to stale fish," Medwin said, "but I suppose most people are."

"I don't know of anything that particularly upsets me," Louise remarked, "except rich food which of course I am not used to."

Medwin laughed and said, "I dote on it. Not that one ever gets it nowadays. And how bored I am with my own cooking!" She held out her left hand. "That's one reason why I'm getting thin. Feel my wedding ring."

Her aunt hesitated; she almost perceptibly shrank from such a contact, and Melvin quickly withdrew her hand and demonstrated, herself, how the ring slipped up and down. It was the only ring she wore. "And this dress," she said, gathering a fold of it just above the waist, "it's getting far too loose for me."

"All the same, you look well," Louise said, unmoved.

"Oh, I'm well enough," Medwin replied at once.

When the trifle—stale cake and jam moistened with custard—was finished, and the plates, which Louise said she preferred to wash later, removed, they sat down by the fire again. Medwin asked Louise if she would like her to go shopping with her, but Louise said no, she had arranged to go out at four. She had little shopping to do, it would take her only fifteen minutes or so.

Medwin told herself, it's now or never, and spoke the words she had been for so long rehearsing.

"Can I tell you now what's troubling me, Louise?" she asked. "I must. I need your help terribly." She sat forward in her chair, elbows on knees, hands clasped in front of her, looking into the gas fire. "I've come to a crisis in my life, and you are the only one who can help me. I'm giving up my job at the hospital, as I told you. It isn't good enough. I'm worth more than they pay me there. I know it and they know it."

"But what other work could you find near your home?" Louise asked. Already, perhaps, she had a suspicion of what was to come.

"That's just the point," Medwin replied. "There isn't anything. And now I have the offer of a job in London at more than double my present salary. An incredibly good job. The difficulty is, of course, that I can't leave mother and father alone until mother's well again. Once I've established myself in this new job, I'll be able to pay someone to live with them—some nice woman who'd be glad of a home, though I couldn't, of course, pay very much. But that won't be for several months. Perhaps three or even four months. You see, I've nothing saved up at all. I gave father the money to have those scrubbing contraptions made. He begged me to. And of course there's the money for Sarah's keep. Louise, do you see what I'm trying to ask you? Would you go and live with father and mother for a few months, so that I can take this job? I swear I won't be longer than that. Oh, if you only knew what it would mean to me!"

There was no doubt now that Louise was listening and with her whole mind.

"I see your point quite plainly," she said slowly, deliberately, "but I cannot say that the idea appeals to me. You didn't, of course, expect that it would. I am used to my own life and my own ways, and my ways are not their ways. We have nothing in common."

"I know, Louise, I know, but have you forgotten how old I am? I'm thirty-two. Charlotte married and began a life of her own before she was nineteen. But ever since I left the secretarial college, I've had my nose to the grindstone. First with Reid and Simmons, then the Ministry of Food, then the hospital. Louise, I have a brain, I'm capable of something better than the work I'm doing—something at least more interesting and better paid. And there's nothing better for me as long as I have to live at home. This job I have the chance of—really, it's as good as mine—a little flat goes with it. Think of it! I shall have no rent to pay."

"What is it?" Louise asked. "And how did you hear of it?"

"One of the hospital consultants, a nerve specialist, told me about it. I think I've spoken of him—he looked after me when I was ill there. Dr. Radnytz. The job is with two middle-aged women who share a big house and are interested in a lot of different things—hospitals, charities, research. I suppose they're very rich. They want a secretary—the one they had has had to go to a sanatorium. Dr. Radnytz has told them about me. I have an appointment—you see, I took a chance—for tomorrow. I'm wild to get this job."

"What made him think you wanted to leave the hospital?" Louise asked. "Isn't he doing the matron a bad turn?"

"No. She's known for months that I wanted to go, but mother's accident prevented it. There's someone standing by to take my place."

None of this is any good, Medwin thought. I might be talking to her in Choctaw. There is no contact. I am wasting my breath, but I shall go on until there is nothing left for me to say.

"You are asking too much of me," Louise said. "More than you realize."

"No, not more than I realize," Medwin replied. "I've thought about it and thought about it, and I know it would mean a very great sacrifice for you. But Louise, it's not only for myself I'm asking it. Mother would so hate to have a stranger in the house now, even if it were financially possible. She seems to want—oh, someone who belongs to her. She's very fond of you, you know. Lately she's been talking so much about the old days, when you were girls together."

"Your mother knows me very little," Louise said. "We were always completely different. Even when we were children I lived my own life. And you know I have no strong family feelings. I'm fond of you, I would do a great deal for you," (just what, Medwin wondered?) "but you are asking too much."

"What else can I do but ask you?" Medwin said, holding on, like a dog to a bone. "Don't you see how wrong it is for me to go on doing work anyone could do, and for so little? You say you'd do a great deal for me. I've never asked anything of you before. Have I? And probably I shall never ask anything of you again. But this—oh, I do need your help now," she cried, "so desperately!"

To this Louise replied.

"You have a comfortable home and a safe job. That is more than most people have. You should stay where you are."

Medwin turned her face away, and tightened the clasp of her hands. She thought, I must say nothing. Count twenty, fifty, a hundred. Let her speak next.

Louise had been turning over in her mind, in the interval, all the difficulties involved. She would now bring them out one by one.

"And Mr. Beedle? Who would look after him? I should have to find another lodger when I returned. He is so tidy, he never leaves anything for me to put away. He always wipes his feet with the greatest care. He has a small appetite and he does not smoke. I should never find anyone like him again."

Medwin knew that no life is what it seems; that Mr. Beedle's life was as vivid a dream of living as her own; that if she felt she had a hold on reality, so did he. But now she resented the little man with his thin hair, sloping shoulders and tie drawn through a ring, because Louise put him before her mother. The memory of him at that moment was as dispiriting to her as a deserted railway junction where one waits for ever for a train to take one where one does not want to go. And at the same time she had perceived and been fascinated by the two women who lived together in her aunt's skin—the prim, dry spinster and the wild revolutionary.

"Couldn't he stay here alone for a few months?" she presently asked. "Plenty of men do live alone. I think as a rule they manage better than we do."

This was brushed aside.

"And there is my work at the library. They could hardly keep my place open for me."

Medwin suddenly remembered the name of the friend who had been called in a year ago to take Louise's place.

"Wouldn't Mrs. Prowse perhaps take it on until you get back?"

This only irritated Louise, who said sharply, "It is always so easy to make plans and arrangements for other people. I'm afraid you really do not see my difficulties."

Medwin sighed deeply. "Nor you mine, Louise."

This is too humiliating, she thought. I cannot go on begging and pleading. She will do nothing. But I will not quarrel with her. We do not quarrel in our family. It is one of our few virtues.

They sat quite silent. Two trams went noisily by. The wind rattled the window. Suddenly, startlingly, Louise asked:

"When do you want me to come?"

Medwin turned quickly and faced her; her eyes were vivid in their blue amazement. Louise still looked into the gas fire.

"Louise! Do you mean—? Oh, if you really would! Two weeks from now, about. Oh, Louise!"

Then that happened to her which happened extremely rarely; which had not happened since her illness. Her too-repressed frustrations and longings seemed to have found sudden release, for she gave way to a violent outburst of crying. She was ashamed, but could not stop. She bent over, like a child, her head on her arms and her arms on one arm of the chair, and wept as if in despair. Louise sat quite still. She did not put out a hand, nor a finger. She realized that in speaking seven words in the form of a question she had now committed herself and could not go back. Medwin's tears flowed like a river between her and her previous determination to stay precisely where she was. Months would be lost from her life, her too-short life, and there was not much time to lose. These months now seemed to her the richest and most golden that would ever be given to her, and she was throwing them away. She had not the consolation of feeling she was doing a kind action. It would lead to nothing, and she did not believe in kindness for the sake of kindness. But where Medwin was concerned, she was weak. Between her and Medwin there was some bond of blood which enabled her at times to *be* Medwin, and for this pleasure she would now have to pay heavily.

The two storms, the one indoors and the one outdoors, were passing, and Medwin went upstairs to the bathroom to bathe her face and make use of powder and lipstick. She came down again restored, and with a quick smile to Louise, who had not moved from her chair, sat down again, and they talked of various things, Medwin racking her brains for fresh subjects, to while away the time.

Before four o'clock, the wind had packed away the blue-black clouds and done with them, and the sky was now a clear and delicate blue, appropriate to winter. The wind still rushed this way and that, drying the pavements, but was in a hurry to get its work done and be gone. And then the sun went down golden, in a death-bed repentance, spreading glory in the dingy street. When it was time for Medwin to leave, Louise put on a coat and the famous hat and went to the tram-stop with her. Medwin tried, once more, to express her gratitude.

Louise said drily, from under the battered hat:

"I am going to do what you ask, but we shall none of us like each other. Your father and I have never liked each other. Why should we now?"

"You'll find him sad and a good deal changed," Medwin told her. And then, more brightly, "I'll come down sometimes on Sundays. I could even spend a week-end now and then, if I slept on the sofa. And, oh, the relief to me to feel that now, at last, I shall be able to pay the doctor's bills."

"I hope the new job won't disappoint you," Louise said, holding her head down. And then with a little preliminary cough, she asked what she must for long have been wanting to know. "By the way, have you by any chance said anything to them about me? I think you know something of my interests. Do they know too? Because if they do, I think it would make my stay with them quite impossible." As she put these questions she poked at a crumpled tram ticket in the street with the tip of her ancient umbrella.

"I have never said one word to them about it," said Medwin, wishing Louise would look up. "Not one word. So you needn't have any doubts on that score."

"I see," Louise said, and then raised her head. "Thank you. Now my dear, here comes your tram. I hope you have a good journey home."

There was no good-bye kiss. Medwin felt that her aunt would not wish it. As the tram stopped she said, "I'll write to you tomorrow night, when I'll have news for you."

She found herself a seat and looked out of the window, ready to wave. But Louise was already walking briskly in the direction of the stores, and did not see her. Something in the small, shabby, anonymous figure moved her, and she thought, "Bless her! I shall be grateful to her for this as long as I live." And then, following on this thought came another. "Poor little beast! How she'll hate it!"

CHAPTER 2

ON THE WAY BACK TO HURCOMB, THE LITTLE STATION IN the deep cutting, Medwin had time to consider this new step she was taking and the events that had led up to it. She did not take her book out of her pocket again, but sat thinking and remembering, her immediate anxieties much diminished by the success of her visit—though now that she had succeeded, she saw, more clearly than before, the many drawbacks involved.

Her thoughts returned to her father, and she thought sadly how he had failed to reach the one goal he ever—so far as she knew—deliberately aimed at: success in business. This he passionately desired. Was there, she wondered, in some old calendar, a date on which one might place a finger and say, "Here he went wrong? Here he made his first irretrievable mistake?" Or in the little boy running about his nursery, were there already all the seeds of failure? For it would be untrue to say that fate had been against him. He had been born to loving, well-to-do, upper middle-class parents, whose only thought was to see their son well set up in life. No, she thought, his judgment has been at fault, he has not seen clearly. The seeds of failure were always there. That is his tragedy—that he had better opportunities than most men, and made nothing of them.

Did he ever, she wondered, admit this to himself? She did not know, but hoped not. There was so much she could not say to him, so much he could not bear to hear spoken that conversation between them was never easy. Nor could she question her mother. Even her daughters could not break, if they would, her deep and loyal reserve.

Their worst troubles began, Medwin thought, about 1925. Before that she could not remember troubles, or was not permitted to know of them. She vividly recalled the house in Victoria Road, part of that charming and unexpected pocket of suburbia in the heart of Kensington. Indeed she knew it well, for she had walked past it, devouring with nostalgic eyes every feature of it, many times since. A medium-sized, comfortable, early-Victorian house painted a deep cream colour, with long windows looking on to a small garden in which were the same two red hawthorn trees she loved as a child. At one of these windows it was her habit and her right to stand watching for her father's return. As soon as he came in sight she would race to the front door, out to the gate, and fly into his arms. He would exclaim, as if surprised, "Well, Poppet! It's you, is it?" pick her up and carry her back into the house, until she grew too big to be carried.

It was at the height of the dancing craze that the change came. Two or three evenings a week her parents would go out somewhere to dance, or couples of their own age—for though her father was the eldest of them all, he loved dancing—would come in and dance in the drawing-room to a gramophone, rugs rolled up and pushed aside, and the long expanse of parquet shining like a yellow lake. In their bedrooms, she and Charlotte would fall asleep to the sound of music and laughter and the shuffling of feet. They were practising new dance steps; everyone was learning the Charleston, and her father and mother were said to be the best dancers of them all. Then these evenings suddenly came to an end and her mother very rarely put on those brief, sheath-like evening dresses which the little girls thought so beautiful.

And then one evening, after her father had come home—it was the only winter evening to stamp itself clearly on Medwin's childhood memory—she and Charlotte were called into the drawing-room and told that the house and everything in it was to be sold at once, and that they must accustom themselves to being poor. Medwin could remember giving a delighted little jump and saying, "Oh, can I go to market and bring home eggs in a basket?" Her mind had formed a Little Red Riding-hood picture of herself with a basket on her arm, and this stayed with her pleasurably for some time.

After that, until the house and furniture were sold and even her mother's evening dresses, furs and jewellery, there was a fearful pause whenever the door-bell rang. Sometimes, after the servants went, it was not answered at all. The little family moved to a cheap lodging house near Russell Square and even Medwin could see how her father's face began to alter and to sag, and his eyes to stare.

Then, she thought, he must have found a job, or one was found for him. She had an impression that it was with a firm of tea-merchants in the City. But working under his juniors could not have been easy for a man past fifty who had once had his own business and was sore with failure. Probably there was a quarrel or quarrels; at any rate, there presently began another period of advertisement answering, and there was an abrupt flitting from these lodgings to others, still cheaper, in Bayswater. Then, again abruptly, this time in the summer, they went into rooms in the country, near Marlow, and the two girls learnt to punt and to swim. Her father went to London every day and probably had another job, but if so, it did not last long and they went back to a second boarding-house in Bayswater. Here they remained, and Mrs. Fosdick found for herself a position as saleswoman in the fur department of a big store, a job she kept for many years, and the girls looked after themselves.

With no school to go to—for Mr. Fosdick would not hear of a Council School for them—Medwin and Charlotte now devised for themselves a life and a system of education that pleased them very well.

So that awkward questions as to their schooling should not be asked, they left the boarding-house every morning before nine and spent their days in museums. With buns in a bag, some bars of chocolate, and money enough for bus fares and a glass of milk at a dairy, they went daily, except Sundays, to the British Museum, the Victoria and Albert, the Natural History

Museum, the National Gallery, and the Tate, and on Sundays their father, who still remained a Fellow, sometimes took them to the Zoo. Medwin made copious notes of what she saw and filled many exercise books; Charlotte relied upon her memory. The two girls talked to their parents' few remaining friends—for borrowings had greatly diminished their number—about mummies or Egyptian tear bottles or South American humming-birds as other girls of their age talked about games or parties or films. Then came another phase. They discovered, encouraged and advised by their mother, the joys of reading, and on cold or rainy days went to public libraries, often the one in which Louise worked, and there spent happy hours. Louise's disapproval of their mode of life increased her dislike of their father and the two did not, at that time, meet. On fine days in the summer they took their borrowed volumes into the park, taking care to sit only on the free seats. In the evenings they would sit curled up in the lounge of the boarding-house with books up their knees, while their mother sewed and Mr. Fosdick rustled his evening paper, reading it through unseeingly once, twice, three times, while he thought his unhappy thoughts.

Guided by their mother, the two girls ran rapidly through Scott, Trollope, Meredith, George Eliot, and read and re-read Jane Austen, the Brontës, and Charlotte M. Young. Then came history, which helped to fit their scattered bits of knowledge into something of a pattern. Sometimes, in their bedroom, Mrs. Fosdick read poetry to them. She was now head saleswoman in the fur department, and Mr. Fosdick reluctantly consented, now and again, to take a humble office job, when extra help was needed, in the same department store. His shoulders became heavy and rounded from his habit of holding his head down.

As they did not mix with other girls of their age, Charlotte and Medwin were hardly aware that their lives lacked anything. They were happy, they thought not going to school delightful. They became complete little Cockneys, and boasted that they knew more than thirty bus routes. They were not allowed to go alone by Tube or Underground, but buses sufficed them, and if they could get the top front seat thought themselves in heaven, and would sit like two love birds, utterly content. They talked to many of their fellow-passengers, a fact they kept to themselves as Mr. Fosdick would not have approved, and made friends of museum attendants, postmen, milk-waggon ponies, other people's dogs, and a Mr. and Mrs. Gribble who kept the nearest stationer's shop, where they often went for afternoon tea. The pretty, coltish, long-legged pair were never apart. Their chief regret was that they were not allowed to mix—again by Mr. Fosdick's orders—with the people in the boarding-house. Good mornings and good evenings were permitted, but nothing more.

As soon as they were old enough, first Charlotte and then, the following year, Medwin (and this one year's daily separation was by far the worst thing Medwin could recall at that time) attended Miss Judd's Secretarial College and did well. To make this possible, Mrs. Fosdick sold her handsome diamond engagement ring, the only bit of jewellery she had left. The girls did not know this until long afterwards; did not even notice, at first, that the ring was gone. When at last they did observe its absence, Medwin one day asked, "Mother, why don't you wear your engagement ring any more?" Her mother flushed and replied, "Don't worry about it, dear. It is where I can't possibly lose it."

Medwin accepted this answer and never asked again. Later she did not have to ask. She simply knew.

Charlotte made her first girl friend at the secretarial college, a girl named Joan Halstead, and for the first time in her life, Medwin knew the sharp bite of jealousy. Joan invited Charlotte to spend part of the summer holidays at her home in Kent, and there seemed no reason why she should not go, for Joan was a quiet, well-brought-up girl to whom no objections could be made. Mr. and Mrs. Fosdick gave their consent, and Medwin spent a night in weeping, for she felt that Charlotte was now lost to her. It was in fact the beginning of their separation, for staying at the Halsteads, Charlotte met Joan's elder brother Harold, twenty-four years old and just starting work in the City, and the two fell in love. He was the first likely young man who had come Charlotte's way, but this fact did not cause her to feel the slightest hesitation. They became engaged a few weeks later, and Charlotte left the secretarial college before quite finishing her course, to be married. Mrs. Fosdick had her doubts about the wisdom of this marriage, while Mr. Fosdick was deeply disappointed that Charlotte was not doing better for herself. But her mother realized only too well how limited were her opportunities. The Halsteads were a pleasant enough family, and she hoped that marriage would at least open up a wider life for Charlotte.

Time was not kind to Charlotte, in that it soon robbed her of her early prettiness. She was too pale, her skin too fine, her features too pronounced. Lovely though she was when she married, she shed this bloom and outward charm after the birth of three children, and put on a look of blonde austerity intimidating to her jocular, robust and sensual husband. This look went deeper than the skin. Charlotte became a seeker after delicate values, a searcher into "purposes" and meanings, and in this search, Harold, an ardent golfer, did not propose to join. Before long he was spending every Saturday and Sunday playing golf. He was a stock jobber, and when markets were poor, golf was his solace and his delight. He won tournaments, he made friends who were only names to Charlotte and sometimes not even that. Playing in mixed foursomes he met a hearty, golfing widow named Mrs. Loveday. The two decided that they were made for each other, and perhaps they were. Mrs. Loveday had an income sufficient for her casual needs, while Charlotte had not a penny and sometimes made inconvenient gifts out of her household allowance to her mother. One day Harold informed Charlotte, without much delicacy, that he was in love with Mrs. Loveday and had been unfaithful with her on numerous occasions, of which he was willing to offer proof. If Charlotte would divorce him, he said, Mrs. Loveday was quite prepared to "stand the racket."

Charlotte received this blow with unexpected resilience. She still loved the hearty, insensitive bonhomous fellow, and all her tenacity rose up to counter this effort of his to free himself. It was not only that she wanted him for the children's sake—for he could be a good, interested and playful father, if only for brief periods—she needed him herself. In her quiet, somewhat etiolated way, he was what she required to keep her warmed and alive. Also, she believed that Mrs. Loveday, whom she had once or twice met, would, in the long run, do him no good.

"No," she said, "never that. Never a divorce. What would the children and I do without you? I love you, and the children adore you. You cannot do this to us."

Doggedly he said:

"I warn you I shall go on being unfaithful to you with Mrs. Loveday."

"That's as you please," she replied. "One day you'll tire of her and be grateful to me. And I would tell any judge, any jury, that I condoned the offence. I suppose you are the sort of man who requires a Mrs. Loveday. But it would be wrong for me to let you marry her."

"Look," he said, staring down at his fists, one placed on top of the other, "is this quite fair to Mrs. Loveday? She wants to marry me."

"I'm afraid the children's wants and mine must come first," Charlotte said.

He never admired Charlotte more than he did then, and he felt guiltily ashamed of preferring a woman who was in every way her opposite. But he went on loving Mrs. Loveday, and they tried to console each other for being unable to marry by drinking too many Scotches and sodas, which sometimes reduced them to self-pitying, unsober and not unenjoyable tears. He cut down Charlotte's allowance because of the expense of wining and dining Mrs. Loveday.

But Charlotte had other things to think about. She went on, as Medwin remarked, cutting bread and butter. She had the children. Richard, the eldest, had a surprising gift for mathematics; Louise scribbled stories in her free hours, the youngest boy, Tony, a comic, made her laugh. And then came the war.

Harold joined the Naval Reserve and went to sea, thus fulfilling a dream of his boyhood. Once he came home on leave and was received with such a warm welcome by his family that he was unfaithful to Mrs. Loveday with Charlotte, with the result that, rather inconveniently, a fourth child was born in 1942. Medwin remembered how surprised they all were, and how ashamed Charlotte was, as if she had been caught out in some regrettable indiscretion.

Mrs. Fosdick, made ill and sleepless by the bombing of 1941, was ordered out of London, and Medwin, then working for the Ministry of Food, had to find a place in the country for her parents to live. This was not easy; not a corner seemed available. One day she heard, through one of the Ministry officials, of a small lodge on the edge of a large estate in Surrey. The house had been requisitioned by one of the other Ministries, but the lodge, one of three, was empty and habitable. She got permission from her boss to go and see it the same afternoon, and she took it that day at a weekly rental of eighteen shillings. It was furnished after a fashion and could be moved into at once. She got two obliging village women to clean it, and three days later Mr. and Mrs. Fosdick took possession. It had a small garden, some apple trees and a wire-netting enclosure for hens.

The problem of how her parents were to live without Mrs. Fosdick's earnings was partially solved by the convenient death of an elderly relative who had gone to New Zealand and died there, leaving her a tiny legacy. It was time. Mrs. Fosdick had reached the end of her strength, had reached exhaustion point. Medwin, in order to help them financially, shared her room with another girl, who worked at the same Ministry. This was a sacrifice she made willingly enough for the sake of her own peace of mind. There was a spare bedroom at the lodge and from time to time she spent week-ends there, and, with infinite relief, saw her mother's health slowly revive.

She had barely got them settled in when the house in which she lived near Baker Street became the scene of an "incident." She returned one evening after dining out to find it a ruin and her room-mate and four other people taken to hospital. Her room-mate died the next day. Medwin was surprised to find that none of this greatly affected her. She felt numb and indifferent rather than shocked. In fact she was shocked only by her own indifference. A friend who worked at the same Ministry and whose husband was a prisoner in Germany, took her into her one-room flat and she remained with her. She was at the office as usual the next morning wearing borrowed clothes, and when her boss looked at her with sharp eyes and suggested that she take a few days off she was surprised.

"Why? I'm all right. There's nothing wrong with me, is there?"

"You look as if you'd had a bad shaking up," he said.

She took more pains than ever over her work as she found she was inclined to forget things, and this worried her, but she kept it to herself.

She was seeing most at this time of Jervis Blair. He was one of a little group of officers and men who, failing to reach Dunkirk, had hidden themselves for a while until they could reach Brittany and escape to England in a fishing-smack. He was badly wounded in the shoulder and when he came out of hospital was employed at the War Office. His devotion to Medwin amounted, she told him angrily, to persecution. Looking back she could see that her anger was mixed with fear. Again and again she told him to go away and leave her alone, and after some painful scenes which still further lowered her vitality, he went, and for months she heard nothing from him. But her mind, like the subconscious mind of the sleeper, went on working at the problem, and one day she suddenly came to the conclusion that she had made a mistake. She missed him unbearably. She made up her mind to ring him up, and then, before she could quite bring herself to do so, met him, during her lunch hour, crossing Piccadilly. She learnt that he was going to the Middle East in three weeks' time.

They stood together on an island with the traffic rushing past on either side and she told him she had been a fool to let him go. He took her hand and, without loosening his tight hold, they walked in step to the Berkeley Hotel, went in and ordered drinks. They decided to marry at once.

Jervis was the son of divorced parents. His father, who had brought him up, was dead; his mother, long since married again and living in the West Indies, meant little to him. He had an uncle and aunt in Norfolk, and he presently sent them a telegram, while Medwin promised to write to her parents that night. They had never met Jervis, they barely knew his name. But she was now thankful to close her eyes to any difficulties or obstacles and leave everything to him. Jervis had little money but good prospects, and his job with a great chemical firm was waiting for him at the end of the war. They were married by special licence and went to the coast of Wales for their honeymoon.

During those two weeks they tried feverishly, touchingly, to build something that would resist all the stresses of time and the war. Medwin fetched from the lodge and took with her the exercise books she had filled with childish notes and comments in the galleries and museums. These her mother had lovingly kept. Sometimes, reading them while lying on the grass above the sea, Jervis would put his head down on his arms and shout with laughter. Once or twice he looked at her with tears in his eyes and reaching for her hand, said, "Oh, you funny kid. Why didn't I know you then?" It was their pasts they tried so ardently and truthfully to share, and Medwin, in this re-creation of herself, this searching out and putting together of all she had been and therefore now was, felt that for the first time she began, through his eyes, to see herself whole.

They need only have concerned themselves with the present. Four months later she was told of his death in the Western Desert. Five months later, Sarah was born in the hospital near Hurcomb.

Medwin did not recover from the child's birth as she would have done had her state of mind been normal. Both the baby and the life she was presently expected to take up again seemed beyond her, outside the little she could now compass. Dr. Radnytz, consultant at the hospital, took her determinedly in hand. Sarah was taken to Wimbledon by Charlotte who said one more would make little difference, and Medwin slowly emerged from the tenebrous uncertainties and self-abasements of a nervous breakdown.

When she had recovered, the Matron asked her to stay on as secretary, as the present one was shortly leaving to be married. This Medwin was glad to do. She could now have Sarah at the lodge, and Mrs. Fosdick was delighted to take care of her while Medwin was at work.

During the flying bomb period, Mr. Fosdick became a warden for the district and even got about, though precariously, on a bicycle until his heart was found to be the worse for it and the doctor ordered him to give it up. For a while the only events were those heard over the radio and read in the newspapers, and it seemed to Medwin that she was destined to spend her life in this backwater, but stayed in it because of Sarah. Then came her mother's accident, and it was now her turn to go to the hospital. Sarah was once again handed back to Charlotte. At about this time the Ministry decided to de-requisition Hurcomb Place, and it then became known that the estate had been bought by a wealthy film producer named Mr. Gordon Schlemmer. This news caused consternation in the Fosdick family, and Mr. Fosdick, who had felt it a disgrace to be living in a lodge at eighteen shillings a week, now lay awake at night dreading that they might be put out of it. His fear that he might be expected to open the gates for Mr. Schlemmer's car was less than his fear of being homeless.

Medwin at once got in touch with the new owner and a few days later met him by appointment at the big house, where she found him sitting at an ink-stained table left behind by the Ministry and going over plans and blue-prints with his architect.

She took an immediate liking to the little man. He was short, squat, ugly, but had charm, and she felt she could trust him. He said she need not worry, that he would not be using the lodge so far as he knew at present. He only stipulated, with characteristic caution, that they would agree to move out at a year's notice if at any time he needed the place for workers on the estate. Medwin consented to do this. There was a look in Mr. Schlemmer's eyes which told her that no such notice would be given. He saw her to the front door and then said that a rental of eighteen shillings a week was too much for the lodge, and that he would reduce it to ten. Her anxiety about her parents pleased him. He looked after his own parents, and handsomely. He considered that she was the right sort.

The night was very dark now and she was glad the train was on time, for the bus was there, almost ready to start. It set her down at a cross-road within a few minutes' walk of the lodge, and she took her torch from her hand-bag and shone it on the road. She hoped that Mrs. Briggs had prepared some vegetables and that the fishmonger had not left cod. It would be a long time before she could bring herself to eat cod again. She went through the little gate for pedestrians beside the big gate and opened the door of the lodge. There was a welcoming smell of wood smoke, and she was glad to be home.

Mrs. Fosdick, whose resemblance to Medwin was striking until a few years earlier, was lying on a couch-bed which could be wheeled from room to room. She wore a warm blue dressing-gown and her hair was untidy because she could not do it herself and that morning Medwin had no time. This distressed her a little, for, like her daughter, she was devoted to neatness. Medwin kissed her and asked if she had had any pain.

Mrs. Fosdick's tired blue eyes had lighted up at the sight of her daughter. Torture would not have made her admit how dull she found her husband's company, how tedious the narrow and dismal route his mind habitually travelled. He was hers, he was her portion, her lot, her life, her choice. His misfortunes had deeply endeared him to her. She had known for nearly forty years that he bored her—they had been married for forty-two—and she loved him devotedly. Her boredom was utterly her own secret. She was not ashamed of it, she had come to honest terms with it. They did not talk much nowadays; there was not much to say. She was always a busy reader and he had his patience cards. She loved him as one may love an inconvenient house, an ill-conditioned child, a dog with tiresome ways. There he was, an old habit. But hers. And she knew herself to be adored even though it was an adoration mixed with shame, pain, regrets and an abysmal selfishness.

She shook her head. "Nothing to speak of. Are you very tired?"

Medwin denied being tired. She went to her father, left a

kiss on the top of his head and handed him the evening paper. Almost the first thing that had caught her eye—as it was meant to do—was a white china bowl full of brown eggs in the centre of the table.

"What!" she cried, quick to take her cue. "Not all those today?"

"Every last one of 'em laid today," her father exulted. "Every blessed last one of 'em. I took the twelfth from under Tibby at three o'clock. I'd almost given up hope of her."

"It's simply marvellous," said Medwin, counting the charming brown ovoids, to please him. "Yes, twelve. You've certainly got a way with them."

He winked, a little heavily. A light stroke to which no one ever referred had slightly affected one side of his face. All his life he had been a firm, solid man, broadly built, with well-covered bones, but now the flesh was leaving the bone and he sagged, his clothes, which were very much pre-war, were far too loose for him. It was a melancholy-humorous face, the face of a sad clown not yet made up for his turn. Whatever came from those lips was likely to be a joke or a moan, but the joke would be without gaiety and a little feeble now, and the moan would be for trivial things. He was a man who could so easily have been easily happy. Avoiding either depths or heights, he could have lived cheerfully, gaily, had he been able to be careless with money, generous to his family and friends. Without money to give him extension and aggrandizement, he had dwindled to what he was now, and did not care to be more than he was. He left everything that was not on his own shrunken, material, day-to-day plane to his wife and daughters. Let them get what good they could from it; he could get nothing.

"We can thank old Chartley," he said, following up the wink. "I did a clever thing when I made a friend of that chap."

Mr. Chartley was a neighbouring farmer who had taken a liking to Mr. Fosdick. Mr. Fosdick went frequently to the farm, it was his favourite walk, and after dark sacks were left, from time to time, just inside the gate of the lodge. Wicked black market dealings were in progress, in which Medwin was deeply involved. She sold the eggs they did not need to the hospital and returned the money to her father. With it he bought himself beer and pipe tobacco. The basic ration they were entitled to for the hens, plus the small amount of kitchen waste, would have produced only a few eggs a week. Mr. Chartley saw to it that the hens got what they needed, and though it was all very illegal, the consciences of the Fosdick's were untroubled. And the hens and his success with them were one of Mr. Fosdick's very few pleasures. It was all, Medwin sometimes thought, that made his present life endurable to him, for he hated the country and longed to be back in London, where he pictured himself as being, somehow or other, better occupied, though he did not know just how.

"What did the fishmonger leave?" Medwin asked, sitting beside her mother for a moment. "Not cod I hope?"

"Plaice," Mr. Fosdick answered for her. "Not that there's much to choose between 'em." And he murmured, casting his eyes upwards. "Cold salmon trout with green hollandaise, tiny new potatoes with green peas. Were there ever such things?" And he smacked his lips.

"If you're patient," said his wife, "there'll be new potatoes and peas in due season." But she could wait no longer. She looked at Medwin and said:

"Well? How did it go? And how is Louise?"

There was a deep groan from Mr. Fosdick at the sound of Louise's name, but the two women ignored it. He was now looking at the evening paper, but would hear every word they said.

"She's very well," Medwin answered, "just as she always is. She sent her love." They both looked quickly at Mr. Fosdick, for they expected an explosion presently and were putting the moment off.

"Did you get caught in all that hail?" her mother asked.

"No. I dodged it. It wasn't such a bad trip." Then, feeling that the sooner it was over the better, Medwin said, "I had a long talk with Louise, and the upshot of it is that she's agreed to come here for a few months."

"Good God!" her father exclaimed, and threw down the paper. "Good God! Louise!"

"Now, Will," said Mrs. Fosdick gently. "It's what Medwin went for."

"I hoped the woman would have sense enough to stay away."

"Then I should lose the best job I'm ever likely to get," Medwin reminded him quietly.

"Pah!" he said. He took out of his sagging coat pocket an

old and extremely dirty pack of patience cards, which he rapidly laid out.

"Don't forget there are still the doctor's bills and the hospital bill to pay," his wife reminded him.

"Let 'em wait," he said, and the two women exchanged glances.

They had heard this so often before. It was what he used to say when tradesmen wrote threatening letters or pealed the door-bell. Was not he himself waiting? Would he not, in all probability, have to spend most of his life waiting? Why should not they wait? Then he burst out, "If you hadn't gone up that damned ladder after those damned apples, none of this would have happened."

Those late winter apples hanging so tantalizingly out of reach on the bare tree—how well Mrs. Fosdick remembered them. She was sure she could manage the ladder perfectly. She had felt free, adventurous, even girlish. Five steps was high enough; now she could reach. Then the ladder, one end sinking into a hole a field-mouse had made, tilted sideways and she fell awkwardly, one leg twisted between the rungs. She lay so for an hour or more in the soaking grass, fainting, becoming conscious of dreadful pain, then fainting again, until Mr. Fosdick, coming back from the farm, found her. She could see those red apples now, brilliant against a blue sky, and recall her feeling of elation as she went up the ladder, elation at doing a foolish youthful thing her husband or Medwin would never have allowed her to do. But she did not like to be reminded of the trouble she had caused by that act of folly, though she felt it was just; that she deserved it.

"When is she coming?" she asked, taking care to show no pleasure at the news, though she was greatly relieved.

"In about two weeks," Medwin said. "She has to make her arrangements, of course."

"Arrangements?" Mr. Fosdick angrily demanded. "What arrangements? Isn't she just an old maid living in a mouse-hole?"

Medwin tried not to smile.

"She has her job, you know, and her house and her lodger."

"Let her keep away from my hens!" he said next. "I won't have her poking her nose in there."

"Louise doesn't know the first thing about hens," Mrs. Fosdick said.

"That wouldn't stop her."

"She didn't want to come," Medwin told him. "She's really making a great sacrifice because I begged her to. Bear it for a few months. It won't be as bad as you think."

"Then you can have no idea," he said, "what I think."

"And now," Mrs. Fosdick said with thankfulness, "Medwin can go to London."

"What does she want to go for?" he demanded of them. "Hasn't she got a home here with us?"

Medwin could almost feel herself diminishing, becoming a child again, the four walls of the room her world. She had not, she thought, wholly outgrown her childhood, as her father's absurd question could produce this absurd effect. Some chord responded. Or had she, she wondered, been so long a daughter that she must be a daughter first and last and always?

Her mother patted her hand.

"Louise wouldn't have done it for anyone but you."

"We've come to that, have we?" Mr. Fosdick next said. "Asking favours of that mean little gad-fly."

They made no reply to this. Mrs. Fosdick said:

"Mr Schlemmer came in this afternoon, to ask how I was getting on."

"And stayed for an hour," Mr. Fosdick put in. "I was cleaning out the henhouse; I was covered with muck, and I couldn't come in because he was here, with his infernal chitter-chatter."

"He helped to pass the time while you were busy," said Mrs. Fosdick tactfully. She liked Mr. Schlemmer and wished he could come oftener, but Mr. Fosdick could not conceal his dislike of him.

"I hear there are some funny doings up at that house," said Mr. Fosdick darkly. "Funny parties. Some queer people staying there, too. The village is talking. They know, I don't. I'm only telling you what I hear. I don't listen to gossip. But I wouldn't see too much of him if I were you."

"I don't," said his wife, smiling, and Medwin suddenly wondered if it could possibly be that her father was jealous of Mr. Schlemmer. She looked at him with new eyes, fascinated by the thought, then got up, saying:

"It's time I went to get dinner."

"Mrs. Briggs peeled some potatoes and scraped some carrots," her mother told her, "and there are some bottled gooseberries all cooked and ready."

"Good," said Medwin, and then, knowing that her father liked it, she said, "I'll make a gooseberry tart."

She went into her room to take off her coat, and as she went she heard her father say, as he bent to pick up the paper again!

"Louise! Good God! I shall spend my days at the farm."

CHAPTER 3

MEDWIN NEVER GOT ON A BUS WITHOUT THOSE YOUTHFUL days with Charlotte coming back to her. From old habit she went up the stairs and looked for a front seat and was lucky enough to find one. She took this as a good omen. No one pushed past her there, the whole beloved, altered yet deeply familiar city was hers for twopence halfpenny. She glanced at her wrist-watch—the one present, other than the wedding-ring, that Jervis gave her. She would not let him give her an engagement ring; that, she insisted, could wait till after the war. It was just half-past nine and she had said that she would be at the house in Mayfair at ten. If she should be early, and she liked to be early, her mind unflurried, she would walk about until it was time to ring the bell.

Today, unlike the day before, there was no wind. It was dull but not very cold. She was hatless and wore the same coat and dress. Would they like her, these two unusual women? Dr. Radnytz was sure that they would, he had in fact no doubts at all, but Dr. Radnytz was biassed in her favour; too biased. That was one reason she was glad to leave the hospital, for he wrote her a foolish letter and she well knew that he had a Polish wife and two children. It was hard to reconcile the writing of that letter with the fact that he was a highly intelligent and honourable man, and she regretted it both for his sake and her own. She knew he did not and would not expect the slightest increase in her liking for him because of this opportunity he had found for her; that would not have been at all in his character. She was grateful to him and thought highly of him, but she wished, sometimes, that she had heard of the job in some other way.

The morning traffic was heavy, their progress slow, and she reached her destination a few minutes before the hour. She admired the house which was wide, dignified and handsome, and bore beside the front door a blue and white plaque announcing that it was once the home of a famous statesman of the late eighteenth century. The steps were of marble and had already been scoured. Bell and knocker shone. Below, the great area into which she glanced was white-tiled and immaculate. She marvelled that there were still people able to live in this pre-war style, with taxation what it was and good domestic staffs hard to come by. The door was opened promptly by a tall manservant in a white jacket, and she was in a wide hall floored with black and white marble, with an Adam staircase curving upwards with easy, eighteenth century grace.

The butler asked her to go upstairs and she was taken past the open doors of the drawing-room, and shown into a library behind it, where a fire was burning. He told her that Mrs. Gresham would be down directly and went out, closing the door.

This room Medwin considered quite perfect, even perhaps too perfect. If she were very rich and could buy anything she pleased she thought she would have a room like this, but she would have liked it to look more lived in, and she would certainly have arranged a few flowers in it. The fireplace and charmingly decorated ceiling were purest Adam; along the mantel were various Chinoiseries of carved jade. Over the fireplace hung a Canaletto, of the London period. It was a Thames scene, lively with barges and small figures, and St. Paul's rose in the distance. She had not spent a large part of her girlhood in picture galleries for nothing; such paintings spoke to her in no uncertain voice.

Was it possible, she wondered, that she would work here? It seemed likely, because on a small table, decently covered by a piece of Venetian velvet, she thought she discerned the box-like shape of a typewriter in its case. She lifted the corner of the velvet and settled the matter. It was a typewriter. But of course, she thought, there might be, and probably were, other rooms and other typewriters. The broad writing-table in the window was Georgian and the green, tooled leather top was without an inkstain. The curtains were of sea-green chintz with a pattern of sea-horses, the green blending with the paler green of the walls. Sofa and armchairs were covered in a honey-coloured brocade. There were other pictures of interest—a James Pryde, a Nicholson, a Sickert, the old and the new harmoniously spanning nearly three hundred years.

From the large windows she looked out over a paved and walled garden, the paving surrounded by beds in which irises displayed green swords. There were small clumps of yellow crocuses in bloom, the first Medwin had seen this year. Was it spring already, or were there warm pipes laid below the earth of the beds? She smiled at the notion, but anything might happen here. At the far end of the garden was a low building with a green door leading into it. She had no doubt that this building faced on a mews and that the lower part was a garage and the upper part the flat in which these ladies intended their secretary to live.

No, she thought, this can't be true. There's some catch in it—they'll dislike me, or I them. And then the door opened and she turned quickly.

A woman she guessed to be between sixty and sixty-five came in, smiling and unhurried. Medwin's immediate impression was favourable, with only the slightest of reservations, to be examined later. Mrs. Gresham was not too noticeably a sitter on committees. She might equally well have been the capable, busy mistress of a large country house harbouring a numerous family. She had the weight suitable to her type and years, and wore a brownish tweed suit and a yellow silk tailored shirt under it. About her neck hung a string of fine pearls. Her eyes were dark and shrewd, her look could both smile and search. She had a broad face, the face of a healthy, not too rapidly ageing brunette who was not afraid of weather. Her hair, worn moderately short, was iron grey. Her skin was somewhat sallow, with lightly etched lines, but the contours were still firm. Firm, too, even unnecessarily so, was her handshake.

"How nice of you to come up from the country so early, Mrs. Blair," she said, the words accompanying the handshake. "I'm Mrs. Gresham. I'm so sorry my friend, Miss Lyddon, isn't here. She had to be at a committee meeting at ten o'clock."

"I'm most grateful to Dr. Radnytz for speaking of me," Medwin said. She had decided to be simple, direct and business-like. These were the qualities she would show; any others she might have they would have to discover for themselves, if they engaged her. She took the armchair indicated by Mrs.

Gresham, who sat with their back to the light, but not, Medwin thought, for a woman's reason.

"I've no doubt we shall have cause to be grateful to him too," Mrs. Gresham said, smiling and showing strong, short teeth. Her mouth was wide, the lips thin and straight, but the rest of her face was in its way, handsome. "As I say, it's a pity Miss Lyddon isn't here, but it doesn't really matter as I am sure we shall entirely agree about you. Dr. Radnytz praised you to the skies, and said how invaluable you had been to the hospital. But I gather you really want to come to London."

Medwin said she did, very much. She was a Londoner born and bred, and had now spent nearly four years in the country.

"Well," said Mrs. Gresham, with a friendly smile, "I should think your abilities sadly wasted there, and, if I may say so, your good looks as well."

Medwin laughed this away. "That's only my country complexion," she said. "I'm quite prepared to sacrifice it."

"Come, come," Mrs. Gresham protested. "Is there a healthier place in the world than London? I doubt it." Then, with a more business-like manner, "I don't know how much our good doctor has told you about us, but let me tell you briefly what your work here would be like. Shall I?"

"Do, please," said Medwin.

"We are a very busy pair," Mrs. Gresham said, and smoothed her bosom with a complacent, downward motion, a trick Medwin had already observed and which was evidently quite unconscious. "We are up to our eyes in every sort of thing. Between us, we would keep you very, very fully occupied. In fact, I'm not sure we didn't shockingly overwork our last secretary, Miss Jones, so you should be on your guard against us. We would even ask you—" and her voice now had in it a questioning note, "to give up one or two evenings a week to us. Could you bear that? You see, we entertain a good deal."

"How clever of you," Medwin said smiling, "as things are today."

"You'll soon learn the secret of that," Mrs Gresham told her, her eyes lively. "Hams. A stream of hams, tinned or smoked, from America. Miss Lyddon has a brother who lives there, thank heaven. Otherwise we shouldn't be able to entertain at all—or very little."

"I'll be only too glad," Medwin said, "to give up any of my evenings to helping you. I have very few friends in London now, and even if I had dozens, you would naturally have the first claim on me."

"How kind of you. I so hoped you'd say that. Miss Lyddon and I like the company of intelligent men and women, and it helps enormously at parties to have someone young and—may I say?—attractive at hand." Then she got to her feet with a quick, energetic movement. "Look, I want you to see where you'd live. You see that green door? That leads into your flat, up a short flight of stairs. Of course it has an entrance into the mews, as well, so you could come and go quite independently of us. Our chauffeur, an excellent man who has been with us for sixteen years, first of all with my husband and myself, has the flat next door with his wife, a nice obliging woman. If you got on the right side of her, as I'm sure you would, she would help you with your cleaning."

"It's all delightful," Medwin said as they sat down again. "I couldn't imagine anything more perfect. May I tell you something about myself? My shorthand and typing are good—first class, I think, and I'm told I have an orderly mind. I hope you don't expect languages. I've never been out of England, and my education was most unorthodox. I don't even speak French. Would that matter very much?"

"Only to you," Mrs. Gresham answered agreeably, "as you are deprived of much pleasure. No, don't bother your head about that. Both Miss Lyddon and I speak French fluently, and in addition she speaks Italian and I speak German. Your other qualifications are quite sufficient. And, if you'll forgive an old-fashioned word, you are a lady. Miss Jones was almost a lady. The difference is enormous."

Medwin felt that Mrs. Gresham had struck a false note without in the least realizing it. What she had just said, though doubtless well meant, jarred unpleasantly. She liked Mrs. Gresham less. She looked at her with lifted eyebrows and said:

"I really didn't know. The word belongs to my mother's generation much more than to mine. People of my age are indeterminate, aren't they? Classless, I rather hope."

Mrs. Gresham made no direct reply to this. She only said,

"I think, since the war, people of your age seem a trifle 'désorientés,' if you know what I mean. But you don't strike me at all as being so. You seem to me to have great poise. Perhaps that's what I meant." And then she added, "Our good doctor tells us you have not had an easy life."

Medwin replied to this, in a low voice, "I suppose it's all a matter of comparisons."

"I understand your husband was killed in the war. I'm so sorry."

"Yes, in the Middle East."

Mrs. Gresham got up with another of her brisk, decisive movements and rang a bell by the fireplace.

"After your early start, I'm sure you must be wanting something. A glass of sherry perhaps." She resumed her seat. "And haven't you a little girl?"

"Yes," Medwin replied. "Sarah, her name is. She's four. At present she's with my sister."

"A delicious age," said Mrs. Gresham, and stroked her bosom downwards. An ungentle bosom, Medwin thought, expensively supported and restrained.

The manservant appeared with remarkable promptness.

"Some dry sherry, Wilson please, and some biscuits or cake." When he had gone again she said, "We are very fortunate in our staff. We are lucky enough to have an excellent Italian cook and parlourmaid—sisters. The rest are English, but they all get on quite happily together. Now I'd better tell you something about Miss Lyddon and myself, and then I'll explain what your work will be, if, as I very much hope, you decide to come to us. Miss Lyddon is the only daughter of the late Admiral Lyddon—created Lord Lyddon of Hartsdown in 1929. One of the really great admirals of the war before the last, the war Miss Lyddon and I call *our* war, though heaven knows"— there was the smile and the gesture—"we had plenty to do in this one. Miss Lyddon adored her father and never married because she couldn't bear to leave him. He really was a most lovable man, I knew him well. Her mother was a Devenny—the brewers, you know—so she has inherited wealth from both sides of the family. I only mention this to explain how she has been able to do all she has done, such as founding her famous Lyddon Home for Crippled Boys near Worthing. She has many other interests besides—research into the cause of infantile paralysis is one of them. She's my oldest friend—in fact we were playfellows and then schoolfellows—and when my husband died in 1937 it seemed a good idea to join forces. I may say"—and she stroked herself—"it has worked quite perfectly."

Medwin did not think of anything appropriate to say in the pause that followed, but there was no need for her to speak, as

Wilson returned with sherry and slices of a particular dark, rich-looking fruit cake. This last, Mrs. Gresham explained, also came from America. She went on:

"As to the house, my husband bought it many years ago. Miss Lyddon lived at Hartsdown till her father died and her brother inherited the place. Then she came here, to me, bringing with her many of her own things." She paused to sip her sherry, then continued. "Now a little about myself—not such an interesting subject as Miss Lyddon"—and she smiled—"but you'd better know what there is to tell. I'm afraid my preoccupations, or some of them, are rather more frivolous than hers. I like people better than she does, and I enjoy entertaining more, though of course she enters quite happily into everything I do in that way."

She paused again and Medwin said:

"Then it would be chiefly letters and invitations you would want me to do for you?"

"That, of course, but equally of course, other things as well. I am on the Board of one hospital, and Vice-Chairman of another. And then I have my own most beloved ploy. I run a holiday home at the seaside for overworked mothers and their children from the East End. I look forward very much to showing it to you."

Medwin began to feel a little overwhelmed.

"Do you really think I can cope with all this?"

Mrs. Gresham smiled her wide, thin-lipped smile.

"Don't imagine Miss Lyddon and I are idlers. We both spend a large part of each day working. I work here, and she works in the room below. She will want you for three hours in the afternoon, I for three hours or so in the mornings. Sundays, of course, are entirely your own, and then you must forget us and think only of yourself. And Saturday afternoons can be yours too, if you want to go away for the week-end."

Medwin said this would suit her perfectly. She then asked about the housekeeping and said she had never run a big house but would be glad to learn.

"Oh," Mrs. Gresham said, "I think we can quite happily leave all that to Miss Lyddon. She loves it. She has her chat with the cook before I am up in the morning and gives the orders then. She will probably want you to go over the accounts with her and the pay books. And there's one thing more. We borrowed a friend's secretary for a month while he was away, abroad. She's already been with us half that time. Do you think you could come to us—I'm presuming, you see, that you will come—at the end of two weeks?"

"That's just what I was hoping to do," Medwin answered. "And as you're so very kind as to say you'd like me to come, I want to say here and now that there's nothing I'd like better. I'm looking forward to it more than I can say."

"How nice. How very satisfactory! Then that's settled." She looked at a diamond bracelet watch. "I mustn't be late. In fifteen minutes I'm due at the Mid-Metropolitan Hospital for Women. I'd like to show you your flat, but that must wait. I believe I told you in my letter, didn't I, what we propose to pay?"

Medwin said yes. "I do hope you'll find me worth it," she added.

Going briskly out of the room ahead of her, and staring down the stairs, Mrs. Gresham said over her shoulder,

"My dear Mrs. Blair, you need have no doubts on that score. You strike me as being quite twice as intelligent as Miss Jones, though she was adequate and we were very much attached to her. Now, can I drop you somewhere?"

Her fur coat, sensible felt hat, gloves and bag were lying on a chest in the hall, and she made herself ready to go out without so much as a glance in the mirror.

"Thank you," Medwin said, "but I'd rather like a walk. I don't know this district very well, and I must get my bearings. In the last four years I've been in London very little, and I want to look about."

"I see," said Mrs. Gresham. She glanced at the hall clock and then went quickly to the door of Miss Lyddon's study and opened it.

"Just peep in," she said. "I always think Miss Lyddon has such charming taste."

It was the same size and shape as the room above, but its panelled walls were powder blue, the curtains were of a faded coral brocade, and along the mantel were pieces of *blanc de chine*. The pictures were all of one type—French eighteenth century portraits in pastel. Mrs. Gresham indicated the one over the mantel.

"I always think that's so like Miss Lyddon," she said. "We think it must be an ancestor, but we can't discover the lady's name it's impossible to trace it. Miss Lyddon has some French ancestors, which makes it still more likely."

The woman in the portrait had a narrow face, a high, rather narrow forehead, large grey eyes under thick dark eyebrows, strong features and white or powdered hair dressed high in the fashion of the period. It was a compelling face full of what is called character, by which is meant, more often than not, an obstinate will. The dress, lightly touched in, was of powder blue silk with knots of coral ribbon. Medwin decided that the room was designed to set off the portrait.

"It's a lovely room," she said, and then added, "but if I may say so, I like yours even better."

"To tell you the truth, so do I," Mrs. Gresham said, closing the door. "But when you see Miss Lyddon you'll realize how perfectly it is her room. Now I must run. We'll expect you two weeks from today. Good-bye."

Medwin watched her into the car. The chauffeur who was to be her neighbour, was forty-ish and had the alert, watchful look of the good mechanic. He tucked the rug around Mrs. Gresham's knees, got into his seat and they were off.

Medwin turned towards Grosvenor Square, where soon the statue of Roosevelt would stand. She felt a stir of hopefulness in the air. London was convalescent; it was forgetting its wounds. Painting was going on, damaged buildings had been or were being repaired, and though the bomb sites were as empty as ever, they had been made tidy for visitors, and London expected visitors. There were window boxes in many windows, with the green tips of bulbs showing through the earth.

Her mind went over the interview with Mrs. Gresham. No one could have been pleasanter, friendlier, more welcoming. Why, she wondered, have I this slight, this very slight reservation in my mind about her? She is the employer of one's dreams. Generous, full of the desire to help, all that a rich, well-educated woman should be, I suppose. Am I put off by that gesture she makes? As there was no one near, she made the same gesture herself. Someone ought to tell her. Why doesn't Miss Lyddon? But probably she's known her so long that she doesn't even notice it. No, it can't be that. People often acquire these odd little habits; possibly I have one myself, though I hope not. It must be something else.

She had now reached Grosvenor Square, and she stood for a few minutes by its newly planted hedge, watching workmen wheeling barrows or rolling paths. Now that the square had been cleared of many of its trees it looked immense. She suddenly felt a most irrational nostalgia for the war years when the square teemed with Americans and their cars and lorries; for days when life was dictated and dangerous; when all that was demanded of one in daily life was obedience and courage. She was at once ashamed, and told herself that whenever she felt she would like her life to be ordered for her again it meant that there was a backwash from that dark wave that engulfed her when Sarah was born. Or was she, in her heart of hearts, somewhat intimidated by the thought of those two women and all the earnest busyness in which she would soon be involved?

Here in the square, not more than ten yards from where she was standing, she and Jervis, in a taxi, had been run into in the dark by a jeep. No one was hurt, but she and Jervis were thrown violently against the door, which luckily held. It had been one of those evenings when she had been imploring Jervis to go away and leave her alone. She had not wanted at that time to marry him or anyone, and it was shortly after, in a final scene accompanied by misery and tears, that she sent him away. Now she was surprised by the vividness and poignancy of the recollection, and she remembered her fear that his wounded shoulder had taken the worst of the impact. So acute was her distress and anxiety for him that she supposed she must have been more fond of him than she knew. She thought she must have grown up with a picture in her mind of the man she would like to marry and that Jervis did not at all resemble this picture. Our lovers, she thought, should be most of all jealous of the men we have hoped and expected to love. Those are their most dangerous, most fatal rivals. She had always wanted to marry someone eight or ten years older than herself, older still in wisdom and experience. Never having had a teacher, it was perhaps that she yearned for. Someone who would be her mental banker, so to speak, upon whom she could draw heavily for knowledge. Jervis was scarcely older than herself. He had left London University, where he had specialized in chemistry, only four years before joining the army, and those four years had been spent with the chemical firm to which he hoped to return. He, unlike herself, had made several light-hearted journeys, with other young men, to the Continent; he had been to Switzerland, France, Italy. But his was still an immature mind, boyish almost, though with a boyishness that was altogether charming. He was all that the gayer, lighter side of her nature delighted in, and there was an understanding and an intuitiveness there that were very far from boyish. Yes, she thought, I fought against him because he was not like the mental picture I cherished and clung to; that I was ready to sacrifice him for. But I ought to have known that night, when I felt that panic fear for his wounded shoulder, how fond of him I had grown. It was just there, in the dark, and I was sick with fear for him. She closed her eyes. I wish he had seen Sarah. I wish that more than anything. If only they had let him come back, just to see her once.

The thought of Sarah started her moving away from the spot, away from the square. I need her, she thought. She is all that belongs to me, all that keeps me from feeling I am only an adjunct to other people's lives. Now that I am to have that flat as my own, perhaps I can bring her there sometimes. And I can spend some of my free evenings with Charlotte in Wimbledon, even though Sarah will have been put to bed. I can spend Saturday afternoons and Sundays with her. I could sleep in Harold's dressing-room, as he is sure to be away playing golf. Yes, there are dazzling possibilities in this job. But I must spend occasional Sundays at the lodge, for heaven only knows how things will go there.

Her heart lighter now, she walked away in the direction of Oxford Street. She decided to buy a hat. She was almost certain that Mrs. Gresham had eyed somewhat unfavourably her uncovered head. I will buy a brown velvet beret, she thought. They suit me, and I saw them advertised for twenty-two and six.

When she had done this, and put the beret on, to accustom herself to it, she rang up the friend, Mrs. Stetson, with whom she shared a room after the "incident" that killed her room-mate. Mrs. Stetson was still working for the Ministry of Food. She had been moved up and now held a responsible position there. Something, Medwin did not know what, had broken up her marriage. There was a divorce, only recently granted, and Medwin, who was a poor correspondent, had heard none of the reasons for it. Now she supposed she would have to hear them, for Diana Stetson hailed with delight the suggestion that they lunch together. For some time there had been a coolness between them, for Medwin did not tell her of her marriage until after it had taken place. But that was forgotten now, or seemed to be, and Medwin thought, as they sat down in the restaurant where Diana was in the habit of lunching, that her friend, divorce or no divorce, looked exceedingly well. She soon learnt that she was not to hear too many details of that affair. Diana had lost interest in it. She was soon to be married to a high-up official in the Ministry, and she talked about that instead. She marvelled that after all this time, Medwin had not re-married.

"I never meet anybody," Medwin said with truth.

"Then it's high time you did," Diana replied. "Remember that every year we grow harder to please and have less hope of pleasing."

After lunch Medwin mused upon what aspect of herself Diana Stetson—soon to be Diana Frederickson—saw. She saw her, no doubt, as a still-young widow in the market for a husband; a still-young woman who would spend her life doing secretarial work unless she married again; no doubt she felt that she was foolishly wasting a wasting asset, and should do something about it.

For old times' sake she walked through the Park from Stanhope Gate to Knightsbridge and looked at the very seats—the free ones—on which she and Charlotte had so often sat with their books. An elderly man once tried to get into conversation with them, sat down on their bench, although they occupied, with their books and lunch, the greater part of it, and asked them what they were reading. Their replies were brief and brusque. They disliked him at sight. There, that was the very bench, just there not far from the Achilles statue. (Now a stout nurse sat on it, with a red-nosed baby in a pram.) The elderly man presently suggested that if Charlotte would walk as far as his flat with him—it was really, he said, no distance at all —he would lend her some interesting books with the most fascinating illustrations, such as, he was certain, they had never seen before. The two girls exchanged glances, collected their belongings, got up and walked away. They were bored by his presence; they merely thought him rather crazy, and wished to put a distance between themselves and him. Not until years later did they know how to interpret this incident. They were armed only with innocence and two pairs of critical eyes. They were nearly grown up, indeed Charlotte could be said to be grown up, before they knew "the facts of life" for Mrs. Fosdick, shy herself, could never quite bring herself to tell them. Charlotte discovered these facts in her first year at the secretarial college and told Medwin. Medwin vividly remembered how the subject was broached. Charlotte, looking very thoughtful and serious, said to her after they had gone up to bed one night:

"Medwin, I'm afraid we're terribly behind the times."

They could never hear those words, "behind the times," used now without a longing to burst into immoderate laughter.

When she was back at the lodge that evening, her mother asked her many questions, her father none at all. He listened to their talk, holding the evening paper in his hands, but they knew he was not really reading it. She described the house and Mrs. Gresham and told what she knew of Miss Lyddon. What was Mr. Gresham, Mrs. Fosdick wanted to know? Medwin said she had no idea, she supposed that he was a highly successful business man, and at this Mr. Fosdick ducked his head as though something had been shied at it. There were now a number of things to lower his already low spirits; that Medwin was leaving them; that Louise was coming; that certain men were able to provide for their families as these two women who were to employ his daughter had been provided for. In this last there was one faint consolation. Those men were dead, he was not. He extracted what satisfaction he could from it. Then he lowered his paper to say!

"I remember Admiral Lyddon. He was kicked upstairs. There was a lot of criticism of the way he handled his squadron during an engagement."

Mrs. Fosdick said, "Really, Will, what a memory you have!"

He put aside the paper and took out his patience cards. This little pack was one of his treasures, for they were not to be bought now. He knew the backs of at least a dozen of them by their broken edges and defacements, but that made little difference when one was playing against oneself. Medwin presently picked up the discarded paper to give it to her mother, asking him if he had finished with it. He said he had, that there was nothing in it. During the war, it was a different matter. Then it was a question of survival. The brutes might have been in England, trampling on our necks; would have been had things gone a little worse. But the post-war world interested him little. He had grandchildren growing up in it, but they did not greatly concern him. Charlotte's were the children of "that fellow," and in any case he rarely saw them. Sarah's father he hardly knew (though he supposed he was a nice enough chap), and he was disgusted that Sarah had to be, as he called it "farmed out." He considered that he had nothing to offer any of them. It had been his dream, once, to buy an old manor house, with, if possible, a lake and a heronry. Then grandfatherhood might have had a meaning. Now it had none, or, if it meant anything it meant only another unpaid debt.

That evening Medwin wrote a formal letter of thanks to Dr. Radnytz. She could not be sure of seeing him at the hospital, and she wanted him to know that everything had gone as he had hoped. She suspected that she would see that sad, ruggedly-boned, intelligent face fairly often in London, for it was evident that the two women admired him greatly.

Two days later she received a letter by the first post in an unknown hand. It was postmarked London, W.1. She knew it was not Mrs. Gresham's writing, for she had previously had a typewritten letter from her signed in a large, sloping, noticeably feminine hand. This letter was not typed, and the writing was small, neat and full of character. She was surprised to see that it was from Miss Lyddon.

"Dear Mrs. Blair," the letter said:

"I am so sorry I was not in when you came the other day as I should so have enjoyed meeting you and setting the seal of my approval, as of course I should have done, on Mrs. Gresham's arrangements with you.

"In case she did not think to tell you, it might be of help to you to know that there is ample room in the basement of the house for any trunks you may have. So do bring with you whatever will make you feel at home with us; any personal belongings that you might regret leaving behind. We want you to fell that the flat is really your own. Let us know what time you will be arriving and we will arrange for the car to meet you. Stevens, the chauffeur, can see to your luggage and arrange for its transport.

"We are greatly looking forward to your coming and we hope you will be happy here. If you see Dr. Radnytz please give him our fond regards. You might remind him that he has not been to see us for some time, but I know, of course, how busy he is.

"Yours sincerely,

"Marietta Lyddon."

A most agreeable letter, Medwin considered, but she could not help smiling as she thought of the trunks she had been urged to bring. She did not own a trunk and had never owned one. Everything she possessed that was wearable in London would go easily into two suitcases. As to other belongings, the bomb destroyed such as she had and she had never replaced them. There were a few photographs she might bring, and half a dozen books of poetry. When she bought books nowadays she bought them for her parents, or for Sarah. For her mother, as Christmas or birthday presents, novels, history and biography; for her father, books on patent law and a great many pamphlets on poultry-keeping.

She was not sentimental about objects belonging to the past, she found they teased her too much with their associations, and she preferred to rely upon her own vivid memories, such memories as children are apt to have who live cut off from their fellows and from the packed life of schools. She would never have kept those exercise books but for her mother. No, Miss Lyddon would get a surprise when she arrived with two moderate-sized suitcases and a small bundle of books. It would be good for those two to see how much it was possible to do without; even, she thought with ironic amusement, for a lady.

The next ten days flew past. She had a brief talk with Dr. Radnytz when she was bicycling home one afternoon. He had been at the hospital, and he overtook her in his car. He stopped to speak to her and she dismounted and stood ready to mount again for she did not want to be seen talking to him in the drive for long. There had already, she thought, been some gossip. Trust nurses to miss nothing. They had eyes in the backs of their caps.

He wound down the car window to say how pleased he was to get her letter.

"But you should not have thanked me," he told her. "I have done a great service to my two good friends. The thanks are due from them."

His speech was correct, his accent indubitably Polish. She gave him Miss Lyddon's message.

"Tell her," he said, his too-expressive, bottomless dark eyes fixed on hers, "that now I shall look forward to coming there more than ever before."

This is what she would have avoided if she could. But he was a Pole, she remembered, and not even ten years of Harley Street could put armour on such as he.

"Well then," she said, one foot on a pedal, "this isn't goodbye, for we shall meet in London."

But he did not let her go yet. He asked quickly about Sarah, and she told him that the child was well and could already pick out a few letters.

"It is sad for you to miss all that," he said. "I wish you were together, for her sake but most of all for yours."

She made no reply to this. She only said that she would see her on Sunday, smiled at him and with another good-bye, pedalled on.

She had more than one reason to feel grateful to him, for she knew that he handled her case with great skill and patience. This little complication was unfortunate. She had never seen his wife, and she wondered to what extent the marriage was unsatisfactory. Or was he, at home, a pleased and contented husband?

She had now said all her good-byes. Tonight she had to pack and tomorrow catch the two-thirty train to London. Louise was due before lunch. With a sudden return of optimism she thought Louise's stay need not be a long one.

CHAPTER 4

"You don't look thirty-two," Miss Lyddon said as they walked across the paved garden. "I should have guessed about twenty-six or seven."

Miss Lyddon was bareheaded and her thick, rather coarse white hair was beautifully arranged, with crisp curls at the back and over the ears. She was wearing a black suit lightened by a fine white blouse and a jewelled ornament. She was slim and tall, and her feet and ankles were exceptionally good. From one of her long white fingers she was swinging two keys attached to a ring and was taking Medwin to the flat.

"Do any of us look our ages nowadays?" Medwin asked. "We really need a new measuring-rod, don't we? We're still thinking of age as our ancestors thought of it, and we're about a hundred years out of date."

"Yes, that's quite true," Miss Lyddon agreed. "I'm sixty-five, and I don't suppose I look it. But one expects not to look one's age and yet one is always surprised when other people don't look theirs. Here we are. These keys are yours, so now let me see you open your own door."

Medwin unlocked the door and put the keys in her handbag, thinking Miss Lyddon's gesture a charming one. She was very much taken with Miss Lyddon and hoped she was not going to like her too much more than she liked Mrs. Gresham, for that, she saw, would not do. Just inside the door was a little staircase and as they went up she noticed on the wall a series of old flower prints. The hall at the top was just big enough for a small table and a chair, but three doors opened out of it; one into the living-room, one into the bedroom and the other into the kitchen; and there was also a linen-cupboard there. The flat was painted a pleasing green throughout, and at the windows were curtains of a kind Medwin had never seen before. Miss Lyddon said:

"I hope you like my *Toile de Jouy.* I bought yards of it in France in 1939."

"It's charming. It all looks so beautifully fresh and gay," Medwin said.

"When war came," Miss Lyddon told her, "everything went straight into storage, and the house was taken over as an Officers' Club. I must say that on the whole they treated it pretty well. We moved back over two years ago. Last year it was all freshly painted, so we feel quite ourselves again."

Medwin laughed with sheer pleasure. "It's the most enchanting little place," she said. "I can't believe I'm to live in it."

The two ladies had put nothing rubbishy here; probably they owned nothing rubbishy. Everything was in excellent taste. In front of the fireplace which was fitted with an electric fire simulating coals, was a deep, comfortable sofa. On the walls were a few good coloured prints. One window looked on the garden, another on the mews, facing a tiny house with a blue door and blue window frames.

"An actress lives there," Miss Lyddon said, and mentioned a well-known name. "Nowadays, actresses make excellent neighbours. Mrs. Gresham has met her, I haven't. She says that off the stage she looks unbelievably dowdy. That seems to be the mode. Come and see your bedroom. I hope you won't find it too small."

It had curtains and a bedspread of the same red and white *Toile de Jouy* and overlooked the garden. There was a built-in cupboard lined with plain glazed chintz, there was a gay little painted bed, and on the bedside table stood a good reading-lamp and book-ends placed back to back.

"I didn't pick out any bedside books for you," said Miss Lyddon, "not knowing your tastes, and I thought you'd probably bring some of your own. Personally I never read anything but thrillers in bed. Mrs. Gresham strongly disapproves on the ground that if they don't keep me awake they can't be worth reading." And she laughed. "It's one enthusiasm we don't share. Do you like them?"

Medwin said she did and Miss Lyddon promised to send over a selection.

"As you saw, I hadn't much to bring with me," Medwin said. "I've never kept house, and during the war I was bombed out of my room and lost the little I had."

Miss Lyddon looked sympathetically at her with curiously striking grey eyes over which arched thick black eyebrows. With a slight surprise Medwin noticed that the roots of the eyebrows were white. But she's quite right, she thought, the effect is excellent.

"I know," Miss Lyddon said, "that your married life was tragically short. I'm so very sorry. And your little girl is with your sister, I hear. Do bring her here sometimes. We'd like to see her."

"I'd love to do that." Now, Medwin thought, there is little left to wish for.

There were footsteps below and Wilson came up the stairs with Medwin's suitcases. He put them in the bedroom and went away. Opening out of the bedroom was the green-tiled bathroom. Hot water and heating, Miss Lyddon explained, were supplied from a furnace in the garage. This warmed and gave hot water to both flats. Medwin felt she must be dreaming. It was too much!

The little kitchen, beautifully fitted and arranged, had an electric stove and a small 'frig.' Medwin, without being ungrateful, could hardly wait for Miss Lyddon to go. She felt that the flat had been waiting for her, that it wanted to welcome her, that there was not even the ghost of poor Miss Jones lingering there. She longed for the moment when she could be alone in it.

But Miss Lyddon was in no hurry. Her work for the day was finished, she said, except that her lawyer, Mr. Fullerton, was coming in at six to discuss some business matters and have a drink. She stopped and switched on the electric fire so that it glowed red.

"About dinner tonight," she said. "If you've no other plans, and as there's no food left in the flat except a few groceries left by your predecessor, I suggest that you dine with us. We shall be by ourselves and you needn't change. We dine at eight."

Medwin thanked her and abandoned the idea of supping off lettuce salad and tomato sandwiches in her new home.

"I'm afraid," she said, "I don't possess an evening dress. I have the usual little black afternoon dress, but that's all."

"Well, don't hurry," Miss Lyddon said. "Prices are fantastic. I doubt if you could get anything fit to wear under twenty guineas." She looked Medwin up and down. "If you wouldn't mind wearing them, I have one or two evening dresses that I believe would fit you. We're about the same height. I'm thinner than you are, but I dare say they could be let out a little."

"That would be a perfect solution," Medwin said. "I certainly don't want to spend twenty guineas at present. How kind you are."

"Not in the least. They'll be things I don't wear. One is too young for me—or so Mrs. Gresham insists. I'll send them over. Oh, by the way, one thing more. Miss Jones was a nervous type and we had a bell fitted up for her just beside the bed. You'll see it. It rings very loudly in Wilson's room, and the theory is that he throws on a dressing-gown—I'm sure he'd do that as he has strict ideas of propriety—and comes dashing over with a key and a policeman's truncheon to deal with any intruder. But nervous though poor Miss Jones was, she was more frightened of ringing the bell than she was of any suspicious noises she may have heard. Anyway, she never rang it. As a matter of fact, the windows that look on the mews are barred, as you see, and the ones facing the garden you needn't worry about. Any burglar who got into the garden would probably turn his attention to the house."

"I'm not a nervous type," Medwin said smiling.

"No, you don't strike me as timid. Now come down and I'll show you how you get out into the mews. Have you got your keys?"

Medwin said they were in her bag and they went down. At the bottom of the stairs was a narrow door across which was an iron bar that could be dropped. Miss Lyddon dropped it and Medwin unlocked the door. It led into a narrow passage at the end of which was another door leading out into the mews. This too was locked and barred. Opening it, Medwin looked out. She felt that the mews was a friendly place. Everyone in it was busy; near by a car was being washed; a milkman was delivering milk; a man rolled a barrel noisily over the cobbles and two boys were playing leap-frog.

"You'll find it more convenient to come in and out this way," Miss Lyddon said, "unless of course you're coming to the house. Now I'll leave you to unpack. If you feel like making yourself a cup of tea, there's about half a pound in a tin, and I told Mrs. Stevens to put a little milk in the 'frig.' There might even be some biscuits somewhere. I always think the first cup of something in a new home is an exciting event, don't you?"

"But it is all so exciting," Medwin said, and Miss Lyddon looked at her with understanding. It was Medwin's way to show pleasure, she was able to communicate it as some people were not, and Miss Lyddon was in no doubt as to her feelings. Making one flat into two, she said, and putting a secretary into the smaller one was her own idea and it was she who paid for the alterations and the decorating. The Stevens were more than willing, as there was now less work for Mrs. Stevens and they were a childless couple. Miss Lyddon said she never felt that Miss Jones knew how lucky she was to be there. That was one of the things that irritated her about Miss Jones.

"We'll expect you about seven-thirty," she said, and with a friendly look and a wave of the hand, went back to the house. An elegant creature, Medwin thought, watching her cross the garden; yes, elegant, that was the word for her. How straight she held herself, yet she had grace. To look like that at sixty-five was a triumph: she had an air of youth about her that Mrs. Gresham had not. She was at Girton, she had said. Yes, that was it, Medwin thought, it was Girton that lingered, it was the atmosphere of women, of young, intelligent women living together, that hung about her; the jokes shared, the clannishness, the friendships, so important and intense, the likes and dislikes so well understood that they need not be spoken. Yes, there was about Miss Lyddon the atmosphere of things understood between women, things that need not be spoken.

Then she put Miss Lyddon out of her mind, and made her longed-for inspection of the flat, for one could only make the sort of inspection she proposed to make when one was alone.

She felt as a dog feels in a new house, she wanted to use all her senses, even the sense of smell, and she did, in fact, put the curtains to her face, telling herself that they smelt French. She fingered things, turned lights on and off, switched on the electric stove, filled the kettle and put it on, opened the frig and put her hand in to touch the little jug of milk and feel how cold it was, for she had never used a frig before, never even lived in the same house with one. The hot water tap ran hot, there was warmth in the radiators, the reading lamp by her bed worked, and she sat on the bed to feel how springy it was. Then she went to the linen cupboard. Half a dozen sheets, half a dozen pillow cases, plenty of towels—green ones—extra blankets, lavender bags. Then back to the living-room. Her dining-table was a drop-leaf table which was placed against the back of the sofa. When the flaps were extended it would easily seat four, even possibly six. She went back to the kitchen. The silver—and it was silver—was neatly arranged in a drawer, and was initialled L. She found biscuits in a tin, made tea and drank it in the kitchen. After she had had her tea and washed the tea things, she unpacked, thinking as she did so that if she had not succeeded in persuading Louise to go to the lodge, all this would have been lost to her. Her clothes when she hung them up looked shabby, but today she did not care. She shook out the "little black dress." In spite of Miss Lyddon's saying she need not dress she would put it on, after her bath. She arranged her half-dozen books of poetry on the bedside table and wondered whether or not she would put Jervis's photograph on her dressing-table. She decided that she would not and carried it instead into the living-room, looking at it as she went. The eyes, loaded with too much meaning, returned her look. It was taken just before he went to Africa, and the eyes were saying, eloquently, how much he was hers. She put it into a drawer of the writing desk, but gently, as one lays flowers on a grave. Better to put it away now, she thought, than put it away later for some chilly reason; some reason at present unforeseeable, but, time and change and loneliness being what they were, probably inevitably. The photograph of Sarah, untouched by any knowledge of death, she stood on the end of the mantel. She had now done all there was to do. She had taken possession of her new home.

But she had to communicate her pleasure, for it brimmed over. She rang up Charlotte in Wimbledon, and Charlotte answered in her usual calm and business-like way. An admirable—indeed a perfect—secretary or personal assistant to some high government official had been lost when Charlotte married, Medwin had always thought.

"Wimbledon 0046."

"It's me, Charlotte. I'm ringing you up from my new flat."

"Oh? What's it like?"

"It's the sort of place single women hope to go to when they die. It has everything, even central heating and a frig."

"Sure you're not just bragging?"

"Come and see for yourself."

"I will. What are your two old women like?"

Medwin laughed, putting Charlotte's fancy and the facts side by side and amused by the misfit.

"What a libel! In their different ways they're both charming. Terrifically active. I shall have my hands full."

"They'll bully you," Charlotte said, not trusting women as employers. "They'll try to make you into a sort of secretary-housekeeper-companion. I know." Her voice was sharpened by suspicion.

"I see the mental picture you've formed," said Medwin, "but you're one hundred per cent wrong. They're not in need of a companion, I can assure you. They're very gay, and entertain a lot and I feel years older than they are. But years older."

Charlotte merely said, "I'd like to hear more in a week's time. How are things at the lodge?"

"I left Louise grimly settling in. She deserves a halo."

"I think it's mother and father who deserve haloes," Charlotte said. "Selfish little beast, she's never raised a finger for any of us in her life. The only thing she ever gave me was a bookmarker that fell out of some library book, and she once gave you a toothbrush."

But Medwin was still feeling grateful to Louise. "It's just that she and father together are dynamite. But there was nothing else I could do, was there?"

"I suppose not," said Charlotte, and added, "No, there wasn't."

"Is Sarah at hand?" Medwin asked. She had not liked to ask this too soon.

"She's in the garden with Karen. I'll call her. Hold on."

Charlotte went away and left Medwin thinking that there was no silence like the silence at the other end of a telephone, no void so blank. Then a small soprano voice spoke, and it was as if man had been made manifest out of nothingness. The voice spoke without punctuation and with catchings of the breath.

"Mummy Karen says maybe I can have a little dog like the little dog Karen has can I mummy have a little dog like Karen has?"

Medwin could feel her heart liquifying with maternal love.

"I don't know, darling. What would Aunt Charlotte say?"

"I'll ask her." There was that silence again, then Sarah was back. She dropped the receiver, picked it up and said, breathing hard, "Aunt Charlotte says we can talk about it on Sunday."

"That's a good idea. I'll be with you all day, darling."

"Good-bye," Sarah then said and dropped the receiver again with a clatter. It was picked up by Charlotte, who said, dryly, as if she knew that Medwin's heart was torn and knew it was better not to seem to know:

"Well, were you pleased with your daughter?"

"I thought it was pretty good," said Medwin, speaking unemotionally. "It's only the second time she's talked to me on the telephone. I'll be there early Sunday morning. About ten." She paused. "Will Harold be there?"

"I think he'll probably be off playing golf," said Charlotte guardedly. The sisters then exchanged good-byes.

Medwin, with a strong sense that this was one of those moments she would look back upon, went across to the house at half-past seven. She felt that she was now caught up in the machinery of time, that for years she had been out of it, marking some time of her own, as a soldier marks time, going through motions and getting nowhere. Her pulses told her that this, this should be the beginning of something. She rang the bell of the garden door and it was opened by Maria, the cook, and they smiled at each other, tentative smiles, explorative, interim smiles, on both sides. "Now that I have come here to live, I hope you will like me," was in Medwin's, and in Maria's there was, "You are not like that other one. What will you be like? But that is none of my business." She was a tall, big-boned woman, handsome in a bold, dark-featured way, with a short, curved upper lip darkened by hair, and a fierce, mobile lower lip. She would be capable, Medwin felt, of violent passions but also of steady and loyal affection. A person to be made a friend of, if possible, though she spoke only a few words of English and refused, Miss Lyddon had said, to learn more. Wordlessly but smiling, she showed Medwin the way to a short flight of scrubbed pine stairs, immaculately clean, which led up into the main hall, and Medwin wondered if she was right in feeling that to Maria it was like opening a door of a cage to a favoured bird.

Hearing voices in Miss Lyddon's room she went in, knowing that an air of timidity, the putting of a head round a door would not be well regarded in this house. Nor was she inclined that way. Years of office life had cured her of shyness. Its manifestations, she early learnt, were rarely pleasing to employers.

The two women were sitting with cocktail glasses in their hands talking to a large, florid, heavily chinned man who, though he was sunk deep in an armchair, bounced lightly to his feet as if the springs of the chair had propelled him.

"Here she is," Miss Lyddon said. "We were just speaking of you. Mr. Fullerton, our new secretary, Mrs. Blair."

Mr. Fullerton not only moved quickly and lightly, he seemed to Medwin to have been pumped full of air. His hand was plump and cushiony, as if blown up; he might have soared off in a breeze at the end of a string and floated overhead, possibly upside down. At the same time he gave the impression of sagacity and his large face was mildly humorous, with witty nostrils. His eyes had the sort of gaiety which is apt to provoke indiscreet talk, but he would have too much tact to allow it to go beyond desirable limits. Medwin was glad he was there, for she found exclusively feminine society a little flavourless. In the hospital she had had her fill of it.

Both ladies were wearing afternoon dresses, and Medwin saw that she had been right to put on her black, however shabby. Mrs. Gresham had on a navy blue taffetas, frivolously full-skirted and nearly ankle length. Miss Lyddon's dress was a clever black satin, the skirt drawn up into a bow on one narrow, unfeminine hip. Medwin did not need to have been to Paris to know that these two dresses had newly come from there. They did not look quite at home, yet, in London.

Miss Lyddon, hostess of course in her own room, poured Medwin a cocktail from a silver shaker with a cold bloom on it. Medwin could count on the fingers of one hand the cocktails she had drunk in the last four years, and they were all, she was thinking, at Mr. Schlemmer's. She sat sipping it with rapt enjoyment. From over the mantel, Miss Lyddon's possible ancestress, done by de la Tour, looked down on them with liquid dark eyes devoid of kindness. Medwin thought she had certainly been a trouble-maker.

Yes, she presently said, in answer to Mrs. Gresham's inquiries, she had unpacked and now felt completely at home. No, there was nothing lacking. It would take more ingenuity than she possessed to think of anything that should be in the flat and was not.

Mr. Fullerton's humorous and gallant nostrils gave point to anything he chose to say. It was plain that he was very much at home here, that he drew up satisfaction from the house, the room, the company of his two hostesses like a vigorous and thirsty plant, nourished himself well upon it, and would always be glad to come back for more.

"These ladies," he said to Medwin, and his nostrils twitched with humorous intent, "are the best housekeepers in London. With infinite daring, and well knowing my appetite, they have just asked me to stay to dinner, and yet I believe they have no dealings whatever with the black market."

"My brother in America is our black market, Archie, as you well know," said Miss Lyddon, filling up his glass. "And my dear man, all we are offering you tonight is baked fresh haddock with tomatoes and onions. Anyone could give you that. I cannot understand why people always feel they must apologise for fish, as if it were some ersatz food."

"Certainly one needn't apologise for Maria's fish," said Mrs. Gresham, stroking her abrupt taffetas bosom.

"I've just met Maria," Medwin remarked. "She let me in. She's like an Augustus John drawing, isn't she?"

Miss Lyddon flashed a quick, approving look at her.

"She is, precisely," she affirmed. "I have one in my room that she might have posed for. I'll show it to you tomorrow."

Mr. Fullerton looked at Medwin with twinkling reproach.

"I knew it," he said. "I knew you'd turn out to be Girton or Somerville. The trouble with this house is that I never meet anyone here on my own low, intellectual level. It's the one thing I complain of."

Medwin looked into her glass. She was half afraid of responding too quickly to the provocative gaiety of those small eyes.

"Unfortunately, I'm neither," she replied. "My education, such as it is, was acquired chiefly at the British Museum. And other museums."

All three now were looking at her. I'm talking for effect, she thought, but saw no reason to be ashamed of it. There was some long-endured restraint that required loosening. The pleasure of candour was a pleasure indeed, especially when in some doubt as to the wisdom of indulging it.

"What?" Miss Lyddon exclaimed, alert and interested. "Why the British Museum? Was your father a curator, or a lecturer?"

"No," Medwin said, "I simply mean that my father couldn't afford to send us to anything but a Council School, and that, I regret to say, he refused to do. So we went off to museums instead. We enjoyed ourselves very much, my sister and I."

"But this is fantastic," said Mrs. Gresham, leaning forward. "Surely, Mrs. Blair, you must be joking. You must have gone to school somewhere sometime. I never asked, but somehow I had the impression that you were at Cheltenham."

"Indeed not," Medwin said. "No, I'm telling you the truth. We had a governess when we were small, and I had a month or so at school when I was eight. After that, owing to my father's financial troubles, nothing at all, until I began taking a secretarial course at sixteen. So my intellectual level," she said, smiling at Mr. Fullerton, "should be low enough for anybody."

"Then the British Museum," said Mr. Fullerton with relish, as though he were tasting something good, "was your Alma Mater."

"Yes, though the Victoria and Albert ran it a close second," Medwin said. "And I think we knew every picture in the National Gallery. We liked the attendants there best of all. We found them the friendliest."

"So you've studied everything," Miss Lyddon said, amused. "Art, archaeology, science, history, what you please."

"We covered a good deal of ground," Medwin said, "in our odd way. My sister Charlotte was devoted to the Natural History Museum. I think that if she were to come upon the buried bones of a mastodon she could put the creature together from memory. She went in for South American butterflies as well."

They wanted to know more. She felt like a story-teller with a group of importunate children.

"And what about literature?" Miss Lyddon wanted to know. "You seem to be pretty well read."

"Oh, that was easy," Medwin told her. "We got our reading done at the public libraries. And in the summer we used to take our books into the parks and read them on the free seats. We took our lunches with us in paper bags."

All this, she saw, had delighted Mr. Fullerton, and had greatly interested the two women.

"What an extraordinary childhood," Mrs. Gresham said. "Then you were left to yourselves all day?"

"Yes. My mother was away all day—she worked at Chalkeley's, and we were supposed to keep away from our boarding houses—we lived in a variety of boarding houses—during school hours. People were not to know that we didn't go to school like other girls."

"But didn't they ask questions?" Mrs. Gresham wanted to know. "Surely they must have asked questions."

"We weren't allowed to talk to our fellow-boarders. My father made a great point of that. We were supposed to find our friends outside."

"But you seem to me quite as well educated as other young women," Miss Lyddon said. "What a comment on our schools! Do you ever feel you've missed anything?"

"More than I can possibly say," Medwin answered.

"Fill up her glass again, Marietta," Mr. Fullerton said. "There's a great deal more she could tell us."

But Medwin now wished to be eclipsed. She had held the centre of interest long enough.

"No," she said with finality, "there's really nothing more. And one cocktail is enough for me. You see how it's loosened my tongue. I'm not used to them."

Then Wilson came in and announced dinner.

The dining-room was banquet hall size and the little party of four had been placed at a round table at one end of the room near the big bow window with its drawn, crimson velvet curtains and at some distance from the immensely long Sheraton dining-table. The room was dim; such light as there was, apart from the candles on the table, came from the two nearest portraits which were indirectly lighted, and these at once drew Medwin's eyes. One was of the late Mr. Gresham who was seated at a desk handling a long silver paper knife and smiling. His look was blandly reassuring, as if someone had just asked him about the safety of some investment of which he warmly approved. A silver-framed photograph of Mrs. Gresham, as a bride, stood on his desk and had been faithfully reproduced. Both painting and sitter seemed to Medwin drearily undistinguished, and it was a pleasure to turn her eyes to the vivid portrait of Miss Lyddon's father, the Admiral. This, Medwin saw, was an Orpen. The Admiral was in Naval uniform with all his medals on, and looked masculine, masterful and self-willed. A forceful enough character to keep any number of daughters at home and in attendance. But Miss Lyddon, she suspected, had stayed at home of her own free will, for there was nothing about her to suggest that she was capable of self-immolation. With his friends, his bountiful way of living, his rich personality—and the portrait proclaimed a rich personality—he must have created a little world in which Miss Lyddon felt excellently herself. As hostess at Hartsdown—her mother died early—she must have found ample scope for her abilities.

Now that she had seen the two women together, Medwin had received the impression that Mrs. Gresham felt herself to be under some disadvantage. By herself her personality was striking; now she appeared subdued, diminished. She seemed, Medwin thought, a watered down Mrs. Gresham, less mistress of herself and of the house, which was, as she already knew, hers, left to her by her husband. Something seemed to have slipped through her fingers. Was it that while Miss Lyddon was the daughter of a famous Admiral, grand-daughter of a famous General and great-niece of a still more famous Lord Chancellor, Mrs. Gresham was merely the widow of a successful business man? As to what or who she was before, Medwin had no idea. So far only Miss Lyddon had chosen to speak of her forebears. Mrs. Gresham had said nothing at all of hers.

The talk, Medwin supposed, was the sort of talk one might expect to hear at dinner-tables in the spring of 1948. There was taxation, there was Russia and the cold war, there was the difficulty of France to form a stable Government, there was the Government at home. This latter topic engaged them for the longest period. Mrs. Gresham thought that the Government, though much abused, was not doing too badly, given all the circumstances; Miss Lyddon did not see how it could have done worse. She was not a woman, Medwin saw, who sat on fences, or hesitated to express her views. Mr. Fullerton agreed or lightly disagreed with first one and then the other of his hostesses, but was difficult to pin down. He knew, he said, so little. This exasperated Miss Lyddon who exclaimed,

"Don't take up such a lofty attitude, Archie. You have opinions like other people and you certainly don't know less than the rest of us. If none of us talked without knowing all the facts, there'd be little conversation."

"I'm always ready to talk, as you know," he said, "but I like to theorize rather than to dogmatize."

"Caution is growing upon you with age," she retorted. "You used not to be so canny."

Wilson served a pleasant white wine with the fish, and Medwin observed that Mr. Fullerton's nostrils seemed more capable of appreciating delicate odours than other people's. He held the glass first to his nose and then to his lips.

"Did I persuade you ladies to buy this?" he asked. "If so how right I was! How very right!"

Medwin hoped he came often to the house, for though there was something of the spinster-bachelor about him—he had never been married—he wore trousers, had the right sort of voice, smoked cigars and made three women more conscious that they were women.

I must have had an ancestor who went mad in a convent, she thought. The matron of the hospital—an estimable woman and a good matron—had taken a passionate interest during moments of leisure in knitting and knitting-patterns ("Look, dear, do you think this pullover would suit me if I made the sleeves long?") and at all times in obstetrics. How good to be out of it all, she thought.

Later she walked across the paved garden in the light of a street lamp that raised its head theatrically over the wall from the other side; a friendly, old-fashioned gas lamp, lighted, she had observed, by a lamp-lighter on a bicycle. It was a fine night and the polished stars were near and clear and reproached her with having mismanaged her life. They told her what she already knew—that soon it would be too late. Was this, she wondered, a recurrent note in the life of everyone—that soon it would be too late? Were we all conscious, she asked herself, of falling behind, of being ambushed by time with no goal reached? I cannot be unique in this, she thought, nor in anything, except that I am I. Everything else I share. And too late for what? For brothers and sisters for Sarah? For success and security? For giving security to my parents? For learning what I am and what I want to be? Well, she asked the reproachful stars, pausing half-way to her door, what are you prepared to do for me? What have you in reserve? Or have you nothing in reserve?

On her way over to the house, two hours or more ago, she had felt that she was stepping into time's current. Now she was less sure. That great house might be a backwater like other back-waters in which she had found herself. She longed for some stretching of the spirit, for some un-cramping release. How was it to be got? To earn a better living for herself and for those who more or less depended on her was not, she knew, going to be enough. She suspected that from neither of these two clever women was she likely to get the mental or spiritual impetus she groped for. No, it would not be from them that she would get more than she already had. She had lived blindly, doing what seemed to her best at the moment. This did not now seem to her good enough, and she needed, not someone else's view or vision, but a clarifying of her own. She pressed the heels of her palms against her eyeballs for a second or two.

Here, she thought, I could become a stalled ox. I must take care. None of it should satisfy me. But I have others to think of. My father, she thought, looking up at the stars again, needs a new suit. And there are bills to be paid. What have you to say to that? But at least let me always see where I am going. Is that too much to ask? That gas lamp sheds a kinder light than yours.

There was a brown paper parcel lying against her door and she picked it up, knowing it, by the weight, to be full of books. She bolted the door behind her and went up to the living-room which welcomed her like an old friend. She opened the parcel and among the books saw a note from Mrs. Gresham.

"I am sending you over a parcel of books," she had written, "some for your amusement and some for your information. I trust my own little book will come under the latter heading rather than the former. E.M.G."

There were some recent novels, none of which she had yet read, a little book she knew she would frequently have to refer to: "Titles and Forms of Address. A Guide to Their Correct Use," and slipped in among these was, "The East End Mother and Her Problems, by Edith Maud Gresham." Medwin opened it, thinking as she turned some pages that it would not be very well written and that the subject would somehow have been made a little dull, but making up her mind to read it before she went to sleep.

She undressed slowly and with enjoyment, then got into bed and took up Mrs. Gresham's book. At the lodge when she read in bed her father, who slept badly and often got up and walked about with the electric torch, would see the light under the door and would knock and say, "Isn't it time you put the light out? It runs up the bills, you know."

She finished the book before twelve. It was slight but it had been written, she thought, with sincerity and feeling. She wondered if Miss Lyddon too had written a book. Probably not, and that was perhaps partly why Mrs. Gresham had. She laid it aside and put out her hand to turn off the light, but before pressing the switch she looked about her. Mine, she thought, and for as long as I please. What will happen to me here? What changes will take place in me? And she wondered what message her predecessor Miss Jones would have left if she had thought of leaving a message Did Miss Jones feel, as she already felt, certain faint, possibly unacknowledged tensions between the two women? Did she find it difficult to steer a steady course between them? What warning, if any, would she have given?

I ought to be happy here, she thought, but something tells me it is not going to be easy to be happy here. This charming flat may have to be earned in unanticipated ways, and a time may come when I won't think it worth the price. Or is it Charlotte who has put the idea into my head? All the same, at this moment I am happy, and I shall allow myself to enjoy to the utmost all this luxury, or what to me is luxury. I shall explore and exploit every physical pleasure that I can get from it. And I am deeply thankful to Dr. Radnytz, and deeply thankful to Louise.

She pressed the switch. The bed was everything a bed should be; a faint, agreeable light came into the room from the friendly lamp which she could not now directly see. She felt cradled in well-being, in longed-for solitude, in delicious, rarely-before-experienced privacy. Her mind roamed back over a succession of bedrooms: her room in the lodge next to her parents' room from which their voices, however low, could be heard; then the rooms she had shared with other girls in London, the room shared with Diana, the room before that shared with Joyce Creswell, who had been killed. For a while, before that again, she had had a gloomy slice of a room to herself in a gloomy house in Kensington, and, after Charlotte had married and gone away, had had her own unshared top-floor bedroom in the boarding-house in Bayswater. Further back still were all the rooms she had shared with Charlotte, back to her childhood. In between then and now were two weeks in a small hotel in

Wales with Jervis, and after Sarah's birth, many weeks in a ward in the hospital. And now there was this.

Sounds came to her in a muffled way from the mews. Someone was garaging a car, but not noisily. There were voices, bidding one another good night, and the sound of doors closing. Perhaps the actress in the little house in the mews, she thought, listening, had been giving a party. There was the far-off rumble of London, so familiar to her ears, and this she could hear or not hear as she chose, and as she gave it her attention or withheld it. Now she withdrew her attention from everything but the physical comfort of being where she was, of being alone, blessedly alone, in her own place. She could have laughed aloud with the sheer pleasure of it. She stretched herself, relaxed, turned on her side and then said a lazy, apologetic prayer, ashamed of not getting out of bed to say it but hopeful of being forgiven so venial a sin. She asked that she might not forget that she lived a dream of her own making, and that it might be an acceptable dream to One to whom all lived dreams returned. So private, so secret were her prayers that she scarcely acknowledged to herself that she said them. Her prayers were part of her living, they were her roots, down in the nourishing dark and the nourishing stillness. She often felt deeply ashamed of not praying until she remembered how constantly she did. Then, not being wakeful by strange beds, she slept.

CHAPTER 5

When Charlotte came to the flat some days later for tea—Miss Lyddon, hearing of the visit, had let Medwin go early—she brought Sarah and Karen who were too young to be left behind. Richard, Louise and Tony were at school in Wimbledon and when they returned home, Richard, the eldest, would be in charge. He could be relied upon to see that nothing went wrong.

The two little girls ate the ice cream that Medwin had gone out and bought for them at lunch-time, and then sat on the floor looking at picture-books, solid, fair-haired Karen reading out the captions to dark, plump little Sarah, who listened round-eyed. Charlotte and Medwin made a tour of the flat which Charlotte said was charming but a little self-conscious. It showed all the signs, she said of having been "done" by a decorator, but Medwin told her that she was mistaken, that Miss Lyddon had done it herself. Charlotte looked into the built-in cupboard in the bedroom and saw the two evening dresses hanging up there, one black, one midnight blue.

"Miss Lyddon sent them over to me," Medwin explained, feeling a slight embarrassment, a slight reluctance to explain them. "I must have evening dresses and I certainly can't buy them. They're not new, of course."

Charlotte made a slight grimace.

"And what's the other one given you?" she wanted to know. She did not like Medwin to be the object of anyone's charity and Medwin was quick to feel this.

"Mrs. Gresham? Oh, just some books, one of them by herself."

"I think I like the sound of that one best. All the same, I wish you were in a government office again."

"Do you?" Medwin said. "You forget, perhaps, that a flat doesn't go with most jobs. I only pay for my food here."

They had now returned to the living-room and were sitting side by side on the sofa in front of the electric fire, feeling momentarily, a little withdrawn from each other.

"I know, I mustn't carp," Charlotte said. "If you're happy, that's all that matters. It's the first home you've had since you were eight. No wonder you're enjoying it. Are you happy?"

"So far," Medwin said, "I'm very happy."

"And they don't work you too hard?"

"Hard," Medwin answered, "but not too hard."

Charlotte presently began talking about Harold. They could discuss Harold in front of the younger children by the simple expedient of referring to him as Colonel Bogey and to Mrs. Loveday as Mrs. Bogey. Charlotte thought there had been a crisis of some sort in their almost married lives. The Colonel, she was sure, had now stopped wanting to marry Mrs. Bogey; she believed he was, in a way, grateful to her for not having consented to a divorce. She had an impression, though she hadn't much to go on, that the association might even be coming to an end. But Medwin doubted this. Harold, she thought, was not the man to relinquish a pleasure even though it had grown a little stale, and he would never find another golf partner like Mrs. Loveday.

"Don't you think," she said, "it's simply that he's now satisfied with things as they are? After all, he's getting the best of two very tolerable worlds."

"I suppose so," Charlotte replied. "All the same, he's spending much more time at home than he used to."

There was always such candour in Charlotte's face that Medwin could see the trouble there, a trouble that Charlotte was ashamed of but could not conceal.

"You don't seem, if I may say so, very glad about it," Medwin told her.

"Well," Charlotte said, "I know I ought to be glad, but the truth is I've got so used now to his being away most of the time that I'm beginning to find him rather in the way. He prevents me from doing the things I've discovered I most like doing. I never dreamt it would be like this. Sometimes I even ask myself if I was right not to let him marry Mrs. B. But then I know that's pure selfishness, and I ought to think of him and not of myself." She glanced at the children but saw that they were absorbed in their books.

"You didn't keep him from it for selfish reasons at the time," Medwin said. "After all, it *was* for his own sake, and for the children's, wasn't it?"

Charlotte paused for a thoughtful, worried second before replying, "I think it was. I hope it was. My feelings were perhaps rather mixed. The trouble is, my life runs in a peaceful, orderly groove when he isn't there, and I like it. But of course it's the children I must think of. Richard is so fond of his father. He said just the other day he envied boys whose fathers came home every night. I know I ought to encourage Colonel B. and I will. But he's so restless, and we haven't a great deal to talk about. When he left me alone so much, I filled in the vacuum in other ways, and now these ways have become very important to me." She hesitated, and then said, speaking more quickly. "When I told him the other day that I was thinking of becoming a Quaker he looked at me as if I'd said I was going to become a Whirling Dervish. He was quite horrified."

"But you never told me," Medwin exclaimed, "that you were thinking of becoming a Quaker."

"Well I am," Charlotte said, and her delicate skin flushed.

"I meant to tell you before, and I'm glad I've told you now. I find that Quakerism fits me like a glove. And lately I've been making some very good Quaker friends. I'm going to join." She looked up and looked directly at Medwin. "I wish you would too. I wish you'd come to a meeting some time."

"Oh, Charlotte," Medwin said, "you know how I feel and how I've always felt about joining things. I don't think I'm a joiner."

"I didn't think I was either," Charlotte said, "but then we were never encouraged to join anything. Father and mother never encouraged us or joined anything themselves. I suppose mother did once, but father never did, so she didn't go on with it. Do you remember when he decided that we ought to go to St. Paul's every Sunday, and he made a great fuss about it, as though we were about to begin a new sort of life, and then we went together just once, and that was the end of it?"

"You and I used to go sometimes by ourselves," Medwin said.

"Yes, but it was chiefly because of the singing."

"I can't seem to fit myself," Medwin said, "into any organised religion," and she hoped Charlotte would not persist in trying to persuade her. She didn't want to discuss her feelings about it even with Charlotte.

"You could into this one," Charlotte said. "I'm sure of it."

"Well, we'll talk about it after you've joined yourself, if you do join," Medwin told her. She remembered when Charlotte had taken up Yogi-ism, before Karen was born. After Karen was born she gave it up because there was no time for it.

"Oh, I've made up my mind," Charlotte said. "It's a tremendous relief, and I feel very much happier." And then she said, a little awkwardly, with the awkwardness that had been a part of her girlhood, "But you are religious, Medwin, in a way. At least you used to be. I thought perhaps Jervis's death might have made you feel you wanted to turn more to religion. We never seem to have time to talk about these things, but that's what I thought."

"It's odd you should say that," Medwin answered. "Jervis's death didn't affect me in that way at all. I don't feel any particular craving to be with him again, and I can't pretend I do. I'd love to think he existed and was happy, but I'd love to think that any of those young men who gave up their lives existed and were happy. I've no special feeling, I mean, about Jervis. We weren't close enough. We had no chance of growing together."

Charlotte's light blue eyes searched her face.

"Then you don't feel," she asked, "that you've lost something very precious?"

"Not so precious as this," Medwin said, and bending down she picked up Sarah and took her on her lap. She's my own, she thought. When shall I have her? This is the time when we ought to be together. She will be Charlotte's, not mine. Her eyes blurred with sudden tears that did not quite overflow. The fresh, childish smell of Sarah's hair and skin and clothes enchanted her. How beautifully Charlotte keeps her, she thought. She felt an anguished, hungry motherliness which was soothed and assuaged when Sarah put her arms about her neck and hugged her tightly.

"She's yours," Charlotte said magnanimously, and looked away. "She's not mine. Don't be afraid of her ever being that. She's quite different with you."

"I oughtn't to be glad when you're so good to her," Medwin said, "but I am glad. When you're bigger," she whispered in Sarah's ear, "would you like to come here and live with me?"

"I'd like to come now," Sarah said, and clung tighter.

Karen picked up the books that lay on the floor, and held them against her stomach. She had a square face, with a too well-formed jaw, a short neck and a square little body.

"Aren't we going home now?" she asked. "Isn't it time to go home?"

"Darling," Charlotte said, looking at her watch, "is that quite polite? It isn't time yet." It was as if Karen wanted her mother to know that she was loyal to her, that she was all hers.

Sarah begged to stay longer, much longer, and Karen said contemptuously:

"What do you want to stay in this little tiny place for I'd like to know, when we have a house and a garden of our own to play in? You are a silly."

There was no doubt, Medwin thought, that Karen was Harold's child. She felt almost ashamed of the greater charms of Sarah. Karen had always been and she feared would always be a bore. Listening to and watching Karen she understood how bores become bores, how they are born, develop and flower into full and perfect borehood. Karen's feet were firmly planted on that road.

She presently put on her coat and walked with them to the Green Park Tube Station. She had used this station daily during the war to get to and from her work, and now it brought back all the more vividly, because she had not used it since, the sights and smells of those times. She remembered again the crowded bunks, the musty odour of old clothes and old bedding and unwashed bodies; she recalled the spectacle of families making themselves ready for the night, or frowsily and wearily emerging to meet another day. What have we lived through, she thought, and how little it shows in our faces now! We live behind masks of resistant flesh, masks that are written upon only by illness, violence or the years. Her own smooth face, she knew, showed nothing of that time; it might have been aware, all its days, of life only as its most serene. The wail of sirens, the thud of bombs, the fears that accompanied them, hidden perhaps, but indubitably there, the long years of anxiety, were not registered. Jervis's love and Jervis's death were not registered. Sarah's birth and the mental turmoil that accompanied it, painful to look back upon, could not now be detected. Her burdens were not to be found there. The face she wore could pass for twenty-five or six, and that, she supposed, was to the good, if she were to count her blessings. But Sarah's hand in hers, the tightly holding little hand in its knitted glove was the greatest of her blessings. Sarah was her justification, her one achievement. She was grateful to Jervis for Sarah, grateful that he had wearied her into the marriage she was for so long disinclined to make, grateful that in doing so he had achieved, with some deep foreknowledge, perhaps, his own happiness and his own justification. Sarah was the name he had chosen, certain, as he was, that it would be a girl. She wondered if she had given Charlotte a wrong impression that afternoon, thought of speaking of it now and correcting it, but could not bring herself to it. No, she had told the truth to the best of her ability. It was better to abide by it, even if she had perhaps shocked Charlotte a little.

At the entrance to the Underground the sisters paused to say good-bye. Their eyes turned simultaneously towards the park, misty and bluish now in the dying light. They had had the same thought.

"It's too dark to see," Medwin said, "but I don't think they're out yet. I looked a few days ago."

"They should be out," Charlotte said. "They always were at this time."

"I'll look tomorrow," Medwin promised. "I'll walk this way on purpose to look."

They were referring to the hawthorn trees nearest to Piccadilly, at the edge of the park. These had always displayed the first spring green that had met their city-enclosed eyes as they walked past or rode by on the top of a bus. They had always looked, year after year, for that first new green, had felt sure, on seeing it, that however cold the weather, their winter was now over.

"I wish we saw each other oftener," said Charlotte, moved by shared memories and old, deep ties.

"We will now," Medwin told her. "But I won't be coming to Wimbledon on Sunday. I must go down to Hurcomb. I've had a letter from mother, and I thought she sounded a little worried. I'd better go and see if anything's wrong."

"I hope there's nothing wrong," Charlotte said. "I wish I could take some of the troubles of the lodge off your shoulders, but with the children——"

"Oh, Charlotte," said Medwin, "as if you hadn't enough on your hands! Don't think of it."

"Forget what I said about your job," Charlotte then said. "It's a lovely job, and I'm glad you've got it, but don't let them impose on you."

They were being buffeted by hurrying travellers and Medwin stooped and kissed the two little girls and watched Sarah turn and turn to wave good-bye, and smiled at Karen's square, never-once-turned back, until all three disappeared. She was surprised at the pang she felt on losing sight of Sarah. Her whole emotional life, she supposed, was now centred upon Sarah, and she felt racked by the parting. She was grateful to Charlotte for those words she had spoken. It was like Charlotte to have understood and to have spoken them. It couldn't have been easy for her to speak them. She had had Sarah for all but the first year of her life.

On most mornings, Medwin worked in Mrs. Gresham's sitting-room, but sometimes she and Mrs. Gresham would move letters and papers through into a room built out at the back, on the ground floor, which was called the office. In this room, Mr. Gresham in his lifetime had kept filing cabinets full of papers which he did not wish to keep in his City office. It was the only room in the house that Medwin did not like, but as Mrs. Gresham kept most of her own papers in it as well, sometimes it was more convenient to work there.

To Medwin, the office was permeated with the personality of the late Mr. Gresham, and she had already come to the conclusion that she would not have liked him. She felt there was probably nothing wrong with him except that he was dry, conventional and matter-of-fact. She pictured him as a typical well-to-do Edwardian, fond of grouse-shooting, and yachting at Cowes, and probably taking the events of the London season with great seriousness. So, she gathered, had Mrs. Gresham once done, but chiefly because he did. It was a relief, she had told Medwin to know that she would never again have to spend four days at Ascot, and three days at Goodwood. She had always, she confessed, found racing tedious. Everything she heard of Mr. Gresham tended to confirm Medwin's impression of him, and when Mrs. Gresham began, as she often did, "As my husband always used to say," Medwin knew she was about to hear some bit of banality. She wondered that Mrs. Gresham felt it worth while to quote him, for she herself was not banal. She was too human, too much given to giving herself away to be banal. She had warm, unexpected impulses, after which she would sometimes be overcome by shyness. She was like someone who had long worn an iron corset, and death would overtake her before she had had time to grow back again into her normal shape.

There was no doubt, however, that she had sincerely admired her husband. She told Medwin that though he had been left nearly a quarter of a million by his father, he rarely took more than three weeks' holiday during the year and almost never went abroad, and there was admiration in her voice. It was there when she said, "My husband died in harness. He wouldn't give up. The very day before his death he was at his office."

Never did Mrs. Gresham let slip any information about her earlier life, nor did she divulge her maiden name, but one day when she was in the office going through some files at Mrs. Gresham's request, Medwin came upon a newspaper cutting that had no business to be where it was. It was a column taken from a Leicester paper, and was dated January, 1933. It described the funeral, in Leicester, at the age of ninety-three, of Mr. Benjamin Boles, and heading the list of mourners were Mr. and Mrs. Ernest Gresham (son-in-law and daughter) and Mr. David Gresham (grandson). She was alone in the room when she came upon this, and was far too much interested to put it down until she had read every word. It was not private, it must have been read by thousands, and she did not see why she should not read it too. It threw an interesting light upon Mrs. Gresham and explained much that had been puzzling before.

Mr. Benjamin Boles must have been an important member of his community, for the paper devoted considerable space to a review of his life, and dealt with it in some detail. He had begun a remarkable career, it seemed, as errand boy in a boot repair shop, delivering repaired footwear to customers. At sixteen, wishing to learn the trade, he left to go into a small boot factory, and gradually worked his way up until, at thirty-four, he became general manager and then partner. His next step was to obtain a loan from a friend which enabled him to buy out the other two partners in the firm and become sole owner. From this time onwards, the business grew rapidly. Whenever new boot-making machinery came on the market, Benjamin Boles installed it. Profits were ploughed back into the factories and in this way he was able to keep ahead of all his competitors. For thirty years before his death, Benjamin Boles and Company had been a synonym for fine footwear, not only throughout Great Britain but in the Dominions and Colonies. The people of Leicester, the paper said, had good reason to be grateful to Mr. Boles and to flock to his funeral, for he had given his city some of its best playing fields, had donated large sums to hospitals, and had presented the Leicester Art Gallery with some of its most valued paintings. Mrs. Ernest Gresham, his only child, was chief legatee, but there were generous bequests to members of the firm, old servants and friends.

Although he took immense pride in his city, Mr. Boles had been determined, the report continued, that his daughter should have the advantages of a foreign education, and she had been educated first in Switzerland, then in Germany. At the age of nineteen she went to Cambridge, but left it in her second year to marry Mr. Ernest Gresham, head of the well-known investment house of Gresham and Protheroe. Mr. David Gresham, the deceased's only grandchild, had recently married a Miss Wickham of Montreal, Canada, and was now in business in Toronto.

All this shed such a revealing light that it was as if Mrs. Gresham had stepped out of a dark room into one brilliantly illuminated. Now Medwin could see all around her, back, front and sides. Now she had a background, she was three dimensional and not flat. She began to know Edith Maud Boles a great deal better and was grateful to the chance that had brought the cutting under her eye. She did not think she would tell Mrs. Gresham that she had read it; there was no good reason why she should. Either Mrs. Gresham herself or

Miss Jones must have put the cutting there by mistake. If Miss Jones had put it there, then Miss Jones had been more in Mrs. Gresham's confidence—(and what more natural, as she had been there nearly two years?)—than Medwin was, or was likely to be. But she was wrong about this, for Mrs. Gresham told her everything that was in the cutting and much more, but that was later.

The two women, she felt sure, had been discussing her situation. Dr. Radnytz had told them something of it, and direct questioning had disclosed more. One morning after getting through a pile of letters, Mrs. Gresham said, pausing to smoke a cigarette (Mr. Gresham had not liked her to smoke, but now she smoked about thirty cigarettes a day):

"Do tell me, Mrs. Blair, is it really true that your father has no means at all? That he's quite literally penniless? Dr. Radnytz gave us that impression, but of course he may have exaggerated it; Poles are somewhat inclined to exaggerate, I find."

Medwin admitted that this was so. Seeing that Mrs. Gresham intended to talk, she turned her chair a little and relaxed. "But my mother," she said, "has about a hundred and fifty a year of her own. And I give them my pension."

"Oh dear!" Mrs. Gresham exclaimed. "It must be a great worry and responsibility for you, particularly while your mother is so helpless."

They managed, Medwin said. Her mother was steadily improving and now her aunt was there.

"At least I hope your sister is well off."

"No, Charlotte isn't what you would call well off," Medwin replied, wishing that Dr. Radnytz had said nothing at all, "but she's a wonderful manager. She has five children to take care of and very little help. I marvel at the way she does it."

She guessed that while Mrs. Gresham knew something of East End poverty, other sorts puzzled her. She could not see how Medwin's parents could have got themselves into this fix, and appeared to feel that there must be some source they could have tapped if they would, and that they ought not to lean so heavily upon their daughter. It was not the first time she had spoken of it. Medwin supposed that while Mrs. Gresham must have known people who had failed in business, they had probably managed to save enough from the wreck to live comfortably on. No doubt to a woman like Mrs. Gresham, sound investments were a natural and inevitable background to the lives of people of the middle and upper middle classes. Medwin was learning to follow Mrs. Gresham's thoughts tolerably well.

"Well, you must certainly marry a man in comfortable circumstances," she said. "You owe it to yourself and your child. I hope you do intend to marry again?" And as it was practically a question, Medwin answered, smiling,

"I don't know that intend is quite the right word. I certainly hope I shall marry again."

"I'm very glad indeed to hear it," Mrs. Gresham said. "It would be a sad waste if you didn't. When are you going to bring Sarah to see us?"

"Whenever you like," Medwin said. "It would have to be a day when there isn't much work on hand."

"You'd like to bring her, wouldn't you? Or do you feel it's better not to interrupt the routine? I mean her routine, not ours. We could always arrange a time."

"I'd love to bring her," Medwin said. "Any day."

"Well, we must arrange it," Mrs. Gresham said, stroking her bosom. "Miss Lyddon was speaking about it just the other day. Bring her to tea. Does she look like you?"

"It's hard to say," Medwin answered. "It's just a little round face at present with dark brown eyes like her father's, and brown hair."

"It's sad you can't have her here with you," Mrs. Gresham then said. "There might be ways and means. Later on, perhaps, when she's a little older. How are you getting on with Mrs. Stevens?"

"Oh, very well indeed. She couldn't be kinder. She gives the place a thorough cleaning out once a week."

"I felt sure you'd get on the right side of her. Miss Jones, for some reason, never did." Then her thoughts reverted to the point she had started from. "Tell me, how does your father spend his time? I always think it must be tragic for a man who has nothing to do. As my husband always used to say, 'Serving time is better than trying to kill it.' He had an absolute horror of retiring."

"My father finds it rather hard," Medwin said. "Luckily he has the hens to look after, and hens can take up a lot of time. He isn't a reader, like my mother, but now and then he busies himself with some invention or other."

"What sort of inventions?"

"He's always getting ideas," Medwin said, "and sometimes they seem to be quite good ideas, but he's never had any luck with them. However, he makes plans and drawings and that helps to pass the time."

"What was he doing when he failed?" Mrs. Gresham wanted to know. "Was he in some business?"

"He had an export business. He must have been doing very well at one time. I think he got entangled in some scheme of someone else's. I think he trusted someone who let him down. He never speaks of it, and neither does my mother. I think she feels it would be disloyal to him to speak of it."

"She must be a remarkable woman," Mrs. Gresham said. "Of course," she went on, "there were a great many big financial crashes in the middle and late twenties, and I had a second cousin who lost everything in the depression of 1929 and '30. He bought a farm in Rhodesia and went out there. I believe he did very well. He's dead now, but his son runs it. I thought it was so brave of him to start afresh at his age."

"A very good idea," Medwin said, "if one has something to start afresh on."

"Well," said Mrs. Gresham, finishing her cigarette, "now I suppose we ought to get to work on that report."

The Mid-Metropolitan Hospital for Women got out an annual pamphlet reporting on its finances and activities during the past year. Mrs. Gresham made herself responsible for this, and she and Medwin now wrestled with it. Medwin admired Mrs. Gresham's zeal, for she fairly sweated over the wording of it and they made little headway. At last, feeling that they were getting nowhere, Medwin said:

"If you'll give me an idea of what you want, I'll try to put it into suitable words. Just an outline would do and then I could make a rough draft for you, embodying the statistics and so on, and show it to you tomorrow. Wouldn't that be the best way? Then you could make what alterations you liked and I'd give it a final polishing up."

"Oh, if you'd do that I'd be most grateful," Mrs. Gresham said, relieved. "It's just what Miss Jones should have done and could never do. She wrote just as I do, without grace or facility, but rather worse. She had no ear."

Poor Miss Jones, Medwin thought, not for the first time. They hang all their annoyances and dissatisfactions around her neck. They are retrospectively angry with her. Now that she has gone she is their Aunt Sally. So no doubt shall I be when I have gone. "What Mrs. Blair never seemed to understand," they will say, "was this and this and this."

What they had not learnt, Medwin considered, was how to make the best use of a secretary, though Miss Lyddon was better at it than Mrs. Gresham. It took a clever man, in her opinion, to train a secretary really well, and clever though these two women might be in many ways, they had not the knack. They had evidently failed with Miss Jones, and it would be part of her own task, she thought, to help them to get the best out of her successor.

By the end of the morning, Medwin had what she wanted. She intended to work on the report that evening in her flat. Mrs. Gresham got up to go at a quarter to one, for she was lunching at an Embassy, and Medwin followed her out into the hall, glad to be out of the room that had remained so very much Mr. Gresham's room, with its sporting prints, gun cupboard and rows of metal filing cabinets

In the hall, Mrs. Gresham's mink coat, crocodile bag and gay little feathered hat awaited her. This time she put on the hat in front of the hall mirror and it did not suit her as her plainer hats did. She seemed to be aware of this and kept Medwin there while she put it on tilted first to the right side then to the left and then to the right again. It only remained, Medwin thought, for here to try it on back to front. She said firmly that it was intended to be worn pulled down on the right side, well over the right eye.

"Well, if you're quite sure. I don't think Thorvald has been as successful with this one as he usually is, and it cost the earth. However, I see now that you're right." She turned away from the mirror and pressed a bell. "I hope you're giving yourself a good lunch today. Women who live alone are notoriously casual about their food. I hope you don't lunch off bread and jam and tea."

"No indeed," Medwin told her. "I'm much too hungry to be casual about my food."

"But you probably feel you ought to economise," Mrs. Gresham said, smoothing on her gloves. "You should lunch here oftener than you do. By the way, I hear Miss Lyddon sent you over some dresses."

"Yes, two. I'm wearing the black one tomorrow night."

"You ought to wear light colours," Mrs. Gresham said, "at

your age. We wear black so much ourselves." She looked at Medwin speculatively. "I'd like to take you to Bertha Mollnar's and get her to make you something nice, but I suppose you wouldn't hear of it." She smiled her wide, thin-lipped smile, and there was a certain shyness in it.

Medwin wondered if Mrs. Gresham had wanted a daughter. She answered, smiling back:

"How kind of you to think of it, but of course I wouldn't let you. I'll wear the dark blue one instead."

Mrs. Gresham, with a little frown, pressed the bell again, but Wilson appeared before she had taken her finger from it.

"Oh, there you are, Wilson," she said. He held up the mink coat for her and she slipped her arms into it. It was one of the finest mink coats, Medwin thought, that she had ever seen.

"When you see Miss Lyddon," Mrs. Gresham said to Wilson, "remember to tell her that Lord Albany has flu and won't be able to come tomorrow night. It doesn't really matter as we already have an extra man or two, but she'd better know."

"Yes, madam," Wilson said, and added, as if faintly shocked by Mrs. Gresham's indifference, "it will be the second time his lordship has had flu this winter."

"Well, remind me to ring up within the next few days to inquire how he is," she said. "He's getting on in years, I suppose, like the rest of us."

As she went towards the door, which Wilson held open, he took a quick look to see that she had left nothing behind.

"Have you your cigarettes and lighter, madam?"

"Yes, they're in my bag. Antonia has promised she won't forget again. If anyone wants me, Wilson, I shall be at the hospital from three-thirty to five."

"Is it the Mid-Metropolitan today, madam?"

"Yes. Good-bye, Mrs. Blair. Remember what I said about your lunch."

She hurried down the steps and into the waiting car, and Medwin returned to her flat, thinking about Mrs. Gresham and glad that Charlotte need not know that Mrs. Gresham had wanted to take her to Bertha Mollnar's to get her a dress. It was just one of Mrs. Gresham's kindly, foolish impulses, and would be forgotten, she hoped, tomorrow. Between her father, the successful boot manufacturer, and her husband, the successful investment broker, she had not, probably, been able to indulge many kindly, foolish impulses. She felt sorry for Mrs. Gresham, and that was something she was sure she would never be able to feel for Miss Lyddon. The two women, so utterly unlike in everything but their activities, had first met, she knew, as little girls, at the school in Switzerland, at Territet. If they had not met at some school it was unlikely that they would ever have met. She could think of nothing that might have brought Mr. Benjamin Boles of Leicester and Admiral Lyddon together.

She went into her little kitchen and made herself a salad. She then opened a tin of tongue that Miss Lyddon had sent over to her. It had come the day before in a parcel from America.

Miss Lyddon was inclined to enliven their work with little jokes and humorous comments. The Girton manner came out strongly, the here-we-are-together-and-we-can-say-what-we-please manner, a manner that might pertain to members of a close-knit, clannish family. Miss Lyddon got through more work than Mrs. Gresham in the same length of time and was easier to work for.

"It's a pleasant change," she said that afternoon, "to have someone here who has a sense of humour. Miss Jones hadn't an atom, poor creature."

"Poor Miss Jones," said Medwin, and added, "and I really mean poor Miss Jones!"

Miss Lyddon threw her one of her quick glances.

"I see you think we're brutal about her," she said, "but she was so utterly worthy and so tiresome. She was all that it's quite unbearable for a spinster to be, if you know what I mean. She made one feel so dreadfully that she had missed everything, which was most unfair as there was really nothing one could do about it."

"All the same," said Medwin, "if she hadn't been taken ill she'd have been here still, wouldn't she? She can't have been as bad as all that."

"She wasn't bad at all. She was a nice, good creature, but she depressed me. No one need be quite so colourless. By the way, I'm glad to say she hasn't got TB. after all. I had the report yesterday. She was simply run down and anæmic. When she's well enough, she's going to keep house for an uncle. And, brutal though you think I am, I'm paying her expenses in hospital—or rather we both are, Mrs. Gresham and I. So now let's get on with that speech of mine."

"You haven't told me much about it," said Medwin, opening a fresh pad.

"Well, I propose to tell you now. Bear in mind that the Lord Lieutenant of the County is coming, the local Mayor, various members of the County Council, and Mr. Walter Birdway, M.P., to say nothing of other worthies, including old Lady Rethwick from Mountjoy House. She's been one of our most enthusiastic supporters from the first, and she's going to say a few words. It's her privilege. As you already know, it's to celebrate the tenth anniversary of the founding of the Home, and of course my Committee will be there in a body. I want to lay particular stress in my speech on how much they've helped me, as indeed they have."

"I saw the list of names," said Medwin. "I rather thought Mrs. Gresham's would be on it."

"No, we decided a long time ago to keep our interests quite separate. I'm not on any of her Committees and she's not on any of mine. It's better that way."

"I suppose it is," Medwin said. They were sitting side by side in Miss Lyddon's room—Miss Lyddon never used the office—at a long walnut table in the window, and Medwin could look across the garden to the little green door of her flat. Miss Lyddon had at her elbow a pile of folders, all of which were labelled, "The Lyddon Home for Crippled Boys," and she now slid this along the table nearer to Medwin.

"Here, in this top folder, you'll find the agendas for the past year, and the Committee Reports. I'd like you to familiarize yourself with the names of the Committee, as you'll meet them all on the day. You know I propose to take you with me, don't you? It's important that you should see the place."

"Well, it's the first time you've mentioned it," Medwin said, with a smile, "but of course I'm delighted to be going. Can Mrs. Gresham spare me?"

"Oh yes, that's all arranged. She's taking you off to her Holiday Home one day soon. Now here in this second folder you'll find all the information you'll need about the boys' activities, especially about the wood-carving they're making such a success of. We're exhibiting an altar screen that they've made, on the day. It will just be finished in time. And then there's the painting, basket-making, cabinet-making, lithography, gardening and so on and so on. You'll find some very good photographs that I had taken last year, illustrating their work. In this third folder you'll find the rough notes I've already made for my speech and when I refer to the founding of the Home, see that I've omitted I, I, I, as far as possible, will you? I particularly want you to watch out for that, and keep it down to the minimum. I intend to devote five minutes to the founding of the Home, three minutes to the work of the Committee, five to the boys' training, hand-crafts and so on, and a good fifteen to the work of the specialists. You'll find all that here in this folder marked 'Medical,' and there are rough notes of what I want to say about it. I want to give special prominence to the work of that young Canadian, Ellsworthy. You'll find a lot about him in the medical file. It will interest you. Then I want to give five minutes to a survey of our plans for the coming year—you'll find a list of them in the first folder—and finally I must devote a good five minutes to the financial report. That's here in this bottom one marked 'Financial.' The whole speech should take from forty to forty-five minutes, not more, or we shall have the Lord Lieutenant taking out his watch. He has to give away prizes at some College or other later. I'm going to drive myself down in the Humber. I get so few chances to drive nowadays."

"Won't it tire you, just before your speech?" Medwin asked.

"My dear girl, I've been driving since I was eighteen. It's second nature to me. My father gave me a Panhard on my eighteenth birthday. We'll start early, so that we needn't hurry, and we can have lunch on the way. I do want you to see everything. You must make a tour of inspection with the rest of us, and then I'll ask the matron, Mrs. Chilvern, to introduce you to some of the boys. They're a splendid lot, really the most gallant little fellows. You've got the date, haven't you? April 9th. The daffodils the boys have planted will be at their best. We're proud of our bulbs."

"How quickly do you speak?" Medwin asked. "I haven't heard you yet."

"I try not to speak quickly, and I'm careful to make impressive Churchillian pauses. But of course we'll go through it and time it. I'd like to inject a little humour into it here and there, so if you see any opportunities for jokes, let me know. One or two might enliven the financial report, and as we're hoping to raise an extra three thousand this year we mustn't give the impression that we're downhearted. We're organizing the usual ball in June at the Winchester, and that always brings in a good dollop, as you'll see from the report. Last year we had three princesses as patronesses. Of course, Mrs. Debenham sees to all that. It's time you met. She's coming to lunch this week and you must come too. She's a great character and a first-class charity organizer. She does very well out of it but why shouldn't she? If ever anyone earned what they get, she does. I wouldn't have her job for ten thousand a year."

"Nor most emphatically would I," Medwin said.

"Ring for Wilson, will you, as you're nearest the bell?" Miss Lyddon said. "It's time for tea." She presently got up and stretched herself and then sank down into one of the armchairs, crossing her slim legs in their sheer, dark nylon stockings. "Tell me," she asked, "how do the dresses fit?"

"I let out the blue one as far as the seams would allow, and now it fits very well."

"How clever you are! I can guess where it needed letting out most." And Miss Lyddon laughed. "I was always as flat as a flounder. You're too young, of course, to remember the days when we were all trying to have flat, boyish figures. I heard of a woman in Paris who even went to the length of having her breasts removed. Our waist lines were down around our hips and our skirts up to our knees. I was in my element then."

Medwin smiled. "I can just remember my mother wearing dresses like that. She and my father—but especially my father—loved dancing, and they used to go out and dance three or four evenings a week. It seems incredible now. But I can remember her coming into my room to kiss me good night wearing a knee-length spangled dress and a bandeau round her head. She was very pretty."

"So that's where you get your good looks from," Miss Lyddon said.

There was no need for Medwin to reply to this, for Wilson came in bringing a tray, which had been awaiting the ringing of the bell. He placed it on a low table beside Miss Lyddon. There was tea for Medwin and chocolate for Miss Lyddon, who hated tea, and there were hot buttered scones in a covered dish, and small cakes. Medwin left her hard chair at the table and sat on the sofa.

When Wilson had gone again, Miss Lyddon said, pouring out her chocolate, "Thank heaven I can eat and drink what I like without being reproached by the bathroom scales. Every time Edith has a bite between meals she goes and weighs herself.

Tell me how you got that odd name, 'Medwin'? I don't think I ever heard it before."

"It keeps cropping up in my mother's family," Medwin told her. "I think it's probably Welsh. My mother's name was Carmichael."

"Tell me something about your sister. Is she good-looking too?"

"She looks more like my father. I think you'd call her handsome. She has regular features and very fair skin and hair."

"No brothers?"

"No brothers," Medwin answered.

"That's a pity," said Miss Lyddon. "A brother might have eased some of your burdens. Or, on the other hand, he might have added one more. One can never be sure."

Now it's her turn, thought Medwin, to discuss my affairs.

In her neatly tailored black suit, Miss Lyddon looked ageless and perhaps sexless. The bold arched eyebrows, bold nose and keen grey eyes were certainly not feminine, but there was nothing unfeminine, Medwin considered, about her approach to life. And certainly she had charm, more charm now, it might be, than in her youth. The crisp, beautifully arranged white hair suited her admirably.

"What a mixture of good and bad fortune your life has been," Miss Lyddon went on to say, sipping her chocolate. Then she leaned back in her chair and crossed her arms behind her head. "Your family troubles have been pretty grim, and you've suffered tragedy, but to balance them you have youth, intelligence, health and good looks."

"All but one of those are diminishing assets," Medwin said. "My only growing assets are—I hope—my intelligence, if I have any, and my daughter."

"Oh yes, do bring her here one day. I want to see her."

"I will, gladly."

"Edith was saying that we must fix a day. Do remind me."

It did not escape Medwin's notice that Miss Lyddon now referred to Mrs. Gresham as Edith which she would not have done earlier.

"I've often regretted not marrying," Miss Lyddon said, still in that easy, relaxed attitude, "but I've never regretted not having children. I'd have made a shockingly bad mother. I like decorative, well-brought-up children in very small doses, and in spite of their silly little minds, but all others bore or disgust me—

with the exception of my cripples, of course. I look upon them as highly interesting problems, and I've always liked problems. I nearly married a problem. Perhaps that's why he attracted me as he did. He was something of a genius." She paused, and then said, "One of my brothers interfered, and I've never forgiven him. He lied about me to the man I loved."

Medwin sat very still, holding her cup. She knew that Miss Lyddon intended to say more and felt that a small, unconsidered word or even movement might divert her. The surprising thing was that Miss Lyddon was saying what she was saying. So surprising was it that she felt she listened with every nerve of her body, every pore of her skin.

"I have three brothers, you see," Miss Lyddon continued. "The present Lord Lyddon, who'll be here tomorrow night, the one in America—my favourite—and this other one whom I never see, though I believe he lives in London. I wouldn't know him if I passed him in the street."

And as she was speaking, Medwin pictured another room, a collegiate room, and two young women sitting in it, perhaps sipping chocolate. It was a moment chosen by one of them, with forethought and for a purpose, in which to make a confidence, and this confidence was not unimportant for it made its own situation and altered a relationship, just as this confidence, made here and now, was designed to make a situation and alter a relationship.

"Why did he interfere?" she asked, and reached for a scone. The Miss Lyddon she had known and had seen almost daily for nearly a month was now changing before her eyes and a different Miss Lyddon was taking her place.

"He disliked me and I disliked him," Miss Lyddon said, still in her easy, relaxed pose. "He was jealous of my father's affection for me. He behaved so badly in the end that my father cut him completely out of his will."

"I can imagine a brother telling lies," said Medwin, "but not a lover listening."

"Ah," Miss Lyddon said, "but that would depend on the tales that were told. There are tales that subtly undermine, that eat away confidence. This man was also my brother's best friend. He knew that he would lose his friend in his brother-in-law. We both saw that as inevitable. Hence the tales, of a very special kind."

"Can one really hate a brother or sister one has been brought up with?" Medwin asked. "I think my family feelings would be too strong."

"Mine are strong too," Miss Lyddon said. "Very strong. Which only goes to show how deeply I suffered. One day I'd like to tell you the story because you have a quick grasp of character, and I think it would interest you." She gave a short laugh. "There were three or four rather unusual personalities involved, if I may include my own."

Medwin smiled at her, and then said:

"Do you never feel you'd like to see this brother?"

"I am not a forgiving person," Miss Lyddon said. "If he were dying and asked to see me, I would not go to him. After what he did, forgiveness would be a sentimental weakness, and as you may have discovered, I am not sentimental."

Medwin said, "No, I wouldn't call you that." She felt a little chilled by Miss Lyddon's ferocity, and wondered if she herself would be capable of it. Then her mind returned to the outcast.

"But don't you get any news of him?" she asked.

"Well, by a very odd coincidence indeed, I do know something of him. After Miss Jones had been with us a year she told me she was related to my brother's wife. I think they were cousins. She said she had not known there was any connection between the two Lyddons, or, in the first instance, that there was a Miss Lyddon here at all until after she was engaged. It was Edith, you see, who engaged her. I was in America at the time. It took Miss Jones a whole year to summon up her courage to tell me. It was so like her. It wouldn't of course, have made the slightest difference. Why should it? She was at liberty to report back to my brother's family and to my brother himself if she liked everything that went on here. In any case, after she had told me, we never referred to it again."

"Has he a family?" Medwin asked.

"Yes, a son and daughter. The daughter was on the stage, Miss Jones said. I gathered that she played small parts chiefly in the provinces. The son was in the Navy during the war. I don't know if he still is."

"Does Lord Lyddon see his brother?" Medwin inquired. Miss Lyddon having made her confidence, having aroused her curiosity, must now take the consequences.

"I imagine James has helped him financially from time to

time, but he never talks about him to me. Never even refers to him. He knows my feelings about Mark too well. You see," she added, smiling, "my brothers were all named after the Disciples. The one in America is Luke, and a brother named John died. I was the only girl."

"I wonder why you weren't given a Biblical name?" said Medwin.

"But I was," Miss Lyddon said, and laughed. "Believe it or not, I was christened Mary Martha, but my parents relented and called me Marietta."

"Which certainly suits you rather better."

"I'm relieved that you think so! I can't say I've ever in my life felt like a Mary or a Martha." She got up and rang the bell for Wilson to take away the tea things, then stretched herself again and sat down at the table. When Wilson had come and gone she said, "Now I've got a tiresome and difficult letter to write. It's to the headmistress of a girl's school I'm interested in, the Barminster Manor School in Dorset. I'm one of the governors, and I've been chosen by the other governors to inquire into some alleged irregularities among the girls. And when I say irregularities, I mean irregularities. What rumour says had been going on under the headmistress's nose almost passes belief. I shall have to go down there as soon as I have a free day and look into the whole matter, but I must first warn Miss Ranscome. A young gardener seems to have been the cause of the trouble—a situation straight out of the Decameron. He appears to have seduced no less than three of the girls—or so our informant claims—and one is said to be in the family way. If the story is true—it came to one of the other governors through a horrified mother—it's going to be difficult to prevent a noisy scandal, and I should particularly dislike that. One of my nieces is there."

"I'm sure you'll handle it with great tact and skill," Medwin said, and she felt that Miss Lyddon would not only handle it well, but would even enjoy doing it. She felt sorry for Miss Ranscome. "I suppose we shall have to word the letter with extreme caution," she said. "By the way, it's the first time I've heard of your interest in Barminster Manor. It wasn't in that list you gave me."

"Wasn't it? Well, you'd better add it."

"I wonder when I'll come to the end of your activities," Medwin said, and opened her pad. She marvelled that Miss

Lyddon found time to blow her nose. No wonder the telephone in that house rang without ceasing.

"Yes, there'll be need for circumspection," Miss Lyddon agreed and began to dictate. "Dear Miss Ranscome." She broke off to say, "Oh, one moment. I propose to call you Medwin. Mrs. Blair is altogether too unfriendly. Do you object?"

Medwin looked up at her with a smile.

"Please," she said, "unless you dislike the name."

"On the contrary, I happen to like it," Miss Lyddon replied. "Edith, of course, can do as she pleases. She's less unconventional than I am. Well, now for it. Dear Miss Ranscome——"

CHAPTER 6

THE FOLLOWING MORNING, MRS. GRESHAM ASKED MEDWIN to look up some of the guests in "Who's Who?" She wanted, she said, to get her facts right before the evening. "Just find out for me if Sir Charles Betchworth was at one time Minister to Bolivia. I think he was, but I don't want to make a mistake. And then look up Mr. Hepburn-Grantley. I can't remember who his wife was. They're Miss Lyddon's friends, but she can't remember either."

Medwin wondered if anyone got asked to that house whose names did not appear in "Who's Who?" and she took the book over to her flat when she went back to dress for dinner just to satisfy her curiosity. She found that only two of the guests were not mentioned in it. One was a foreign diplomat newly appointed to London, and the other was a recent discovery of Miss Lyddon's, a Scottish bio-chemist who was to sit next to Medwin at dinner. She had early discovered that both Mrs. Gresham's and Miss Lyddon's names were in "Who's Who?" Mrs. Gresham's for her founding of the Holiday Home for East End Mothers, for her book, and for the fact that she was on the boards of two ancient Charities to which she had been appointed in the place of her husband; Miss Lyddon's because she had been given a C.B.E. for her founding of the Lyddon Home for

Crippled Boys and because she had been for three years head of a women's Ambulance Service during the war.

Medwin dressed unhurriedly and with enjoyment. As she took a hot bath she told herself that this would probably be the best part of the evening. She did not expect, though she could not have said why, to enjoy the party itself so much as suffer it with grace, and, she hoped, helpfulness. There were to be nineteen guests, eight women and eleven men. Both Mrs. Gresham and Miss Lyddon said that they preferred uneven numbers and more men than women, as it prevented that tiresome pairing-off after dinner when each guest talked to some other one person for too long unless moved on, and that was too much like playing general post. They preferred to form people into three or four groups and start them talking. It was evident that they had given much thought to these dinners, which had become an important part of their lives, particularly, Mrs. Gresham said, since the war, when there was so little entertaining going on. It had become, Medwin thought, amused, a sort of rite. The two women were the high priestesses, and she, though not a virgin, was to be the young attendant vestal in the temple.

When the dress Miss Lyddon had given her had gone over her head with a rustle she almost wished the evening were at an end, for she felt that none of it would equal the enjoyable preliminaries. She zipped the dress up the side and went to the long mirror. Unless a too sharp eye detected the marks of stitching, the dress might have been made for her. It was of stiff dark blue silk and simply cut. The neck was square and low, the sleeves long, the wrist tight-fitting and the skirt dramatically full. Sewed into the waist band was an exalted name. But if Mrs. Gresham had said the dress was too young for Miss Lyddon, she was perfectly right. Medwin inked her old black evening bag which was threadbare at the corners, and presently crossed the garden, hearing her door click behind her with some regret.

The two women were dressed and waiting and the cocktails were already in the drawing-room when Medwin got there, but she was well ahead of the guests. Mrs. Gresham wore a black lace dress and all her pearls; Miss Lyddon had on a dress of supple grey satin and was wearing a Lyddon family heirloom, a diamond necklace over two hundred years old with earrings to match. She looked extremely handsome.

A fire burned at either end of the room, which ran the whole width of the house, the splendid chandeliers were lit, the green and gold brocade curtains drawn, and Medwin saw the room in its full beauty. Only one thing failed to please her. The flowers had been done by a firm of flower decorators and looked she thought, like set pieces at a fireworks display. She turned to Miss Lyddon and said:

"Would you let me do the flowers some time when you're having a party?"

Miss Lyddon was smoking a cigarette, a thing she very rarely did. She said in a voice that had a discernible edge:

"You'd better ask Mrs. Gresham. I'd prefer not to have flowers here at all. It's a lovely Adam room full of lovely things, and in my opinion it's like decorating the Parthenon. We never used to put flowers in the great saloon at Hartsdown, and that was an Adam room, too, though larger of course."

"They probably did decorate the Parthenon once," retorted Mrs. Gresham. She was helping herself to a preliminary cocktail.

"Anyway," said Miss Lyddon, "I've no doubt Mrs. Blair"—and Medwin thought she accented the name—"could do the flowers better, if flowers we must have. These remind me of the front windows of a café."

Medwin was not slow to feel that there was a tension in the air, a certain acerbity in the voices of both women. She wished she had not mentioned the flowers.

"Well, to me," Mrs. Gresham replied, "the room looks dead without them."

"Dead?" said Miss Lyddon, the hand holding the cigarette raised in astonishment. "What an extraordinary idea! I connect cut flowers with death. Perhaps I've been to too many funerals."

It struck Medwin that neither of the women had commented on her dress, though both had looked at it as she came in. She went to a consol table below one of the mirrors and slightly loosened some stiff-looking carnations.

"How I loathe carnations," Miss Lyddon exclaimed, her eyes following her. "I always expect to see a card attached, 'With the Compliments of the Hotel Manager'."

It was a relief to Medwin when the butler who assisted Wilson at dinner parties announced Lord and Lady Lyddon.

She turned to see a very oddly matched pair. Unlike his sister, Lord Lyddon, though by no means short, was as round as a large robin and his stiff white shirtfront and waistcoat described a handsome curve. His cheeks were full and red and slightly pendulous, and the only resemblance to his sister lay in the thick arched eyebrows and grey eyes. It was, in effect, a schoolboy's face Medwin thought, and he looked a little sulky, as though he had just been scolded for not washing behind the ears, and besides, had not wanted to come, but the eyes were shrewd and clever, and the big round head suggested no lack of brains. Lady Lyddon, though probably no taller, looked taller; she stooped slightly and had a plain, honest, excellent face that seemed to belong to an earlier period; it might, in fact, have looked out of a Victorian bonnet. Her dress of dark red velvet was badly made and pinned to the front of it was a heavy, ugly cameo brooch. She could not have been much over forty-five but her looks proclaimed that she cared nothing at all for the fashionable world and very little for her appearance. Miss Lyddon kissed her with affection, as, too, did Mrs. Gresham. She was so utterly unlike what Medwin had imagined that she could scarcely keep her eyes off her. If ever good nature and simple honesty beamed from a face, it beamed from Fanny Lyddon's. She had a confiding manner, and spoke as if she were imparting secrets, and when she asked a question seemed to hang breathlessly upon the answer.

Medwin thought afterwards that if the party had consisted solely of themselves and the Lyddons she would have enjoyed it, for she was extremely taken by Lady Lyddon, and amused by Lord Lyddon. He said occasional droll things without changing his sulky expression, and when not actually engaged in conversation and even, occasionally, when he was, would wander off to look at some book or ornament. His eyes blinked sleepily, and Medwin only discovered later how much they saw. The majority of the guests were friends of his; he was on first name terms with most of them, but if he felt any pleasure in meeting them there it was not discernible in his manner. His wife, on the other hand, put herself out to be pleasant to everyone, engaging one after another in what appeared to be, but Medwin knew was not, an exchange of secrets. A pair of amiable eccentrics, she thought, and she could not help wondering if the outcast brother at all resembled Lord Lyddon.

Medwin's experience of dinner parties was so slight that she had no preconceived idea of what such a party as this should be like, but nevertheless she felt, when it was over, let down. There remained a blankness; something was missing; there was always the feeling that the party was working up to some agreeable climax that it never reached. The people in it did not come together; the groups formed so carefully by Mrs. Gresham and Miss Lyddon were never productive of anything, so far as Medwin could judge, but inconsequential talk. There was no spontaneity. Nothing emerged. Just what she had hoped would emerge, she hardly knew, but in spite of her earlier doubts and her feeling that she would be glad when it was over, she had nevertheless hoped that something might.

What, she asked herself, do Miss Lyddon and Mrs. Gresham get out of these parties they give so frequently and at such trouble and expense? She did not feel that the parties were given in order to bring people together who might want to meet. It was a form of exhibitionism, perhaps, a thing that took many forms. "Here we still are," the two women seemed to say, "in spite of two devastating wars. We have not disappeared from the scene and do not intend to, yet. We still wear clothes that come from Paris, keep a handsome house, provide lavish meals, and know everybody. We are interested and interesting. We are to be reckoned with."

Her best moment was when Lady Lyddon beckoned her out of the group in which Mrs. Gresham had placed her, to join her on a sofa. She was no good at all, Lady Lyddon said in her confidential way, at high-brow talk. She only had four subjects: bird-watching, aquatic plants, the education of the young, and her husband, and none of those was quite suitable for dinner-parties. She told Medwin that she had a married daughter and a daughter at school, and that they had lost their only son in the war at the age of nineteen, a tragic fact with which Miss Lyddon had already acquainted her.

"I don't really like London," she said, during their talk. "I never have liked it. No one ever hated 'coming out' more than I did. I once went to a dance and hadn't a single partner, and I'm sure that's a record. I had no looks and no conversation, but as I didn't like young men, I didn't take it too much to heart. I'd already met my husband when I was fifteen. I knew I'd marry him some day, or if I didn't, that I'd never marry anybody. Now tell me how you like it here and how you're getting on. I think you must be very strong to cope with all the work you have to do, and very clever to be able to."

Lying in bed later and thinking over the evening, Medwin knew that for her by far the most agreeable part of it had been meeting Lady Lyddon, who was completely natural and a "character." She wondered if she had made her liking too apparent and half suspected that it had something to do with the quite unnecessary sharpness with which Miss Lyddon later spoke of her sister-in-law. Since the previous afternoon, when Miss Lyddon had chosen to put their relationship upon a friendlier basis, she had known that there would be difficulties in her path that had not been there before. She had felt, when summoned to sit on the sofa with Lady Lyddon, that this might not altogether please, and was somewhat prepared, therefore, for Miss Lyddon's tartness.

After the departure of the guests it appeared to be a habit with the two women to linger in the drawing-room and discuss the evening. They helped themselves and Medwin to orangeade, and Miss Lyddon took off her ear-rings, which were heavy, and was toying with them in her left hand. Mrs. Gresham was now in one of her blandest, most bosom-stroking moods. She had thoroughly enjoyed herself. As far as she was concerned, the evening had gone off extremely well. Miss Lyddon was disposed to dispute this; she did not consider it, she said, by any means one of their most successful parties.

"Well, if I may say so, Marietta," Mrs. Gresham said, "it was unfortunate that you asked that queer little Scotch scientist. It's always a mistake to try to mix people."

"You know so much more about these things than I do, Edith," said Miss Lyddon with a yawn, and then added, as if ashamed of this near approach to rudeness, "you're the party-giver. I wouldn't mind if we never had another of these big dinners. They're not my idea of fun. One can never get sense out of more than a dozen people at one time. Well, it's pretty late. I think I'll go to bed."

"I suppose it's time we all went," said Mrs. Gresham, evenly. Then she said to Medwin, as if determined not to pander to any folly of Miss Lyddon's, "I'm glad you got on so well with Lady Lyddon. We're devoted to her. But so is everyone who knows her."

"Yes," Miss Lyddon said, still playing with her earrings, "I often think that one of the best things James ever did was to allow Fanny to marry him. He'd intended to live and die a bachelor," she said, looking at Medwin, "but Fanny made up her mind to marry him when she was a mere child, and in the end she got him. It took fifteen years of patient and determined pursuit."

"Aren't you a little unkind, Marietta, to say that?" Mrs. Gresham protested, and set down her glass sharply.

"But why unkind?" Miss Lyddon inquired, lifting those bold eyebrows. "Fanny would be the last person to resent it. And it happens to be perfectly true. I never can see why it should be discreditable for a woman to know what she wants."

"I shouldn't imagine," said Medwin, feeling that it was time for her to speak, "that Lady Lyddon was ever in any doubt about that. In which," she added, "she's very much to be envied."

"Dear Fanny," said Miss Lyddon, "she's the kindest soul in the world, but I wish her kindness wasn't so apt to remind one of the lady of the manor bestowing coal and warm red petticoats upon the poorer tenants. After all, she was only the daughter of an archdeacon and hadn't a penny to her name." And she smiled. "But that's Fanny's way." She didn't wait for Mrs. Gresham to speak but said, quickly, "I think the dress looks very well on Mrs. Blair, don't you, Edith?"

"Well," Mrs. Gresham said, after a second's pause, "it's a little sombre. I'd like to see her in lighter colours."

"You'd better take her to see Bertha Mollnar," said Miss Lyddon, with a short laugh, and Mrs. Gresham took this up, in spite of its plainly intended sarcasm, and said:

"That's just what I'd like to do, if she'd let me."

"But I love this dress," said Medwin, wishing she were anywhere but in that room. "And this silk will wear for years."

Miss Lyddon got briskly out of her chair. She dropped her ear-rings into her bag and snapped it shut.

"I dare say Bertha Mollnar would make her up something very charming for sixty or seventy pounds," she said, lightly. Then she yawned once more, patted the yawn away and remarked, "Well, I really am off to bed. Good night, Edith. Good night, Mrs. Blair. Sleep well."

She went out of the room, and still Mrs. Gresham lingered. She lit a final cigarette and said:

"Do try to persuade Miss Lyddon to take a holiday, if she speaks of it to you. She really ought to. She always gets a little nervy and irritable when she needs a holiday. I can feel it at once."

"Is she thinking of taking one?" Medwin asked.

"She's been toying with the idea of going to see an aunt of hers in Ireland. She ought to go. The aunt is nearly ninety and has been begging her to come. She has a most charming place. Miss

Lyddon's very fond of her, and I'm sure it would do her good."

"She couldn't go just yet, of course," Medwin said. "Perhaps towards the end of April or the beginning of May."

"Don't you think yourself her nerves are a little on edge?" Mrs. Gresham asked, without looking at her.

Medwin was not going to risk being quoted as saying so, though she did not think Mrs. Gresham capable of such unfairness.

"No," she said, "I hadn't noticed it, but I don't see why she shouldn't take a holiday. She hasn't been away, she told me, since last August."

"Well, try to persuade her, if she speaks of it," Mrs. Gresham said, and got up. Then she asked, "You don't mind, do you, going over to your flat in the dark, alone?"

"Not in the very least," Medwin assured her. "There's the switch at the bottom of the stairs. I'm not at all nervous."

It was after midnight when she got into bed. She was a little disturbed by the irritability and unkindness Miss Lyddon had displayed, and lay thinking about it before turning out the light. But the two women, she said to herself, had known each other since childhood. What more natural than that they should get on each other's nerves now and again? The wonder was, surely, that they got on so well. Still, it had been a little deplorable.

She wouldn't have cared, she thought, or she would have cared less, if she had not felt herself to be involved in it, but she was quite sure that she was. Both before and after the party she had been conscious of tension, with herself as the core of it. She tried to imagine just what had occurred to cause this tension, then gave it up as not being worth her while. Whatever it was, it would have vanished in a day or two. Her conscience was clear. But she could not quite forget the expression in Miss Lyddon's eyes when she had once or twice looked across the room at her while she was sitting talking to Lady Lyddon.

Absurd, she thought, but nevertheless she was sure she was not mistaken. Miss Lyddon was an intensely possessive woman, capable, she knew, of strong antipathies and jealousies and of an equally intense pride. A woman with less humility it would be hard to find. Medwin knew herself to be at present the object of her liking, and once having bestowed this liking she would keep a close and possessively watchful eye upon the recipient of it. She did not think there was anything more in it than that, and it was enough.

Well, Miss Lyddon might have been a different woman, she thought, if that brother of hers hadn't interfered. And she supposed she would have to hear that story one of these days. She'd been swinging between those two, she told herself, ever since she'd been there. Now she'd swung over to Mrs. Gresham's side, and this was something to be regretted. She did not want and must not be on either side, but discreetly and comfortably and safely in the middle. She must learn to regard them both in a large, human, understanding way; to be merely amused by their foibles and to approve and admire their many admirable qualities. But as to these, she admitted, she had not yet wholly made up her mind. At times she regarded her employers as two spoilt and shamefully lucky women who did their good deeds very much in the public eye; who required, in fact, plenty of limelight for their performance. She did not envy them a single quality or a single possession. She would have hated to be in the shoes of either; even in imagination the thought appalled her. No, she had not arrived at any conclusions about them yet, and perhaps it was better that she should not. Let them be and flourish and strike attitudes and get what they could out of living; it was no concern of hers. They were, like anyone else, facing the unknown dark, and facing it as best they knew how. (Plagued, both of them, also, with thoughts of death duties, she knew; that added millstone the State binds to the necks of the ageing rich.) They did not seem, either of them, to be interested in whether or not they were to meet total oblivion, total shipwreck, or find themselves wading to some other shore. They had never spoken of any such contingency, nor hinted at it. Mrs. Gresham went, rather ashamedly to church, a fact Medwin had only chanced to discover by seeing her one morning about to step into the car, prayer-book in hand. She had paused on seeing Medwin and had said, with heightened colour and a faint air of embarrassment, "Oh, good morning, Mrs. Blair. I'm just off to church, as you see," and had waved prayer-book and gloved hand from the car window. Miss Lyddon, she knew, never went to church and was disposed to believe what she could see. She had once heard her say that man had invented God because he was ashamed to accept responsibility for the mess he had made.

Very well, she thought, wishing her brain would stop its aimless activity, the dinner party was over; there would be another soon and she would get used to them. She was not likely to meet anyone who would be more than passingly interested in her, or in whom she was likely to be more than passingly interested. She had liked Lady Lyddon for her unusualness and her naturalness, but if there was a possibility of friendship there, it was one she had better deny herself. Miss Lyddon would care nothing at all about the friends she made outside her circle; inside it, it would be quite another matter.

But still she could not sleep. There had been too much of everything that evening. Too many people whom she had tried to place and remember, too much (for her) unprofitable talk out of which nothing emerged, too much to eat and drink, far too much that was unpleasing between the two women. Better to think about her own affairs. Better to think about the lodge and her visit there last Sunday. She had hardly had time, since, to review the day, and there had been much that required reviewing.

Walking from the bus stop to the lodge she had been aware of the loud clear fluting of blackbirds. The day was dull, but not cold; it had not been a cold winter, and now it seemed to be dissolving into an early spring. City-bred though she might be, she had a quick ear for country sounds and a quick eye for such things as primrose clusters in which flower-buds were well forward, and for the first shiny celandines. These were not trivialities to her, they were events that marked her year and her memory. She regretted that Sarah was not being brought up in the country but in a street of small gardens and ugly, semi-detached houses whose fronts were made uglier still by garage doors. She did not regret having been brought up in a city herself because she knew she had managed to keep country-conscious and country-minded. Growing-things and the seasons were ever-present to her. The skies and clouds were objects of delight and interest to her from childhood, and she always knew, and was surprised if other people did not, whether the moon were waxing or waning. Now she breathed the country air with delight, and was thankful that Mr. Schlemmer showed no sign of wanting to use the lodge, and that he had recently had it repainted at his own expense. Her parents, she thought, might be far worse off, and she wished her father had discarded his absurd prejudice against Mr. Schlemmer, a prejudice which was partly due to his being in films and partly due to his belonging to a race which excelled in the very ways in which her father had himself so longed to excel. He could endure to look upon the comfortable prosperity of Mr. Chartley. It was a fine thing to see the English farmer prospering. But Mr. Schlemmer's prosperity deeply affronted him.

She went to the door of the lodge and opened it, pushing aside a heavy curtain which was hung there to keep out draughts, as the door opened straight into the living-room. For the first time she saw her mother in the wheel chair which had been borrowed from the hospital. She cried, pleased by the sight, "Oh, mother! How lovely to see you sitting up!" and in almost the same breath, so as not to give offence, "Hello, Louise! How are you?" and kissed her mother and then Louise without pausing to see if the latter kiss were expected. Mrs. Fosdick had been mending a pillowcase and Louise was altering a blouse of a very ugly striped material. Mrs. Fosdick's hair was untidy, as she found it difficult to keep her arms raised long enough to do it properly, and Louise was unable at any time to do her own hair, let alone her sister's. Hers was a wild scribble of grey about her face and was drawn into a knot behind and skewered with long metal hairpins. Medwin thought she saw something more than the usual pleasure and relief in her mother's face at the sight of her.

"Where's father?" she asked, and pulled off her small round felt hat. "Busy with the hens?"

"No," said Mrs. Fosdick, "he's over at the farm. Oh, I'm so glad to see you, darling. You look wonderfully well. I'm so glad you're here."

"I'm glad too," Medwin said and went towards the door of her mother's bedroom. "I'll just leave my coat and hat in your room."

"Would you mind leaving them in Louise's room this time?" Mrs. Fosdick asked quickly. "It's sure to be much tidier than mine."

Medwin glanced at her mother in some surprise but did as she was asked to do. Louise's room had been hers; it was at the back of the lodge, facing the hen-run, and she was no sooner inside than she saw that the hen-run was now deserted. The hens had all gone and the place had a forlorn, abandoned air. Medwin stood taking in this fact and then realized what must have happened. Her father had gone to stay at the farm. That explained his absence today. The hens had had to be given up as neither her mother nor Louise could look after them. Her father had found life under the same roof as Louise intolerable. This move might have taken place very recently, perhaps only the day before, as her mother would otherwise have written to tell her. Her mother had wanted her to go into Louise's room knowing that she would see the empty hen-run and put two and two together. She did not want to have to explain or even refer to her father's absence in front of Louise.

So that, thought Medwin sadly, was what all her planning had come to. Her father had gone to stay with the Chartleys, and as he couldn't pay them he was there as a guest, or as an object of charity. She thought that Louise could be counted upon to get lunch, and she could discuss this turn of affairs with her mother then. She returned to the living-room.

"Did you get the books I sent you, mother?" she asked, and Mrs. Fosdick, meeting her eyes, knew that Medwin now knew that her father had gone. She said, and her face showed her relief:

"Yes, dear. I would have written if you hadn't been coming today. I'm most grateful for them. Louise has been reading the new Agatha Christie aloud to me."

"I don't find detective novels as absurd as most novels," Louise said. "The average novel disgusts me. There is scarcely a word of truth in any of them, or any attempt to present the world from an intelligent and enlightened angle. But if someone is murdered, he's murdered, and the crime must be solved. That at least makes sense."

"I wonder you can endure being a librarian," Mrs. Fosdick said with a smile.

"I have learnt to hold my tongue," said Louise.

"Then I'd better send some more detective novels," Medwin said.

"Not for me, dear," Louise answered. "I have my own reading to do. And I take little walks and with the cooking and housework I am not idle."

"She's been so good to me," Mrs. Fosdick said.

"I don't want gratitude," Louise said, "though of course the work here is much harder than the work at home, in my own house, where everything is far more conveniently arranged." She gave a dry little cough and bent her head to bite off a thread. Medwin, who could not bear to see anyone bite threads, took a pair of scissors from the table and laid them in her lap.

"Thank you dear." Louise folded up the blouse. "I have finished. And my teeth are very good you know, thanks to the uncooked food I eat. Now I think I'll go for a little walk and leave you to talk to your mother. I'll be back in time to get lunch."

"No, no," Medwin said. "I'll get lunch. I brought down a tin of tongue. Miss Lyddon gave it to me. She gets a lot of parcels from America."

"What a lovely treat!" Mrs. Fosdick said. Louise went into her room and came out wearing a coat and the battered hat.

"I shall walk to the village and back," she said, looking at the clock. "It will take me exactly twenty-five minutes each way. As you know, I walk very quickly." She did not linger but went closing the door firmly behind her.

Mother and daughter looked at each other.

"So that's what had to happen," Medwin said. "Father has cleared out."

"Don't worry about it, dear," Mrs. Fosdick pleaded. "I guessed it would happen. I'm awfully sorry for you, after you'd managed everything so well. They simply couldn't endure each other. Either Louise had to go or your father, and it seemed better for him to go."

"He's at the Chartleys, I suppose."

"Yes. They like him, and I believe he helps Mrs. Chartley in the kitchen. He doesn't mind doing little things there that he wouldn't dream of doing here because he couldn't bear us to see him doing them."

"Yes, that's all very well," said Medwin, "but he can't stay there without paying for his board and lodging."

"He got eight pounds for the hens," Mrs. Fosdick told her, and added, "he sold them to Mr. Schlemmer."

"Oh, God!" Medwin cried, and then was ashamed, for she was not in the habit of calling flippantly upon the Deity. "How did he manage to do that?"

"Mr. Schlemmer was here, as it happened. He came to see me, to ask how I was, and your father decided to come in and talk to him. You know that as a rule he climbs out through the bedroom window if he sees him coming. Well, he did this time, but he came back through the back door and shook hands with Mr. Schlemmer as if he were his best friend. He said he'd decided to go away for a visit and as he couldn't leave the hens he was going to sell them, and did Mr. Schlemmer know of anyone who might like to buy them. Mr. Schlemmer said how many and how much—you know his abrupt way—and they agreed that eight pounds was a fair price. Mr. Schlemmer took out his pocket-book then and there and paid it. He said he could always manage to keep a few extra hens. He sent for them about an hour later, and since then his gardener's been down with a dozen eggs for me." She laughed helplessly, and tears came into her charming blue eyes. "What could I do? I just let them settle it between themselves. Oh, dear, your father is so funny!"

"He's very funny indeed," Medwin agreed unsmilingly. "Very. So now he's got eight pounds. Will he give any of it to the Chartleys?"

"I hope so," said Mrs. Fosdick. "I asked him to. All this," she said, "happened the day before yesterday, rather late in the afternoon. I'd missed the post, so I thought I wouldn't write, but would wait to see you. There's such a lot to tell you, darling, I hardly know where to begin, and now I find I've begun in the middle."

"The last time I came," Medwin said, "I thought it was all working quite well."

"Well it never did work really well. I don't think any of us thought it would, but there seemed no sign of an immediate explosion, and your father kept out of Louise's way as much as he could. But of course she's very provocative. She attacked all his most cherished beliefs. She even attacked Mr. Churchill. I knew then that it couldn't go on. She called him a lackey." She laughed again and put her handkerchief to her eyes. "Where does she get these extraordinary expressions from? It's as if she'd been reading 'Pravda.' Your father said she was a something or other Communist and she said he couldn't hurt her feelings that way, and she didn't lose her temper which of course made him lose his. But that wasn't what made him finally leave."

"You'd better tell me the worst," Medwin said. "Go on."

"It's pretty bad," Mrs. Fosdick told her. "I hate to tell you, and I think in a way your father was ashamed of himself though of course he wouldn't say so. Oh, Medwin!" she cried. "I'm so sorry for him! He wasn't meant to be like this. Why did things always have to go so badly for him?" And she bit her lower lip, which trembled.

"Mother," said Medwin, laying her hand on her mother's knee, "he's always had you. He doesn't know how lucky he is."

"Yes he does," Mrs. Fosdick said and blew her nose. "But that only makes it worse, feeling as he does that he's let me down.

I wish he wouldn't. There were ways in which he might have let me down but he never did. Well," she went on, "after that argument about Mr. Churchill your father could hardly bring himself to speak to Louise. He seemed to brood over it. Then the day before yesterday, in the afternoon, Louise went out for a walk and your father was sitting here, playing patience. I was in the bedroom, trying to do my hair. Suddenly I heard Louise's voice. I heard her cry out, 'What are you doing in my room? How dare you!' I wheeled myself in here as fast as I could and I saw your father coming out of Louise's room very red in the face and Louise following him, looking like a witch full of righteous wrath, if you can picture such a thing. She'd come in quietly—you know he's getting a little deaf—and found him on his knees in front of her suitcase, which she keeps under the bed. He told me afterwards that he was sure Louise kept subversive literature in there and he was looking for it."

"Did he find any?" Medwin asked quickly.

"I don't know. I doubt if he had time to look properly. She had come back unexpectedly for her umbrella, as it looked like rain. There was really nothing he could say. There he was, in her room, looking through her things. He told her that after what she'd said about Mr. Churchill he had a right to search her room, that he was certain she was a dangerous person and up to no good. Louise was quite white and shaking. She said she wouldn't put up with such treatment and that he'd better leave the house. Of course he said he wasn't going to be ordered out of his own house, whereupon she said it was your house, not his and she had a better right to be here than he had. You had asked her to come, and she wasn't going until you agreed to let her go. Besides which, I had to be taken care of. I begged him to apologize but he wouldn't listen to me. He came straight in here and began to pack his things. I realized then that it would be best for him to go at once, and I tried to telephone for a taxi, but the wretched telephone wasn't working. It's been out of order such a lot lately. Louise had just gone out, and I wanted her to go up to Mr. Schlemmer's to telephone for a taxi from there, so without thinking I got up to run after her."

"You what, mother?" asked Medwin, horrified.

"I know, darling, I'm terribly sorry, but I suppose you have to know. I forgot my crutches, I just got up and ran after Louise. At the door I collapsed. She heard me and ran back and the two of them picked me up. Then she hurried up to Mr. Schlemmer's and telephoned for Dr. Tenby. That's how Mr. Schlemmer happened to come here, to ask how I was, and how he happened to buy the hens. He took your father over to the farm himself later, in his car."

"But your hip, your hip!" cried Medwin, anguished.

"I'm coming to it. Dr. Tenby got here very quickly. He doesn't think I've done it any real harm, but he wants me to go over to the hospital tomorrow morning for an X-ray. He's arranged for the ambulance and everything. Don't worry, darling. He seemed quite certain there was no real damage done. When I come back from the hospital I'm to go back to bed again for a week or so, just as a precaution."

"Oh, mother, mother!" Medwin said, shaking her head. "Just as you were getting on so well."

Her mother put out her hand.

"Forgive me," she said. "I'm not in any pain. I'm sure it's all right."

Medwin made up her mind to ring up Dr. Tenby that evening. It didn't matter about her father and Louise. That had its comic side. It would be a change for her father to stay at the farm and for her mother to be without him. They had not been separated for a night, she thought, for fifteen years.

And then her mother asked:

"Medwin, do you think your aunt is quite right in her head? She's become so queer. I can hardly blame your father for being suspicious, though of course it's quite silly. What harm could she do?"

"I think she's a little peculiar," said Medwin, "but quite harmless." And being on dangerous ground she asked, "Tell me, how does she cook?"

"Well, I wouldn't like to be Mr. Beedle," her mother said.

Her mother was eager to hear about her work and about Mrs. Gresham and Miss Lyddon, and Medwin described it all in a way that was flattering enough. She might be critical of the two women herself, but she would not criticize them to her mother. She went on to tell her about the dinner party and the people who were expected, and about the people she had already met.

"I wish you could see your father this afternoon," Mrs. Fosdick said. "It would interest him so much." She laughed. "He could look them all up in 'Who's Who?' Did I tell you about his going to the Auction Sale at the Grange and buying a 1939 'Who's Who?' for two and sixpence? It was badly inkstained. He came home with it like a dog with a bone." She added, "I saw him put it into his suitcase to take to the farm."

"You're wonderful about father," Medwin said.

"If you love someone," her mother said, "it isn't hard to see the reasons for the funny things they do. It helps him to feel he isn't entirely out of everything."

"Oh, mother," Medwin said, "I'll do things for you some day. I'll take you to Italy, I swear I will. Or anywhere you want to go."

"Medwin," her mother said, "I wish you wouldn't worry about money. You're doing wonderfully well. We have all we really need—except that I know your father wants a suit very badly—and Sarah is being well looked after. Please don't worry. It was because your father worried so that he got into difficulties. He wasn't satisfied with enough. I want you to be satisfied with enough."

"Well, I will be," Medwin said, "when I have it. And I'm not like father. I take after you."

In the afternoon, rather against her will, Medwin walked to the farm to see her father. Even at a brisk pace it was a good half hour's walk, and she marvelled that her father had walked it so often. The road leading up to it was deep in mud and cow-dung, and she wished she had worn rubber boots. It was an old, rambling, sixteenth century farmhouse, immensely strongly built with huge chimneys and great curving oak beams. She picked her way up to the door and knocked, and one of the Chartley children, a not very bright boy of eight or nine, opened it. He stood staring as if he had never seen her before, and she put her hand on his head and said, "Hello, Charlie, may I come in?" He stood, still staring at her, and she went into the living-room, looking for Mrs. Chartley. There was no one there, so she went on into the kitchen. This was a big, stone-floored, low-ceilinged room, and at the far end of it she saw her father standing at a sink peeling potatoes, a sack tied about his middle. In spite of what her mother had said the sight brought her up short. Never before in her life had she seen her father performing any sort of household task except boiling a kettle and filling a teapot.

She called, "Hello, father. You seem very busy. I've come to pay you a visit."

At the sight of her he dropped the knife and the potato he was peeling into the basin with a splash and shamefacedly began to undo his apron.

"Don't bother," she said. "I'm not a stranger. I'm just Medwin. How are you?"

"I'm glad to see you," he said, still fumbling, but she knew he was too much embarrassed to be glad. "Mr. and Mrs. Chartley have gone over to Hart's Cross to look at a bull. They'll be back soon. Won't you sit down? I told Mrs. Chartley I wouldn't mind peeling a few potatoes for supper, as I had nothing in particular to do."

"You sit down," Medwin said, undoing the sacking for him, "and I'll go on with the potatoes." She was glad to have something to do, for her father was uneasy, and she thought it would be better if they didn't sit looking at each other.

"Well," she said, when he had sat down in a kitchen chair, "tell me about things. I hear there was a little trouble at the lodge." Her anger with her father was evaporating, and the sight of him shamefacedly fumbling with the apron had touched her.

He coughed and said, "Well, yes, there was. I'm terribly sorry about your mother. I wouldn't have had that happen for anything."

"I suppose," said Medwin, "that Louise is pretty difficult to get on with, but I hoped you'd put up with a little annoyance until I could make other arrangements." And then she felt ashamed of the way her words sounded. She had not meant to take this superior, scolding tone with him. He was not in a position to resent it, and the sad, sagging lines of his face reproached her.

"But I've no doubt," she said, "that she was very provoking."

"Provoking," he said, and gave a short, bitter laugh. "For the first time in my life I understand why people commit murder."

"Oh, father!" she said, smiling at him, "do try to keep a sense of proportion."

Her levity had outraged him. She knew it when she saw the look in his eyes.

"You mustn't say that to me," he said, and his face was working. "You don't know what you're saying. That's an evil and dangerous woman. I weigh my words, I don't speak lightly. She's evil and dangerous."

"Louise wouldn't hurt a fly," she said. "She may have some foolish notions but she's good. She's kind and good."

"Kind?" he asked. "Good? What makes you think so?"

"Well," she said, "I feel it. I know Louise pretty well."

"She's a Communist," he said, and he watched Medwin to see what effect this announcement would have on her.

"Well," she said, "and what if she is? You once called her an old maid living in a mousehole. What harm can she do?"

"She works in libraries," he said, and the colour of his face darkened. "She corrupts the young. She wants to see blood run. Plenty of blood."

Medwin finished the potatoes and stood the pot on one side. She wiped her hands on the piece of sacking and went and sat down beside him at the table.

"Well," she said, to calm him, "she can't do any harm here. Just as soon as mother is better, she can go back to her mouse-hole. Meanwhile, father, I hope you're comfortable. How much do you think we ought to pay the Chartleys for your board?"

He coughed. "It's all right. I have some money."

"I know. Mother told me about your selling the hens."

He looked embarrassed again and she wished she had not put it so bluntly. It was almost the saddest part of it that she could not seem to avoid hurting him.

"Technically, I suppose, the money belongs to you," he said, looking down at his feet, "as you bought the hens."

"That doesn't matter. I wish I thought that Mr. Schlemmer had really wanted them."

He straightened up a little. "He got a good bargain and he knows it. I only hope he lets your mother have some of the eggs."

"He's sent some down already," Medwin told him.

"I don't like leaving your mother to that terrible woman," he said, "but I'm all right here. The Chartleys are good friends of mine and they don't want me to pay them anything."

He wanted that eight pounds, Medwin knew. He wanted, probably, to buy a suit with it.

"We must pay them at least two pounds ten a week," she said. "Please promise me you will."

"Well, if you insist. I tell you they don't want it." He stared in front of him and then said, "That fellow Schlemmer. Don't you think your mother sees too much of him?"

"No, of course not," Medwin said. "Why do you ask?"

"He drops in too often. He's bumptious, full of bounce and

brag. Once I used to do business with such people, but I object to knowing them socially."

"Father," Medwin said, "Mr. Schlemmer knows socially, as you put it, far more important people than we are. He drops in from sheer kindness. He's a very kind little man."

"You think Louise is kind," he reminded her.

"Well, certainly Mr. Schlemmer is."

"Your mother is making a mistake," he said doggedly. "I've told her so."

Medwin said with a smile,

"I should think that after forty years of marriage you could trust mother's judgment, even if you don't trust mine."

"You couldn't call him a gentleman," he said.

"Why?" Medwin inquired. "I could."

"It astonishes me," said her father frowning, "to hear you say that. It shows you haven't the faintest notion of what the word means."

"All right," Medwin said, with determined good humour, "you tell me what it means."

But he was saved from this necessity by the arrival of the Chartleys, a big, stout, upstanding couple with loud, cheerful voices. Medwin stayed for another fifteen minutes and talked to them, but refused Mrs. Chartley's offer of tea saying that she must get back to the lodge. She had a word with Mrs. Chartley apart and arranged with her that her father should pay two pounds a week. She refused to accept more.

"He's no trouble," Mrs. Chartley said, when they were back in the kitchen again, "and we all like him." She patted Mr. Fosdick's shoulder. "He's to stay just as long as he likes."

Mr. Chartley looked at Medwin with twinkling eyes.

"Seems like that aunt of yours is a pretty tough customer," he said.

Her father, she thought, as she walked back to the lodge, had not shown any interest in her job. He had not asked a single question. But then there had not been much time and his mind had been taken up by other things. He seemed contented there. No doubt he talked to the Chartleys about his early life and early successes, and about the people he had known. It was a pity, she thought, that he had taken it into his head to be jealous of Mr. Schlemmer. How little people changed as they grew old! How little they discarded! She pondered this fact, and it seemed to make her father's situation still more pathetic, but she gave her mother a cheerful report of him, and at half-past five left the two women about to resume their reading of Agatha Christie.

On her way to the bus she was overtaken by Mr. Schlemmer in his car. The headlights picked out her familiar fawn-coloured coat, and he called to his chauffeur to stop. He switched on the light in the car, and she saw that his face was beaming.

"Get in, get in!" he cried. "This is a real pleasure. I'm driving up to London, and I'll drop you right at your door. Reason as follows. Big American film producer comes to London, old friend of mine. Tonight we dine and talk, tomorrow I bring him to Hurcomb Place and we talk some more. As dollar-earner, as American citizen, sometimes I get extra petrol. So. Here I am. How is your mother?"

Medwin told him she was to be X-rayed tomorrow.

"Too bad she fell. A wonderful woman, your mother. I tell you so, Sam Schlemmer. Don't you forget it. When I see her, I think better of the human race."

She had never been alone with Mr. Schlemmer before, and on the way up to London he told her something of his history in short, jerky sentences. His parents had emigrated with their two children to America from Vienna forty years earlier. They had settled in New Jersey, but he, after many vicissitudes, had worked his way to California. He had become interested in the film business, starting as a messenger. Every year he had improved his position, every year he had saved money. He had learnt the film business from every angle, and for nearly twenty years had been successfully producing films himself. He had become an American citizen, and, finally, he had built himself a big house in Beverley Hills.

"Finally? Did I say finally? Listen. I am sick of bathing pools, night clubs, cocktail bars and dry, burnt-up Californian hills. Plenty people like them. All right, they can have them. For me, green grass, fine old trees, old houses. Three years ago I come to England, I buy a place. Now don't laugh, maybe I become a British citizen—no, subject. You think that's funny? All right, it's funny. I don't care. I want to die an Englishman. I want to be buried in the churchyard at Hurcomb. It's cosy." And he laughed himself.

Medwin, amused, said why not, there were worse ambitions.

"Well," he said, "all right, I'm ambitious. Ambitious to make some good English films, ambitious to die an Englishman, and be buried in an English churchyard. If that's funny, all right, it's funny. I don't care."

Once, during the drive he said, "Now, your father. There's an unhappy man. My, I'm sorry for him. Doesn't like me, that's O.K., that don't worry me. Everybody can't like Sam Schlemmer. But you got to like something. My, it's sad you get so you don't like anything."

The rain came on, as it so often did on Sunday nights, and before they reached London the streets were shining. But the drive did not seem as long as she feared it might. He asked her if there were anything her mother wanted.

"Perhaps some eggs, when you can spare them. And she looks forward to your visits," she said, as the car nosed its way down the mews to her door.

"Wonderful woman. Brave as a lion. How are those two rich dames you work for? I've given money to that Crippled Boys' Home. Anonymously. That's Sam Schlemmer's way."

She thanked him and said good night; then she switched on the light, bolted the door and went upstairs. Everything seemed to be waiting for her, everything welcomed her. She was glad she had gone, but she was glad to be back. She rang up Dr. Tenby and he told her not to worry. The X-ray would show if there were anything wrong but he did not expect to find that anything was. He would ring her up on the following night and report.

The following night he did ring up to say that all was well. Another two weeks on her back, and provided she did nothing foolish her mother should soon be making steady progress again.

There it was; there was really not very much at the moment to trouble her and there was no reason at all why she should not sleep, except that there had been rather too much of everything. Dr. Radnytz had given her some sleeping pills when she was ill, and there were still half a dozen or so left in the box, for she was very rarely sleepless. Now she brought them out of the drawer of the bedside table, intending to take one, and put out her hand for the glass of water. But before her hand reached it the telephone rang, almost in her ear. It was like a scream in the night. She picked up the receiver, her heart giving a great thump of fear. It could only be, at this late hour, that something had happened to her mother or to Sarah. But it was a stranger's voice that spoke, and clearly he had got the wrong number.

CHAPTER

7

"IS THAT YOU, GWEN?" THE VOICE ASKED.

With enormous relief, with gladness, she said, "I think you must have the wrong number."

"Isn't that Grosvenor 0099?"

"Yes, but it can't be the number you want. There's no Gwen here." Then it flashed across her mind that Miss Jones's name was Gwendoline and she said quickly. "Or did you want Miss Jones?"

"I do want Miss Jones. That's her flat, isn't it?"

"It was. She isn't here now."

"Where has she gone? I knew nothing about it." There was surprise and disappointment in his voice.

"She's been ill," Medwin said. "She's in a sanatorium at present."

"Been ill, has she? Poor Gwen. I've been away and didn't know. She's a relation of mine. How is she now?"

"Much better, I'm told, and coming out soon. Would you like her address? I can get it for you, if you'd care to ring up again tomorrow."

"Thank you. I'd be very glad to have her address. Might I ask if you're her successor?"

She answered, "Yes. I am."

There was a short silence, then he said:

"I wonder if I might call at the flat. I left some things of mine there."

"I think if you left some things here, Miss Jones must have taken them with her," Medwin said. "There's nothing here now."

"I don't think she'd have taken them to the sanatorium with her," he said. "I think they'll probably still be there. Would you mind if I came and looked?"

"I would mind, very much," she said. "You can take my word for it that there's nothing of yours here."

He laughed and said:

"I'm afraid you wouldn't know, you see. There's a hiding place. Only I can't very well explain on the telephone. It sounds such nonsense."

"I quite agree. Then if there's a hiding place, tell me where it is and then I'll get the things and post them to you."

There was a pause, and then he said:

"Please let me come and get them. It would only take a minute or two." And then he added, "My name is Lyddon, Robert Lyddon. Gwen Jones is my mother's cousin. I was often at the flat when she was there."

At this, something like an electric shock went up Medwin's spine. She leaned back against the pillow and was silent.

"Hello," he said.

"Yes, I'm still here," she said. "I was thinking."

He said, quietly, persuasively, "Please let me come. Could I come tomorrow evening between six and seven? I won't put you to any inconvenience, I promise you." And as she did not reply, he said, "Are you still there?"

"Yes," she said, "and still thinking." But she knew now that she was going to say yes. "Oh, very well," she said at last, "but I hope it won't take you long as I have to go out. You'd better come at a quarter to seven."

"Thank you," he said. "I hope I didn't wake you. Gwen Jones used to read in bed till long after midnight. Good-bye."

She hung up without another word. She did not like what had happened, and although she had been taken completely by surprise, she now had the curious and rather bewildering impression that it had all happened before, that it was a word for word repetition of a conversation that had already taken place at some vague and unfixable time. The peace of the night settled round her again, but she was not at peace. What would she be opening her door to tomorrow? Disloyalty and deceit? She could not tell Miss Lyddon. She could not let her know that Miss Jones had frequently seen her hated brother's son there. She could not possibly disclose this, and would therefore be embarking upon a course she felt she would have been wiser to avoid. But how avoid it? She believed the man when he said there were things belonging to him in the flat. It would hardly be an invention. But, she wondered what and where? Where could there possibly be a hiding place, and why, if indeed there were one, had he made use of it? Had he and Miss Jones some connection with that underworld that she knew of only through the newspapers? The idea was totally absurd. Miss Jones was not that sort of woman. But she might have been deceived. Lonely spinsters have been deceived before. Possibly the family of the dispossessed brother had taken to evil ways. But she would have sworn that was an honest man's voice. Well, it was unlikely that she would be hit on the head, and if his looks belied his voice she could slam the door on him. But where, she wondered, in that small flat could such a hiding place be? More wide awake than ever, she got out of bed, threw on her dressing-gown and began to search for it. Only the hall was panelled and she pulled and pushed at the panelling without success. She tried the back of the linen-cupboard and of her own cupboard, but they offered no solution. She went back to bed and took the sleeping pill. Nothing else could help her now and tomorrow would be a busy day.

But the conversation she had just had went on repeating itself in her head, and the talk went round and round and sometimes she altered it, giving it a different ending and said she would post the things to him and that was final. Then she regretted this, was thankful she had not said it, and recaptured the actual words that had been spoken, with satisfaction. She would look at least once upon Miss Lyddon's nephew, she had reserved for herself the choice of shutting him out or letting him in, she had taken the sensible decision. And with this certainty she slept at last.

During the morning Miss Jones's name came up as it so often did and Medwin took the opportunity of asking Mrs. Gresham the name and address of the sanatorium, adding, quite unnecessarily as she afterwards thought, that she knew of someone who might like to hear of such a place.

In the afternoon Mrs. Debenham was coming to discuss plans for the ball at the Winchester. Medwin did not look forward to Mrs. Debenham's visits. She was the only person she had met in that house for whom she felt any antipathy. Or was it simply that Mrs. Debenham did not like her? She was an Irishwoman and strikingly handsome, with a head of red-gold hair and hard, brilliant blue eyes. She had been the hunting-mad daughter of a distinguished but impoverished family, and married disastrously and now made an excellent living out of organizing charity entertainments. She knew "everybody" and "everybody" knew her. She had a shrill laugh which Medwin deplored, she told Irish stories inimitably but too often, and she also told scandalous stories of well-known people that she would have been wiser to have kept to herself, especially, as Miss Lyddon remarked, as they were almost certainly true. Miss Lyddon insisted that she did not really like her, but she was obviously much amused by her, and was pleased, Medwin thought, by Mrs. Debenham's fulsome admiration. When Mrs. Debenham flattered, it was like being hit by a big wave on a beach. People were bowled over in spite of themselves.

Medwin lunched with the two women alone, and everything seemed once more calm and normal between them. They laughed about the Scotch bio-chemist, particularly when Medwin told them how at first, he had refused to eat the ham, suspecting black market dealings. Miss Lyddon, especially, seemed now in high good humour. Mrs. Debenham was not expected until five-thirty, and Medwin and Miss Lyddon got through several hours' work and sent for tea at the usual time.

"Come and sit on the sofa," Miss Lyddon said, patting the place beside her. "You look tired, and that's something one woman can say to another without causing alarm and despondency."

"I didn't get to sleep till nearly three," Medwin admitted. "I expect my brain was over-stimulated."

"Not by the talk you heard last night," Miss Lyddon returned. "Whatever Edith may say, I thought the evening dragged. I wonder what those French eighteenth century salons were like. I'm willing to bet anything they weren't all they are said to have been, and that they caused plenty of yawns. By the way, while I think of it, what about dining with me tonight? Dr. Radnytz is coming, and Edith is going out. Archie Fullerton is coming too, so we shall be four. Dr. Radnytz is pining to see you again."

"I'd love to come. Why doesn't his wife ever go out with him?" Medwin asked.

"My dear, she's a completely round little tub, speaks very bad English and sulks. She came once. Never again. Now I want to talk to you about Edith. Don't you think she ought to take a holiday? I thought she was dreadfully tetchy last night. That's a word my father loved, by the way. It seems to me that she's nervy and irritable. It's time she went to Canada to see her son, but she says she has too much to do, that she can't let down her committees and so on and so on. All nonsense, of course. It only needs a little intelligent planning."

"Is she thinking of going?" Medwin asked. Now she thought, I shall have to take care.

"She keeps putting it off. She dotes on David, and his wife's just had another baby. There'd be no currency difficulties; they have a nice house in Toronto and she could stay with them. Do try to persuade her to go. If she speaks about it to you, I mean, of course."

"Well," said Medwin, "if I see an opportunity I might, but I don't imagine she'd listen to me. Why should she?"

"She thinks very highly of your good sense," Miss Lyddon told her. And then she said, "You know, Edith's tragedy is that she's absurdly sensitive about her background. Her father was a boot manufacturer in Leicester—has she ever told you? No, I thought not. He was quite a remarkably character, and a father to be proud of, but Edith has always felt, all her life, that she's been handicapped by not having been born into good society. Did you happen to notice last night when I said jokingly apropos of her scolding me about asking Dr. McIntyre to dinner, 'Of course you know so much more about these things than I do,' how she coloured up at once and looked hurt? I had to apologize to her later. It was tactless of me, perhaps, to say it, even in fun, but it shows that she's tired and out of sorts."

"I think you both do far too many things," said Medwin. And the sound of her own words encouraged her to say more. She was tired of never speaking frankly. And she felt that what she wanted to say ought to be said. "I think you both take on far too much. Why don't you concentrate on one or two things that really interest you? You on your Crippled Boys' Home—I don't think remote control is good enough—Mrs. Gresham on her Holiday Home, or perhaps the Mid-Metropolitan. She's off this afternoon to a cocktail party in aid of something or other—oh yes, recreation grounds for the children of East Copping—and tonight she goes to a dinner in aid of the Disabled Somebody or Other's Pension Fund, and your engagement book is crammed with things of the same sort. You dissipate your energies. I don't see why you do it."

"Well," said Miss Lyddon, drawing away the better to look at her, "so you've got that off your chest?"

"Yes," said Medwin, "and there's more to come."

"Don't stop," Miss Lyddon said. "I've seen disapproval in your eye on many occasions. So that's what you really think, is it?"

"I'm afraid it is," Medwin said. "You scatter yourselves so. It seems to me wasteful and pointless. Are you annoyed at my saying this? I've wanted to say it for a long time."

"You can say precisely what you like to me," Miss Lyddon told her. "I look on you as a member of the family. Well, I suppose there's some truth in it, but once on a committee I hate to get off. People are so ready to say, 'She's not as young as she was. She must be getting on for seventy.' And what could I do if I didn't do these things? Slack about the house? Read novels? Go to films? Heaven preserve me from that sort of life. I'm stronger than I've ever been. I never felt better in my life. What do you want me to do?"

"Concentrate. Concentrate on a few things, or better still, one. You often tell me how interested you are in those crippled boys. You only see them about twice a year."

"Have you got it into your head," Miss Lyddon asked, "that I do these things for snobbish reasons? Because of course that's too absurd. I've always been able to know all the people I wanted to know."

"I don't know why either of you do it," Medwin said. "It puzzles me very much."

"It wouldn't occur to you, I suppose, that one simply wants to help?" Miss Lyddon asked, with sarcasm.

Medwin hesitated and then asked what she had long wanted to ask.

"Couldn't you give money without all this nonsense about cocktail parties and endless committees of smart women all wearing their best hats?"

Miss Lyddon remained unruffled. She said patiently, "My dear child, it isn't enough to give money oneself. One has to persuade other people to give it as well. And the only way to do that is to appeal to their snobbishness or their fondness for being in the public eye. How many people would give anything at all to charity unless they were induced to do so by the opportunity of being seen at some smart ball, or mixing somewhere or other with the socially important? Human nature is human nature. We're not all angels. It's the way the whole thing works. It's the way of the world."

"What do the socially important get out of it?" Medwin wanted to know.

"Come, come!" Miss Lyddon cried. "Where's that perspicacity of yours? Everyone likes a bit of limelight. And the socially important have to keep on the go or they'd soon cease to be socially important."

"I suppose you've put your finger on it," Medwin said.

"Drop out and you're forgotten in a surprisingly short space of time, whoever you are. Speaking for myself, I like to be busy. It's fun having influence and getting one's own way. It's fun pushing people about and getting things done. And why should you grumble at my getting a lot of things done, or helping me to get them done, if they're things that ought to be done? Tell me that."

"That's unanswerable," said Medwin, feeling that she had said enough. "And forgive me if I've been impertinent, but—" and her eyes smiled, "it's your own fault if I have."

"You've been very impertinent," Miss Lyddon said, "and I like it. That mouse Miss Jones would never have dared to say 'boo' to a goose, or," she laughed, "to a couple of geese. But remember, I've only been speaking for myself, not for the other goose. What Edith gets out of it all is entirely her own affair. You'd better ask her, if you want to know."

A few minutes later, Mrs. Debenham came. Miss Lyddon had told Medwin that she need not stay unless she wanted to, and she therefore went back to her flat thankfully before six.

At a quarter to seven precisely the bell rang, and to Medwin the sound was charged with portent. She had been waiting for it and when it came it was not just the door bell ringing, but a summons to the unforeseen. For the rest of my life, she thought, shall I remember going down these stairs to open the door? Or is it just an incident like any other incident? Because it does not feel like one.

It did not feel like one. That was the odd thing. It had not last night. And as she walked along the narrow, uncarpeted hall, her heels making sharp taps, she had an impression that she was not alone, that Miss Lyddon walked with her. That was her conscience, no doubt. She opened the door feeling that she might be letting in the sea, something that not all her will power could push back again.

Her first impression was that he did not altogether like his errand. Hat in hand, straight brown hair brushed close to his scalp, he looked a neat, compact and solid man, standing squarely on his feet, looking politely apologetic, as if wishing that he had not found it necessary to come. That he was a Lyddon there was no doubt. There were the eyebrows and the nose, both somewhat modified but unmistakable. He was sunburned, which, at that time of year, stood out. "He'll sing me songs of Araby," flashed, inconsequent and foolish, across Medwin's mind. She opened the door wider. The trafficker in drugs theory could be smiled at on some other occasion.

"I'm afraid this is very annoying for you, to have to let a complete stranger into your flat," he said, and came in.

"It doesn't matter," she said. She closed the door, and he stood flat against the wall to allow her to pass.

"I gather I need hardly show you the way," she said, with a half-smile.

"Hardly."

She went up the stairs, he following her, laying his hat on the hall table as he passed. He wore no coat. In the living-room she turned and faced him.

"If there's a secret drawer here somewhere," she said, "I ought to know about it, oughtn't I?"

"You shall," he said. "I doubt if burglars would be able to find it. It might be useful to you."

They were now taking each other in in great eyefuls. Each presented to the other a camera-face, unshuttered, shamelessly taking impressions.

"I'll get the things now," he said, looking away. "I promised to be quick." He hesitated. "A knife is required. I forgot to bring a pocket-knife. May I get one out of the kitchen drawer?"

"I'll get it for you."

"No, please," he said quickly. "I know where it is."

He went into the kitchen and she heard him open the table drawer and close it again. He came in with a small vegetable knife in his hand. The look of embarrassment had returned to his face.

"Do you want me to go away?" she asked. "Or shall I simply shut my eyes?"

"There's no need to do either," he said. "But I shall have to ask you not to stand just where you're standing."

She said, "Oh, I see," and moved to the sofa and sat down.

He turned back the hearthrug and then went down on his hands and knees. He contrived to maintain a surprising amount of dignity in the process.

"I expect this seems very childish," he remarked.

"It might be childish," she said, "or it might be anything

but childish. You may keep drugs in there for all I know."

"I might, I suppose," he agreed. He applied the point of the knife to a crack between two short boards.

"We found this place quite by accident," he said. "The boards used to creak when Gwen stood on them, and she asked me to see if I could stop them creaking. I investigated and found this. I think it has something to do with the electric wiring."

One of the boards came up, and then he removed another, revealing a large space between the floor and the ceiling of the room below. He put his arm in and took out a parcel loosely wrapped in brown paper. As he lifted it up one end of it came open and out fell a shower of articles: a pair of blue pyjamas, a toilet case, a clean shirt, hair-brushes, a small parcel fastened with red sealing-wax. Medwin thought it would be kinder not to help him, and she watched him gather them all up and place them on a chair in silence. Then he replaced the boards and rug.

"Now," he said, standing and looking at her, and his colour had deepened, "perhaps you understand my reluctance to let you get the things yourself."

"Please don't feel you need to explain anything," she said. "It's none of my business."

"After that," he remarked, "I see I shall have to explain. Gwen often used to let me spend the night here. On that sofa. Naturally she didn't want my things left lying about the place, so we decided to hide them in there. It's as simple as that."

"Nothing," she told him, "could possibly be simpler."

They looked at each other guardedly.

"I'd better get you some string," she said, and got up and took some out of the drawer of the desk. He thanked her and turned, with the string and the paper in his hand, towards the chair. It now seemed that there was nothing more for him to do but to tie up the parcel and go. But he was Miss Lyddon's nephew, and she did not propose that he should go just yet.

"Why don't you sit down first," she said, "and have a cigarette? There are some in that box."

"Aren't you in a hurry to go out somewhere?"

"Not particularly," she said. "There's plenty of time."

"Then I will." He sat down in an armchair but he took a cigarette from his own case and lit it. She had half expected him to say, "Do you mind if I smoke a pipe?" She thought he looked like a pipe-smoker, and he considered that pipes should be permitted or condoned only within the family circle.

"Do you know Gwen Jones?" he asked.

"No. I've never met her. Naturally I've heard a good deal about her."

He spoke seriously, leaning forward a little as if what he was about to say mattered to him:

"Whatever you may have heard, Gwen is one of the best of women, and a staunch friend."

"I've heard nothing whatever to lead me to think otherwise."

"Good. I just wanted to make that plain. She's always been incredibly kind to me. She can't be more than ten years older than I am, but she's treated me like an indulgent aunt. I'm devoted to her. That little parcel done up with sealing wax is a birthday present for her. I expected to be back a couple of weeks earlier, and now it's overdue."

"I see," she said. "And that was why you wanted to come at once. Well, I have her address for you now." And she took a slip of paper out of her pocket of her skirt and gave it to him. He looked at it, thanked her, and put it into his pocket-book.

"Do you know what was the matter?" he asked. "Did they wear her out between them?"

"I don't think the work here is as hard as all that," Medwin answered. "But of course, she may not be strong."

"Strong enough," he said, "when she came."

"At first they were afraid it was T.B.," she told him, "but it wasn't. It was just that she was badly run down and anæmic."

He looked down at the hand that held the cigarette, and slowly clasped the wrist with the other hand and then unclasped it. He appeared to be debating whether or not to say something, and deciding not to say it. He looked up, and his eyes, blue and light and colourful as twin jewels in his sunburned face, fell on the picture of Sarah. "Yours?" he asked.

"Mine," she answered.

"Is she here with you?"

"No. She's too young. She's with my sister."

He paid Sarah the tribute of a smile, then he said, "I have a son. He's eleven, and at school."

"I supposed you were married," she said, then felt annoyed with herself for having admitted that she had, one way or the other, given it her thought.

"I am," he said, "and I'm not. It's a long story."

She made no comment on this, and at the same time decided, for some cautious reason, not to tell him anything about herself. Let him think what he liked. It was no concern of hers what he thought.

"Are you home for good now?" she asked.

"I'm out of the Navy for good. Where to go from here isn't yet apparent. There are one or two alternatives. But I mustn't hesitate much longer. I'm thirty-seven."

"Attractive alternatives?" she inquired.

"I'm not dazzled by them. One would take me abroad. I've been abroad too much. And yet there may be nothing to keep me here."

She said, "You have a sister, haven't you?"

His eyes scarcely changed their expression, but he took this in, she saw, with all its implications. He took in, she was sure, much.

He asked, looking at his hand again, "And what else have you heard?"

"Very little," she told him. "The barest facts. She spoke of your father only once."

"I see. You're in her confidence, then?"

She hesitated. "She seems to want me to feel that I am. It's not, particularly, my wish."

"So that when I said my name was Robert Lyddon, you knew."

"I knew."

He eyed her steadily, before saying, "And you wondered if you ought to see me, knowing what you know. Well, you have seen me. There's a resemblance, as no doubt you've noticed. I've seen her from that window, and she's comically like my father." He put out his cigarette and stood up. "The whole thing concerns me very little."

"I don't think family quarrels ought to be carried on into the second generation," she said. "They do harm enough in one." She too got up, and they stood facing each other. He then turned towards the chair where his things lay and she was moved to say, "I wish I could offer you a drink, but there's nothing in the flat."

His eyes became lively and amused. He gave her plenty of time to see that he was refraining from saying something he could have said and would have liked to say. And then he changed his mind and said it.

"Yes there is," he said, and he tried not to smile, "but I would have to take up the floor-boards again."

This made her laugh outright. "How absurd!" she cried. "What a pair of conspirators you seem to have been. Well, get it out then, if you like. You can play host and offer me a drink."

His face now cleared up completely. A tight, preoccupied and intensely thoughtful look had suddenly smoothed into geniality.

"Now that's friendly of you," he exclaimed. "That pleases me more than I can say."

He appeared to put confidence in her now, her laughter had simplified and eased the situation. She thought, soon, if this were to go on, he'd make himself at home here again. "I'll get the glasses," she said, and went to the kitchen, hearing him call after her:

"And some ice."

She thought he was relieved that she would not again be a witness to the taking up of the floor-boards. He had carried it all off well enough the first time. It was not easy, under her gaze, and there had been the laughable matter of the things dropping out of the parcel. It struck her that they had not laughed, either of them. They had not been on that footing. She returned to find him waiting, with two bottles on the table; a bottle of gin and a tall bottle of Dubonnet. He took the tray from her and set it down beside them.

"It's what Gwen liked," he said. "I kept her supplied. But she was no drinker. She wouldn't touch it unless I were here to drink with her."

"I'm afraid," she said, "I would not have been so moderate."

He nodded towards the hearth.

"There's more there," he said. "Another of each. Please look upon them as yours."

"Oh no, I couldn't possibly. You must please take them away with you."

"Not I," he said. "I'll have quite enough to carry as it is."

"Then you must come back and get them another time."

He made no answer. He was preparing the cocktails. When he held out her glass to her she took it, saying:

"I never imagined that your visit this evening would end like this. Please sit down again. I'm not dining till eight, and it will take me fifteen minutes to dress."

"I take it," he said, sitting down, "that you'll be dining over there, in that case." And he looked towards the house.

"You're quite right."

"Well," he said, "I don t think it can be an easy job, for anyone."

"In some ways, not," she said. "But interesting." Then she changed the subject. "Your sister is on the stage, isn't she?"

"She was. She married last year. She had a hard time, and I'm glad it's over. She seemed to me to have everything but luck."

"Then she's married happily?"

"Very, I think." He was looking into his glass and revolving the ice in it. "You wouldn't, I suppose, care to tell me something about yourself?"

"Oh," she said, "if you like, though I don't talk about myself easily. I never know which facts to bring up from the well. What do you want to know?"

"If I answered that truthfully I would seem presumptuous."

She passed this over.

"I'll see what I can do. My parents live in the country. My little girl lives in Wimbledon with my sister who has four children of her own. I have never been out of England. I consider myself very lucky to have this job and this flat. During the war I worked for the Ministry of Food." She ran down and stopped.

"Thank you," he said. "It is interesting as far as it goes."

"I told you," she said, "that I was no good at this."

"I shouldn't have asked. Then may I talk about myself? I think I'd like to, in view of the fact that you already know what you know."

"Please," she answered. "Why not?"

He settled himself into his chair, holding his glass on his crossed knee.

"My father, villain or hero of this little piece, is an odd, difficult but lovable character. At least, he has been much loved by his wife and children. My mother died a year ago, and he misses her, and I miss her, deplorably. He's left London now, for good, and lives a few miles from Oxford. When my grandfather died, my father was a young barrister. He abandoned all idea of making a career at the Bar when my grandfather cut him off, and took up tutoring law students instead. He has been a tutor all his life. It was to please him that I went into the Navy.

It was not my choice and I never believed it was my vocation. I got out in 1935, took a job and married. Then when the war came I went back into the Navy and served right through the war and after—until last autumn in fact. Now of course I'm out for good." He paused and then said quietly and without emphasis, "In 1945 I came home on leave and found that my wife had fallen in love with someone else. It hit me very hard. Now it's like looking back on a fire or a flood—just one of those things that happen to people when they're least expecting them." He looked up at her and said, "If you'd prefer not to hear this bit of personal history please tell me. I can stop here."

"I would like you to go on," she said.

"Then I will. I believe all would have gone well enough but for this mischance, and it's one that can overtake honest and well-intentioned people. While I was away she met a man who wasn't too much caught up in the war to have preserved for himself a certain amount of liberty. He was a member of one of those war commissions that came and went between London and Washington. A bachelor of forty or so, and fancy free. He didn't fall lightly in love; it was a serious and painful matter to him, I believe, to have fallen in love with a woman who was married, and not unhappily, but neither of them appeared to have taken any of the steps they might have taken to avoid seeing each other. It's curious how seldom people do. Then, when the harm was done, she sent him away and was miserable. I came home and found her in this state. She told me then what she ought to have told me earlier, her excuse being that she couldn't bring herself to write it, and we resumed our married life after a fashion. During one of my absences at sea they met again. She assured me that it was by chance and I believed her. Anyway, the whole thing flared up once more. Finally I said I would go abroad and leave her to make up her mind once and for all whether she wanted to throw in her lot with him or stay with me. She told me that if she did leave me she would give up the boy entirely. She refused, she said, to impose a divided loyalty on him. He's a delicate child and highly strung. I think that but for this she would have made up her mind long ago. When I returned the other day I saw her at once—she's been living with her mother—and she begged me to give her two more months. I couldn't very well refuse. It means too much to both of us. I think that in the end she'll go and I'm prepared for it. If that's what she intended by this delay she's succeeded better than she knows. The trouble is that, feeling as I now do, I can't see a very happy future for either of us if she decides to stay, though no doubt it would be better for the boy."

"But the waiting," she said frowning, "the terrible waiting."

"I'm in a state of suspension," he agreed, "and though not precisely swinging between heaven and hell, at least swinging between the old life and the new one that I hope to make for myself. However," he leaned back in a more relaxed attitude, "it has taught me a great deal. It has taught me the folly of marrying for any reason but the best, for one thing."

She did not ask what this was. She thought she knew, and she now wished to turn the talk to more general topics.

"So you're not altogether unhopeful," she said, "in spite of the state the world's in."

"Why should I grumble? At present I've no plans for improving it and no time. People no worse and probably better than I am have made it what it is. Criticism's cheap. I'll wait till I see a chance to put my back into it."

"That's honest," she said. And then she looked directly at him and asked, "Why did you tell me all this about yourself?"

"Instead of asking if you'd read any good books lately?"

"Well, yes. I'm curious to know why."

He answered, "Let's put it that it's because you're my aunt's secretary and in her confidence."

"But naturally I shall have to tell her I've seen you."

"Naturally."

There was a little silence, then she asked,

"Do you know your uncle?"

"I have two. Do you mean my Uncle James?"

"Yes."

"I don't know him. My father dislikes him extremely, almost more than he dislikes my aunt. He has offered my father financial help in a way that made it quite impossible for him to accept it at times when he badly needed it. He hears sometimes from the brother in America, but not often. You see they both consider that my father, because of something he did about forty years ago, is a blackguard and a cad."

"Because he broke up your aunt's love affair?"

"She's told you that, has she?"

She said, "I ought not to have spoken of it. That's the worst of having met you. I shall be led into deceit and disloyalty. That's why I hesitated to let you come."

"How utterly vile," he exclaimed, "family quarrels are! My father's whole life has been undermined, eaten away by this thing. He's like a tree that has been devoured inside by white ants. I refuse to let it touch me, in any way. I refuse to let my life be altered one jot by it. What might have been is no possible concern of mine. I have my hands full enough with what is."

"You're absolutely right, of course," she said. "It's affected your aunt's life too. She's never forgotten, and she can't forget."

"Well," he said, "let them go on wallowing in it until the end. My father did what he thought right—or so I believe. The consequences were tragic, but he did what he thought he ought to do for friendship's sake. Perhaps he put his friend before his sister. Perhaps he was wrong. I don't know. I don't care." He got up and took her empty glass from her. "Let's fill up again."

The room now seemed to Medwin to be overflowing with him. It was no longer the same place, with his voice and his solid presence. Unconsciously he was at his ease there, it was a legacy from Gwen Jones to him. He now moved with the same certainty and assurance he must have moved with before, and the fact that the flat had a different tenant was ceasing to alter it for him. He filled her glass again and put it beside her, and then refilled his own and went back to his chair. He was intent on his thoughts and the things he wanted to say.

"So please don't feel," he said, as if he had offered some proof that no need for it existed, "that you're being disloyal by talking to me here. I bear her no ill will. None. I know this is hers. I know that; but after all, it's the one thing I've not been dispossessed of, so to speak. It's not much, but it does, it suffices. And Gwen was generous with it. I am glad that you can find it in your heart, this once, to be generous with it too. I assure you, I feel not the slightest guilt or shame in being here because it is hers, and she," he moved his head towards the windows, "is there. I have an affection for this place. Here, for me, London ends. It doesn't penetrate these walls. For nearly two years now, this has been, at odd times, a very happy place to come to. And now, please tell me, what is she like? What is she *really* like?"

"But surely, Gwen has told you?"

"She's tried. Good heavens, how she's tried! But it's beyond her. And it's your picture of her I want. Gwen stood in such tremendous awe of her. You don't stand in awe of her; you never would. The other one gave Gwen no trouble, or only a normal amount, but my aunt was always much more than life-size. She looked at her with a magnifying eye. You see, Gwen is a humble soul; proud, but humble in the face of what she conceives to be real superiority. And my aunt seemed to her one of the really superior people."

"In what way superior?" Medwin asked. "It's important to know."

"Oh, in most ways. Brains, ability, charm, skill, birth, personality. If Gwen didn't at times hate her, I'd say she worshipped her. It was that admiration for my aunt that wore her down. No outlet, you see; it was all locked up in that small, spinster body, and I've no doubt nipped pretty cruelly if ever it showed itself. Admiration from the wrong quarter can be an insult to some."

"Yes," Medwin said. "All that I can picture well enough."

"But with you, it's quite a different matter. You meet her on her own ground—or rather better. She'd give her eyes to be young like you, to have what you've got."

"What I've got? And what do you imagine that is?"

"Your life ahead of you instead of behind you. Let's put it, if you like, no higher than that, though one could put it a very great deal higher. Oh, you'll be all right, you'll keep your head, you'll see all round her, and she'll envy you your youth. She'll shake her feathers in it, like a bird in a fountain."

And that, Medwin thought, looking at him with startled eyes, is precisely what she does. He understands her, better even than I do, who am with her every day. But he is of the same blood, and he has had Gwen's eyes to see her through. Now he wants to see her through mine."

"But," she said, "it's one thing for you to talk freely of her, and another thing for me. She employs me; more, she's exceedingly kind to me. If I talked of her it would only make me feel ashamed and remorseful."

"Yes," he said, "I understand that. With Gwen it was different. She had to talk of her and I was her one safety valve. She was so tremendous to Gwen. As I see it, there need be no tragedy in spinsterhood, if things can be kept more or less in their right proportions, but if there's no man, no child to love, something more often than not, has got to be blown up into hugeness—and worshipped. If it's a career, well and good. Or God, or humanity. With Gwen, it was *her*. No reasoning could prick that balloon. And she'd had to wait for nearly half a century to find it, such as it was. Hence, I'm afraid, the sanatorium. She was in a fine state of nerves and misery and abasement when I last saw her."

"Poor, poor Miss Jones," Medwin said, half aloud, and thought the tragedy was that this admiration, excessive and perhaps unwilling, gave pleasure neither to the giver nor to the object of it. But she felt she must change the subject, however fascinating to her, for remorse was already lifting its head.

"And where have you just come from," she asked, "with that sunburn?"

He smiled, acknowledging the purposeful break, and said, "From Nairobi. I had three months out there, with friends, on their farm. That's one of the two possibilities I spoke of. Farming with them. I have to consider it."

She wanted to ask him what the other was, but did not wish to display more curiosity than was seemly. And he did not say, perhaps waiting for her to ask.

"Nairobi," she said. "It's a name to me, like other names. A place people come back from with a sunburn."

"Don't waste time," he said, "regretting that you haven't travelled. If it's something that's to be added to you, no doubt it will be, but you've world enough, in all conscience. Does anyone require more, in fact, than this island holds? Shakespeare didn't."

She smiled.

"Then it's very unfair that I should share with him only what he had not got."

Their eyes met and once more they were unshuttered. In his eyes she saw, clearly enough, that he thought it inconceivable that they should not meet again, and in hers, for him to see, was this knowledge, and her acceptance of its truth. He got up, looked at his wrist-watch and said:

"I'll soon be depriving you of that irreducible minimum, fifteen minutes for dressing. I must go."

She reached the chair with the things on it before he did. She did not want to see him doing up that parcel. She did it for him, deftly enough, and handed it to him, compact and safe.

"Thank you, for that," he said, "and for much else." He went towards the door thoughtfully, looking down. She thought she had never met anyone who so obviously turned things over in his mind, not slowly, but with appreciation of the consequences of words and acts, a seeing before and after. He looked up and said,

"I'll telephone one day and find out if I may see you again. I'm quite aware of the disadvantages of your seeing me again; in fact of your having seen me at all. In the meantime, perhaps you'll think it over."

"I will," she said. "I'll think it over."

Without good-byes, they parted. He went down the stairs and along the little hall and shut the front door behind him as he must have done so often before. She dropped down on the sofa. She could not dress yet, she could not hurry away to her bedroom and then across to the house without allowing the ripples made by that large stone to reach the furthest edge and vanish before other, smaller stones set the water in motion again. Within an hour, out of nothing, out of nowhere, this awkward happening had made its not altogether welcome but unforgettable appearance. A character had walked on the stage who seemed quite capable, if permitted, of stealing a very large part of the show; a character far too distinct and vital to be suitably confined to a single entrance, however much further entrances might complicate the plot and give it a bias not planned for it. She had to try to see, as he had tried to see, what the consequences of his further appearances might be. She could easily say, when he telephoned at some future time, "I've thought it over and it's quite impossible that we should meet again. It would make my position too difficult and too ambiguous. And there are other reasons which I need not state. Good-bye." That would be a simple matter, and final, quite certainly final. And it was not loneliness, she was sure, that made this finality undesirable. If she were lonely, and she supposed she must be, she was only half aware of it. If a real need there were for male companionship of a sort that young and attractive women enjoy, she was not too much troubled by it. She had a fastidious wish to keep her life neat, as she kept herself and her surroundings neat. She had seen too many young women submerged by intractable flotsam of their own accumulating. Other earthier needs certainly there were, but to the perfect fulfilment of these she was prepared to make, and had made, long-range sacrifices. She was optimistic enough to believe that these would somehow be met and satisfied in the most-to-be-preferred way, and calmly took her chances on it and refused short-range solutions. What her optimism was based on, she did not know.

Now, she thought, staring at the clock, you have left me seven minutes. I can dress, if pressed, in five. That gives me two minutes more, to make up my mind. For I must make it up now, while the impression he left is still vivid. Am I to see him again, or am I not? Can I reconcile a secret acquaintanceship—there is no need for it to be anything more—with Miss Lyddon's nephew, with my conscience? What harm is there in such an acquaintanceship? I should be keeping something from her that she has a right to know? Nonsense. She has no such right. I do not tell her of my friends' comings and goings. The flat, she has assured me often enough, is to be regarded as my own. If she quarrelled with this man's father, is that any concern of mine? None whatever. I have always detested family quarrels, and this one is as remote in time and place and circumstance from me as it could well be. On the other hand, if I continued to see this man, her nephew, could I look her, frankly and without shame, in the face? That is morbid and ridiculous. Of course I could. As for the other matter, the fact that he is married—though the marriage may be breaking up—need not enter into it at all. I am not thinking of falling in love with him. Our interest in each other is based on Miss Lyddon. And we are both, I suppose, a little disengaged at the moment, a little at a loose end, and could make use of an ear to talk into. Another time I would let him talk more, and I would talk more myself. And besides, she told herself, getting up from the sofa with a quick, decided movement, her mind made up, I want to see him again, if only once more, and there is no possible reason why I should not. So all is well.

She went to her hanging cupboard and opened it. It will have to be the little black dress again, she thought. Well, that is good enough for Mr. Fullerton and Dr. Radnytz. If Dr. Radnytz has not yet recovered from his not very creditable feelings towards me, perhaps the fact that I am looking dowdy will assist. But I fear he won't notice.

She was at the house at eight, and Maria let her in. Medwin, for her own amusement, was learning a little Italian, and this had greatly pleased Maria. It was a remarkable thing, Medwin thought, that the staff got on as well together as they did. Maria and Antonia were fiercely Miss Lyddon's servants, Wilson belonged heart and soul to Mrs. Gresham, as did Stevens and Mrs. Stevens. Davis, the second housemaid, was the only one who seemed to Medwin to be neutral. If the partnership should ever be broken up, there was no knowing which way Davis would go, and she was too thin, Miss Lyddon had once jocularly remarked, to divide well, if Solomon's were to prove the only solution.

Dr. Radnytz as she had feared, was much too glad to see her from the point of view of the conventions. His Polish pleasure shone from his bottomless dark eyes, and Miss Lyddon's lips and Mr. Fullerton's nostrils twitched with amusement. Both enjoyed this un-English demonstration, both were unkind enough to let Medwin see that they were enjoying it. She was glad Dr. Radnytz did not come often. He had attended Mrs. Gresham, the latter had told her during a crisis of nerves ten years earlier, and had remained on friendly terms with both women. What caused this crisis, Medwin had not been told. Mrs. Gresham she at first thought, seemed on the surface less likely to have been a sufferer from nerves than Miss Lyddon, but on second thoughts this was probably not true. Miss Lyddon had the better cushion against nervous ailments, a robust and even at times coarse sense of humour. She enjoyed a joke with a stock-exchange flavour, and had a sharp nose for amusing improprieties. No, it must be that Mrs. Gresham would always be the most vulnerable, would be the readiest sufferer, if suffering there were. What Dr. Radnytz possessed, in addition to a warm, Polish romanticism, was a profound understanding of mind sickness. He had, Medwin suspected, a battlefield within himself and had only to search a little within its regions to find and match and comprehend the combats in the minds of others. But he also had a steady and assured optimism, and held out such a bright certainty of healing that his patients fixed their eyes upon this goal and reached it without too much awareness of the ground they crossed. She herself, after Sarah's birth, doubted that she would ever recover from the melancholy fit into which she had fallen. He had shown her this as laughably absurd; the hand which he had held out to her had all but shaken with tender mirth. The horror was behind her, she recalled, even while she was passing through it.

And then, knowing all that he knew—but waiting until she was entirely herself again—he had allowed his feelings for her to overflow into an impassioned, painfully self-revealing letter. A puzzling incident, involving a man who saw so clearly into his own mind. Well, he had trusted her, she supposed, to understand; more, to help him. It was a case of patient, heal thy physician. He had no doubt done himself some good by his confession, and looked to her to absolve him. She had absolved him, burning the letter before his eyes one day at her office at the hospital and never again referring to it. Nor did he, but whole or in ashes, the letter was there between them, as no doubt, he being the romantic he was, it was intended to be.

On the whole it was a pleasant, friendly evening. Miss Lyddon displayed her liking for Medwin as something which did great credit to Dr. Radnytz, who had doubtless prophesied it. Mr. Fullerton smoked two cigars, was humorous in his somewhat outmoded way, and was like a great, contented cat, returned to a beloved hearth. He invited Medwin to go to a play and supper with him the following week, a thing which seemed now to have become a monthly habit with him. Well and good. The theatre, otherwise, did not come her way. As Medwin, after the two men had gone, said good night, Miss Lyddon remarked, putting a light hand on her shoulder,

"I always enjoy these *little* evenings so much."

If she did not say, Medwin thought afterwards, "When Edith is not here," it was almost as good as said.

CHAPTER

8

THE WEEK WHICH PRECEDED THE CELEBRATION AT THE Crippled Boys' Home was an especially busy one. There was a large cocktail party, the purpose of which was to form a committee to raise money for a certain charity in which both women had lately become interested. There was also an unusually large dinner, and two luncheon parties. Lord and Lady Lyddon were unable to come to the dinner, but Lord Lyddon contributed half a dozen fine plump cockerels from Hartsdown. The cocktail party Medwin found hard to bear. Mrs. Debenham had collected over sixty women, and an exalted lady took the chair. The auctioning off of various donated objects formed part of the proceedings. These things had been arriving all during the previous day. There was a case of whisky, a case of gin, some assorted liqueurs, various pieces of jewellery, a set of china, a painting of little merit contributed by Mrs. Gresham, some hats, a fur coat and a Persian kitten. Mrs. Debenham was the auctioneer, and performed this duty with remarkable skill. The bidding was brisk and provided not a little excited rivalry, and when Mrs. Gresham bid up to two hundred pounds for the case of whisky there was a storm of applause. Medwin was kept busy taking down the names and addresses of the successful bidders and collecting their cheques. There seemed to Medwin to be an air of conscious well-doing about the whole proceeding, as though everyone were thinking, "How good it is to feel that one is *really* helping in this pleasant, comradely fashion," and the display of spring hats was quite splendid.

She could not help seeing that Miss Lyddon was maliciously enjoying watching her play the part of an unwilling Hebe to this feast of goodwill and public generosity, and it was all made worse for her by the presence of Mrs. Debenham with her screaming laugh. The chairwoman, a stout, elderly and dignified duchess, seemed perfectly willing that Mrs. Gresham and Miss Lyddon should make whatever use of her name they pleased, and she listened to the bidding with bland surprise. "How very clever you all are," her not very intelligent old eyes seemed to say, "to have all this money to spend. I don't know how you manage it. A hundred pounds! How splendid! Two hundred! How generous! Of course I will occupy a box on the night of the special performance of 'Hell's Lovers'; of course I will make an appeal from the box. And in the end those dear little children in Lower What's-its-Name will have their Day Nursery, and I hope I shan't be too old to open it when the time comes. Bless their hearts!"

"You see," Miss Lyddon had said to Medwin, "we've found time for still another charity. Now what have you got to say?"

"I'm not going to say it," Medwin answered. "I know when I'm beaten."

It was early in that same busy week that Medwin had a letter from her father telling her that he was coming up to London to buy himself a new suit. He simply could not, he said, be seen wearing the old one any longer. She need not send him a cheque, he still had most of the eight pounds, and if he found a suit, he could pay half the price of it down, if required, and half when the alterations were completed. Mr. and Mrs. Chartley, he assured her, were perfectly willing to wait for their money. One reason he needed a suit so badly was that he was going to get in touch with someone, who he believed, would quite probably take an interest in his scrubbing invention, and he couldn't call on them looking as shabby as he now did. Medwin at once sent off a cheque to Mrs. Chartley for five weeks' board and abandoned all idea of buying herself a new suit.

For the ceremony at the Crippled Boys' Home, Miss Lyddon wore a new grey tailor-made and a smart little grey felt hat with quills in it.

"We'll have a picnic lunch in the car," she said, as they started off. "There's chicken mayonnaise and a half bottle of white wine. I'm going to enjoy this. Do you know what I was thinking this morning, Medwin? I was thinking that I'd like to take the car over to France this summer. Would you like to come with me? I don't see why I shouldn't take a couple of weeks' holiday, and you'll certainly need one by that time."

"You oughtn't to tempt me like this," Medwin said. "There's nothing I'd rather do, but if I did take a holiday—and I don't think I deserve one yet—I'd spend it with Sarah."

"Dear me, I wish you didn't have quite so many responsibilities," Miss Lyddon said. "You'd be an ideal travelling companion. And it's time you had a look at the Continent, heaven knows."

"It is indeed," Medwin agreed.

"If Sarah were only a little older we might take her along. I could feel my lifelong distaste for small children vanishing when you brought her to the house the other day."

"It's very nice of you to make an exception of her," Medwin said.

"Well, she's really a little poppet. Edith was quite pathetic, I thought. She so obviously wanted the child to like her the best."

"I thought Sarah showed considerable tact," Medwin remarked. "She appeared to like you both equally."

"She gets that from her mother," Miss Lyddon said. "Your own efforts along those lines I find highly entertaining."

"Do you?" Medwin said, and felt suddenly cold.

"Aren't you sometimes just a little amused at yourself?" Miss Lyddon asked. "You're so bent on showing no partiality. Oh, and you're perfectly right. Edith would not take kindly to any discrimination, unless, of course, it was shown to her."

"Does anyone enjoy being discriminated against?" Medwin inquired.

Miss Lyddon shot her one of her bright, keen glances.

"Come, come," she said. "Can't we ever talk frankly to each other?"

"I enjoy frankness as much as anyone," Medwin said, "but it's a luxury I sometimes have to deny myself. And," she added, "you know that as well as I do."

"Now don't try to snub me," Miss Lyddon returned. "We're having a little holiday at the moment. Let's enjoy ourselves. You know I like you and look on you as a friend. Edith doesn't look on you as a friend. It would take her years to arrive at friendship with you. She mistrusts herself. With her background, you see, she's bound to wonder if she's doing the right thing. Do you remember the night of the first big dinner party after you came to us? I'd called you Medwin in front of her, and she'd been scolding me. She reminded me that I'd never have dreamt of calling Miss Jones Gwen, which is true enough. She was highly indignant."

"I wondered what was wrong that night," Medwin said.

"Well, now you know. I don't take kindly to lessons in deportment from Edith. She'd like to take short cuts to the things she wants but hasn't the courage for fear of making a *gaffe*, and she can't bear it that I'm not the same. I often think Papa Boles made a mistake when he educated her above her station, so to speak. I believe she'd have been happier in her own *milieu*."

"What brought you together, you and she?" Medwin asked.

"If you'd seen her as I first saw her!" Miss Lyddon answered. "I was desperately sorry for her. She was the most awkward, wretched, tongue-tied little creature. We first met at school in Switzerland, you know, as children. She couldn't speak one word of French, and she spent her time crying. I took her under my wing, and after that, I could never shake her off. Oh, not that I wanted to. Don't misunderstand me. I was extremely fond of her and still am. But I couldn't have shaken her off if I'd wanted to. And then, poor dear, she had such a dull life with Ernest Gresham. He was really an unmitigated bore."

"Then," said Medwin, "she hasn't had much fun in her life."

"She's been happier since we've been together than at any other time. I'm convinced of that. As for fun, she's had as much as she was capable of extracting from life. Who can have more? She was very fond of Ernest and I doubt if she knew what a bore he was. Then, of course, she adores David, who, I must say, does her credit."

"But she never sees him now," Medwin said.

"That's her own fault. She ought to go to Canada this summer. Hasn't she begged you to persuade *me* to take a holiday? Come now, be honest, be honest. Tell me."

"Oh," cried Medwin, "you two make things very hard for me if I'm not to tell lies. She said you thought of going to Ireland and that I should urge you to go. She mentioned an aged aunt."

Miss Lyddon laughed delightedly.

"Don't take it so seriously," she cried, glancing at Medwin's face. "I knew she had. Do trust me a little. I'm not in the least likely to take umbrage. Well, I'm not going to Ireland unless my aunt sends for me, and so far she hasn't. Now just relax and be natural."

"I am natural."

"You're not a bit natural when you get it into your head that I'm being unfair to Edith, or that I might be the cause of your being unfair to her. I'm devoted to the creature, and I don't think there's another woman of my own age I could live with. There, does that satisfy you? As for you and me, I've always made friends with whom I liked, and where and when I liked. If you want me to be your friend—and I want to be—tell me so. If not, we can go back to being merely employer and employed. But I shall regret it extremely."

"If we're to be friends," said Medwin, speaking slowly and choosing her words with care, "there must be no strings attached. I must be free to conduct my side of the friendship in my own way."

"You shall, you shall! What a bully you make me out to be! Friendship to you evidently means rights. To me—" and she laid her left hand lightly for a moment on Medwin's arm, "it means obligations. I want so much to *do* things for you. There's that wretched pride of yours I know, and I'll try to respect it. But I do want to say this. Treat me like a friend. Come to me if you're in any difficulty. If I can help, in any way, let me help. Will you?"

Medwin gave her a quick smile.

"If I need help, I promise that you will be the first person to hear of it: will that do?"

"It will do very well. Thank you."

They drove on in a silence that to Medwin echoed with words just spoken. At last Miss Lyddon said:

"By the way, I never finished the story of my quarrel with my brother. I'd like you to hear it, and as we may not have a better opportunity, I propose to tell you now." She glanced at the clock. "We'll pull up somewhere at a quarter to one and have our lunch."

She drove on with skill and assurance. It was easy to see that, as she had said, she had driven all her adult life. It was a pleasure to be driven by her, but Medwin knew it was not going to be a pleasure to hear the story she was about to hear. She had made it anything but a pleasure by letting Miss Lyddon's nephew into her flat. If she could have warned Miss Lyddon without implicating Gwen Jones, she would have done so now. She would have told her all the truth.

"Even Edith," Miss Lyddon said, "doesn't know precisely what happened. She wouldn't, I always felt, have been either emotionally or intellectually able to understand. She was brought up a narrow Nonconformist, and though she's not one now, it's a state of mind that few outgrow. She would have scolded me; she would have pointed out to me how much I myself had been to blame. No, it would have been quite impossible to have told her.

"It happened three years after I left college. I was keeping house for my father at Hartsdown and acting as hostess to his and my brothers' and my own friends. I wish you could have known my father; I wish you could have known something of life as it was then lived by people of his kind and position. All the beauty and spaciousness and rich glow of those days has utterly gone now, and to my mind it's a sad thing for England. Hartsdown had been in the Lyddon family for over two hundred and fifty years, and it's a family—I can say this to you—which boasted a great many distinguished men and women. My father, as I think I told you, inherited it from his uncle, Sir Brian Lyddon, a great public servant. My mother, of course, was less well born. She was a Devenny, and the Devennys were brewers, but they had been brewers and wealthy brewers for several generations, and were people of brains and culture. My mother was very charming and very talented. She played the piano exceptionally well and was a water-colourist of some excellence. I wish I had inherited her talents. Only Luke did. He's still a good pianist. At the time I'm going to tell you about, I was twenty-five, and enjoying every moment of my life. There had been the Boer War to shock and distress us, but a far-away, unmechanized war still had some glamour and glory and it had left few marks. My father was on friendly terms with most of the clever and interesting people of his day, and as it seems to me now, looking back, they were as thick as blackberries.

"I can hardly remember a time when Hartsdown wasn't full of visitors. People were always coming and going, and I was made much of, flattered and, occasionally, courted. I wasn't of course, a young woman to everyone's taste. I was too tall and too thin, though I suppose I was striking-looking enough with my jet black hair, clear, pale complexion and grey eyes. My features, of course, were more suitable to my father and brothers than to me, but I had my share of admirers. Up to that time there had been no one whom I even considered marrying. I was perfectly heartfree as far as men were concerned, but I had made a friend at college who played a tremendously important part in my life. Her name was Catherine Harrington. The fact that we were such close friends at college caused Edith much suffering, and we quarrelled, I'm afraid, though we made it up later. Poor Edith, she went through a bad time. That was the reason she rushed into a marriage with Ernest Gresham during her second year at Girton. However, dull though he was, I think it was on the whole the best thing for her. My brothers never took to her very much, and it was always a little difficult to fit her in at Hartsdown. Catherine, on the other hand, was continually there.

"She was very beautiful and very, very brilliant. Too brilliant, perhaps, and too beautiful for her own good. It used to delight me simply to look at her face. I have never seen a face quite like it, and never shall again. You know yourself the sheer delight of looking at a perfect thing. It seemed to me that I could never look my fill. She had the brownest eyes I ever saw, and it was a brown with a good deal of red in it, and she had a mane of magnificent, wavy, chestnut hair. She was a poet, and if she had lived I believe she would have been in the first rank of modern poets. She wrote verse as other people write letters; it flowed from her, and some of it was outstandingly good. None of it, I think, was trite. When I say she was my best friend I mean that she was separated from my other friends, and outdistanced them, by miles. I preferred her company to that of anyone else's; in short, I adored her. Yes, it was a kind of adoration. When she looked at you, she more than looked. It was an intense and burning gaze. She captivated my father completely, and my brother Luke was desperately in love with her. She didn't want to marry him or any of the many men who loved her. She had too much else to think about and to do. I have never known anyone who lived quite so intensely. She wanted to touch everything, to taste everything. She was insatiable. I was closer to her, dearer to her, than anyone, and I, you see, didn't in any way threaten her liberty, or attempt to divert her from her chosen path. For my part, she was everything I most admired and loved, and everyone else I had met up to that time was thrown into shadow by her.

"One day my brother Mark, who was a young and briefless barrister at Lincoln's Inn, came to Hartsdown bringing with him a friend he had made in Germany the year before. We had heard a great deal about this friend but had not yet met him. His name was Giles Haverford. Yes, of course you've heard of him. Who hasn't? But in those days he was merely a young physicist who had been teaching at Bonn University. He had a professorship there. His mother was German, and he was bilingual. He was something completely outside my experience. He was terrific, quite the most splendid-looking man I had ever seen. Not in the least conventionally handsome, but immensely striking and impressive. You may have seen photographs of him in later life; at thirty-four he had a great head of thick dark hair, intensely blue eyes and rugged features full of character and intelligence. He had been married, and his wife, a young Danish girl, had died in childbirth. It was obvious, even then, that he had genius, and he also had a temper that was not to be trifled with.

"Well, this remarkable man fell in love with me. Perhaps it would be more accurate to say that he made up his mind that he wanted me and was going to marry me. Love seems, somehow, too soft and tender a word to use where he was concerned. He confided his intentions to Mark.

"Mark and I had never really liked each other. Possibly we were too much alike. We roused each other's antagonisms and tempers in the most extraordinary way. He had, I think, the same admiration, perhaps even adoration, for Giles that I had for Catherine. I don't know if people had deeper friendships in those days than they have now, or if it was simply that we had more leisure to devote to them. Or if they were the fashion then. At any rate, it seems to me that there is nothing nowadays to compare at all in intensity with the friendships I can look back upon.

"I think Mark was pulled in two directions when Giles told him he wanted to marry me. He was afraid that he would lose his best friend, and at the same time he was proud and flattered that Giles wanted to marry a member of his family. As for me, I had already fallen wildly in love with him. I never did anything by halves, and though I adored Catherine no less, I wanted with all my heart and soul to marry Giles. Catherine and I had as yet no secrets from each other, and I told her at once. The effect on her was a thousand times worse than I had ever imagined it could be. She threatened to commit suicide if I married him.

"This was a terrible blow to me, as I need hardly say, and I realized all too well that I had got myself into a truly dreadful situation. The scenes with Catherine were heart-breaking, frightening. She accused me of being a traitor, a stabber-in-the back, a false friend. She said I was killing her as surely as if I were giving her hemlock to drink. Oh, I can't begin to tell you the dramas, the miseries that then took place. But there was one thing that I could not do. I could not give Giles up. I wanted him as I had never wanted anything in my life before. I was sure we could have a wonderful life together.

"Don't believe it, my dear, if anyone ever tells you that it's impossible to love two people at once; that one love drives out the other. It's simply not true, as I can testify. I felt as if I were being slowly dragged apart. Some decision had to be made, for Giles was going back to Germany and wanted his answer. I felt that there was only one thing for me to do—to play for time. I told him I loved him and I promised to marry him, but I asked him to wait a year. I was optimistic enough to think that within a year, this complicated knot could somehow be untied, some happy solution reached. Little by little, I thought, I could loosen Catherine's too tight hold upon me, and mine upon her. I thought I saw how, over a period of time, it could be done. I thought that gradually, barely perceptibly, I could diminish her affection for me, even though I loved her as much as ever. That was my plan, and when I told Giles that I would marry him in a year's time, but that the engagement must be kept secret, I was certain that eventually all would be well.

"I hadn't reckoned with my brother Mark. I had thought

very little about him during this crisis. Giles told him, confidentially, that I had promised to marry him, and that he had agreed, at my request, to wait for a year. I suppose I ought to have foreseen the effect upon Mark. I ought to have made Giles promise not to tell him. There we were, all four of us bottled up at Hartsdown together, with our conflicting loyalties and emotions. Mark, it seemed, was furious because I was going to make Giles wait for a year. Or that was the reason he afterwards gave for what he did. He thought I was playing fast and loose with his friend. Without telling me, he went straight to Catherine and told her that I had promised to marry Giles, that we were secretly engaged, and that it was only her hold over me that prevented an immediate marriage. He said he thought it was high time that she left Hartsdown and that he, on his part, hoped never to see her there again.

"Catherine appeared to take this quietly, and waited for some confirmation or denial from me. She waited four days, and I said nothing at all. In the midst of my own emotional crisis it never occurred to me, never for a single instant, that Mark would go to her and tell her that I had become engaged to Giles. What those four days must have been to her I can never bear to think. She gave no sign. On the surface, everything was precisely as usual. Then, on the night of the fourth day she slipped out of her room in her nightdress and drowned herself in the lake."

Miss Lyddon slowed up behind a van to allow an oncoming car to pass, then overtook it and went on. She was waiting for Medwin to speak, and Medwin knew that she must speak, though so absorbed had she been in Miss Lyddon's story that it was only with an effort that she could find words, and bring herself to utter them.

"That," she said, and her throat felt dry with listening, "is one of the most dreadful stories I ever heard."

Miss Lyddon did not turn her head. She went on,

"If Mark hadn't interfered, if I had been given that year I asked for, what a different life mine would have been! When Catherine's body was found and brought to the house, I locked myself in my room. I saw no one, I refused to touch food, I was like a demented creature. Giles tried to see me; I only begged him to leave me alone. He went to Mark, and asked him if there had been anything more than ordinary friendship between Catherine and me. Exactly what Mark said I shall never know, but he gave Giles to understand that there had been.

Giles left the house immediately, and shortly after, he wrote me a terrible letter. I never saw him again. He returned to Germany, and the letters I wrote to him were never answered. Not many months after this he married Ellen Fothergill, the daughter of Fothergill the astronomer. They had a large family of sons and daughters. Five years ago, as you may remember, he died."

"Yes," Medwin said, "I do remember."

"It's time for our lunch now," Miss Lyddon said. "As soon as we come to some little quiet by-road, I'll pull up." And then she said, "What a mistake it is to imagine that people necessarily change as they grow old! I am what I was, with much, I suppose, added, but so little taken away. I still have dreams in which I see Catherine alive and happy and in which I find Giles again, and these seem to grow more and more vivid as time goes on. When I find Giles we hold out our hands to each other; everything is understood, and then it is such a relief, such joy as I have never known in actual life. I melt with happiness."

Medwin turned her head and looked at the gaunt, lined, still handsome face, with the smile which accompanied these last words still on the lips. It's true, she thought we never do cease to be what we were. We only lose the things and people we love, and our bodies decay. That is all it is. We are the same, pitifully the same, but no one knows it. Only we ourselves know it. My father is the same lightfooted man who used to love to take my mother dancing, and would come tiptoeing with her up the stairs, so as not to wake his sleeping daughters. And to him I am still one of those sleeping children and he is bewildered to find himself where he now is. This is a thing we who are still young should try to remember, but we are bound to keep forgetting it, just as I know I shall keep forgetting it. And tears for all who grow outwardly old yet are inwardly young came to her eyes, and Miss Lyddon, turning her head just then, saw them, and Medwin could not find it in her heart to say "These are not for you, or only partly for you." There they were, and it was better to say nothing.

It was a day, quite apart from Miss Lyddon's telling of her story, that Medwin knew she would always remember. She had not before seen so many crippled children together, and he sight of their eagerness and activity and their laughter and forgetfulness of self, even if only on that special, and to them, exciting occasion, moved her deeply. She liked the matron and established friendly relations with her. The matron said, referring to Miss Lyddon, "If only she could give us more of her time," and Medwin refrained from saying, "She could if she would," and only said, "Yes, what a pity it is that she has her hands so full." Everything went off well, and Miss Lyddon's speech met with noisy approval. She spoke, Medwin thought, extremely well, adding many little original remarks and comments that gave liveliness and humour to what she said. Tea was served in the main hall, and the Lord Lieutenant then hurried off to give away prizes at an agricultural college. He said to Miss Lyddon, as he left, "Well, this is one institution I hope the State won't take over."

On the return journey to London, Mis Lyddon gave lifts to two members of the Committee, so that there was no opportunity for further private talk, for which Medwin was thankful. She spent the evening alone in her flat, with much to think about. She saw how the death of Catherine Harrington, added to the broken love affair, had raised up a wall between Miss Lyddon and her brother, and she understood how remorse and regrets had made Robert Lyddon's father "like a tree that has been devoured inside by white ants." And she now felt that there could be no further surprises where Miss Lyddon was concerned. Not a glance of her eye but she could interpret, not a touch of the hand or a smile or a word but would not fall into easy place. And having been the recipient of her full confidence, she knew that she walked a difficult road, and that nothing would ever again be simple, straightforward and unbeset between them.

Some days passed and Robert Lyddon did not telephone, and his not telephoning did not surprise her, for in it was the character of the man. That he would have liked to telephone she had no doubt, and in his refraining was revealed how fully he was aware of her fear of being led into disloyalty. She began to think that she might, in fact, have stressed this fear unduly. Then something occurred which drove Robert Lyddon at least temporarily from her mind.

CHAPTER 9

ONE MORNING WHEN MEDWIN AND MRS. GRESHAM BEGAN their work, Mrs. Gresham appeared to be more than usually preoccupied, her thoughts more than usually unassembled. She was of two minds whether to begin with her personal letters, to plan a short speech for the opening of a bazaar, or to work on the wording of an appeal for funds for the Mid-Metropolitan Hospital. She had been asked to make a draft of this last and submit it to the committee the following week. She finally decided to begin with her letters, then broke off after the second one to say:

"I think I'll leave my correspondence for the moment. Let's get to work on the appeal. Did you try your hand at drafting a letter to go with it?"

"Yes," Medwin told her. "Don't you remember I showed it to you the day before yesterday, and you suggested some alterations? I made them last night."

"Of course, of course," Mrs. Gresham exclaimed with a slightly embarrassed air. "How stupid of me! It had quite slipped my mind. Have we the letter here?"

"I put it in the hospital file in the office," Medwin said. "I'll go and get it."

"No, wait a minute," Mrs. Gresham said. "There's something I want to talk to you about first. Suppose we stop for a few minutes and have coffee? I had my breakfast very early this morning because I woke up early. I had one or two things on my mind and couldn't sleep."

Medwin got up and rang the bell, wondering what it was she was about to hear. Mrs. Gresham seemed, she thought, a little flustered, a little worried and uncertain.

"We might do just one more letter while we're waiting for the coffee," Mrs. Gresham suggested, "and then we won't be interrupted. I ought to write to Farebrothers about those gold shares they wrote to me about. Just take down the letter now, will you?"

Fifteen minutes later, when Wilson had brought in the coffee tray and gone she pushed back her chair and said:

"Come and sit here on the sofa, Mrs. Blair. I think I had better get this thing off my mind as soon as possible. I have a feeling that you'd rather I told you, and as I haven't promised not to tell you, I will."

She stroked her bosom, was silent for a moment, her lips closed in a straight, thin line, and then said:

"A few days ago your father came to see me."

They were sitting side by side on the sofa, and the low table with the coffee tray on it was in front of them. A silence fell upon the room, the house and upon all London. Not a car hooted, it almost seemed that not a wheel turned. Medwin sat rigid with what she had heard. And now the whole aspect of the room changed for her. It became a room her father had violated with his presence; she saw it through his enviously admiring eyes. Mrs. Gresham became the "someone I think might be interested in my scrubbing invention"; someone who might, if only his luck would turn, be instrumental in bringing about an improvement in his fortunes. He had come there much as he had gone into Louise's bedroom, knowing very well that he was doing something he ought not to do, but by now he had justified his action completely. He was no doubt thinking that this was the sort of house he and his family ought to have had. This, he was no doubt saying to himself, was the style in which he and his family ought to have lived.

"Go on please," Medwin said. "And I don't want any coffee. This has made me feel rather sick."

"Oh dear!" Mrs. Gresham cried, and there was confusion in her face, "please don't take it like that, Mrs. Blair. I was afraid you might be a little upset because of course I knew he'd come here quite without your knowledge. I didn't know whether I ought to tell you or not. Then I thought he might tell you himself one day, and you'd feel I hadn't been frank with you. So in the end I made up my mind to tell you. Wasn't it best that you should hear of it first from me?" And she asked this almost eagerly, as if in a hurry to be absolved.

"Certainly, if it had to happen at all," Medwin said. "Well, you've seen him, and now perhaps you understand how he could bring himself to do such a thing. He's like a shipwrecked man on a raft who's driven to cannibalism to keep himself alive."

Mrs. Gresham gave a shocked little laugh.

"Oh, please!" she cried, "don't put it like that. Surely you exaggerate! There was no reason, as far as I'm concerned, why he shouldn't have come. When Wilson brought in his card I admit I was a little surprised. It was an old business card, with a City address on it crossed out. And he had written at the top, 'I hope you will be kind enough to spare half an hour to Medwin's father to discuss a matter of considerable importance.' I could hardly say no, could I? Or tell Wilson to say I was not at home. He called in the afternoon—it was last Tuesday—when you were busy downstairs with Miss Lyddon. He was lucky because as it happened I was quite alone and actually had half an hour to spare before going to the hospital. So things," she added, smiling, "really turned out very well for him."

"How do you mean?" Medwin asked, and she spoke coldly because her mind had leapt ahead to what was coming. "I hope you gave him no encouragement whatever."

"Well, my dear," Mrs. Gresham said, "after all, he *is* your father and an elderly man and I suppose he's been unfortunate. No doubt it's been partly his own fault, but that's no business of mine. He showed me his scrubbing machine which he'd brought with him. I don't know what Wilson could have thought."

Medwin bit her lip and was silent.

"It's really quite ingenious," Mrs. Gresham went on, "though I don't suppose there's a char in all London who could be induced to use it. As I tried to point out to him when he showed me how it worked, it isn't just a case of passing a soapy brush over a floor but of scrubbing vigorously and at close quarters and exerting real pressure. That you cannot do, I said, at the end of a stick. Still, housewives might use it, I suppose. I don't know much about such things. However, he wouldn't listen to any criticisms. He said the only thing lacking was the money to launch it. He told me he wanted to apply for a patent. but that at the moment he was so financially embarrassed that he couldn't even afford the necessary visits to London. He said that if he could only stay in London for a few weeks he was sure he could get the thing under way. He seems to think he's invented something quite useful as the carpet sweeper or box broom or whatever it's called, and he asked me for the names of people I thought might be interested. He said I'd be doing my friends a real favour by letting them in on it. I suppose all inventors feel like that."

"And what did you say?" Medwin asked.

"I told him I couldn't see my way to giving him any names. What I did do was to lend him last year's copy of the 'Directory of Directors'. He took it away with him and said he would study it."

"But you've something more to tell me," Medwin persisted. "I know it."

"Well, promise me," Mrs. Gresham said, and lightly touched Medwin's arm, "that you won't be angry. I really didn't know what to do for the best. You can see what an awkward situation it was. In the end, as my time was getting short, I gave him a cheque for two hundred pounds. Now, my dear, don't look at me like that. What is two hundred pounds? Three new dresses, perhaps, from Bertha Mollnar's, or a sum I might have given to some charity or other. And for him it may possibly mean a complete change in his fortunes. But I admit I wasn't thinking of him so much as of you. You have far too many burdens."

"I am not going to thank you," Medwin said. "You know that. The whole thing is outrageous, and I feel deeply humiliated."

"Oh, Mrs. Blair!" pleaded Mrs. Gresham. "What else could I have done? I could hardly give your father five pounds and send him away, could I?"

"He was quite aware of that," Medwin said.

"And on the other hand, nothing less than two hundred would have been the slightest good to him. I really felt it ought to have been more. What I felt I couldn't do was to send him to people I know in the City. If I lose the money, and I fully expect to, it's no great matter, but I don't want to be the cause of other people's losing theirs." She paused. "He was extremely polite," she said, "and has very courtly manners." Then she laughed—"and he insisted on giving me an IOU. Now don't look so tragic. You'd never have let me help you, and if I choose to help your father, that's my affair."

For an instant Medwin covered her eyes with her hand. Then she dropped her hand and said:

"How I wish you hadn't seen him without first telling me!"

"That would have been pointless," Mrs. Gresham said, "as of course you'd have asked me not to see him. Now I'm glad I've told you. I was afraid all this might somehow affect our pleasant relationship. That's what really kept me awake this morning. And that would have been too sad." She made the familiar gesture. "I've really grown very fond of you, you know. In many ways you're the sort of young woman I'd have liked my son to marry."

And there are other ways, thought Medwin, remembering that the daughter-in-law came of a wealthy Montreal family, in which I would not have done at all. But she was touched by the tribute and believed it to be sincere. She said aloud:

"There's no higher compliment from a mother. Thank you. But at the moment I can't divert my thoughts to Canada or anywhere else. I don't think there's the smallest likelihood of my father being able to interest anyone in his invention, so I look upon the two hundred pounds as a loan and I mean to repay it."

Mrs. Gresham got up then and said, almost brusquely,

"Well, it isn't a loan, however you choose to regard it, and I never meant it to be. I never lend money, never. Neither did my husband. I give it, and if I choose to give it to your father, that's my affair. If it makes his fortune, well and good, and he can repay me if he likes. If not, at least I hope he'll get some fun out of it. Now, work."

She went to the writing-table, sat down and began turning over some papers very busily. Medwin got up and sat beside her, but her hands were in her lap.

"Will you promise, at least, not to let him have any more money on any pretext whatsoever?" she asked.

"I won't give him any more without first telling you. I promise you that," Mrs. Gresham answered. "Now let's get on with that appeal."

"Just one thing more, please," said Medwin. "Will you tell Miss Lyddon?"

Mrs. Gresham gave her abrupt, nervous little laugh.

"I don't feel I have to tell Miss Lyddon everything I do, and actually I see no reason why I should tell her this."

"Thank you," Medwin said. She felt that Mrs. Gresham would not now tell Miss Lyddon except for what might seem to her some very good reason, but she could not rule out the possibility that some very good reason might present itself, and she foresaw that Miss Lyddon would not take the matter lightly. Oh well, she thought, that's their affair; I can't expect Mrs. Gresham to keep it to herself for ever. She knows that I'd rather she kept it to herself, and I must be content with that.

There was nothing more to be done; what had happened had happened and she had to bear it. She thought of trying to get the money back from her father, but by now she knew he had deposited the cheque in the Hurcomb branch of Barclay's Bank, with whose manager he sometimes had a glass of beer at the Rifleman's Arms. It was too late, even supposing that she could persuade her father to relinquish it. She felt, as she had told Mrs. Gresham, humiliated. Humiliated by her father's shocking visit, humiliated by Mrs. Gresham's "gift." To regard it as a gift was intolerable to her. She felt that these two women were little by little putting her in chains; one by her confidences and her difficult, exacting friendship, the other by giving money to her father. She did not know which might one day drag heaviest upon her.

She was going to the theatre with Mr. Fullerton that evening, and she left early, in order to be on time. As she hurried across the garden she wished, not for the first time, that later and more civilized hours for playgoers might not be long postponed. She marvelled at the uncomplaining, unprotesting attitude of her fellow-countrymen who were obliged to go straight from work to theatre unwashed and unfed, and later eat a probably indigestible meal at a certainly indigestible hour. They had come to look upon it not as a war-measure due for disappearance but as an Act of God which He would possibly repeal in His own good time. But her elders, she supposed, were too accustomed to inconvenience and too weary to protest, while her juniors knew nothing better. However, it was preferable to not going at all and Mr. Fullerton was a suave, avuncular and playful host to whom the cost of such an evening, and supper at the Ivy or the Savoy Grill, meant nothing, and whose witticisms, to which a close collaboration between eyes and nostrils seemed to give birth, were sometimes worth remembering.

And it was a relief to Medwin to find that Miss Lyddon not only accepted Mr. Fullerton's friendship for her but was eager to further it. She was pleased when he took her out. Obviously Miss Lyddon could not on any grounds whatsoever feel jealousy where her good-humoured solicitor was concerned, and this was something to be thankful for.

Medwin spoke, during the evening, deliberately and with purpose, of Lord and Lady Lyddon, and referred to Miss Lyddon's other brothers—"she tells me she has two others"—but Mr. Fullerton was not to be drawn. Whatever he knew, and he doubtless knew much, he would not utter it, and it would not be from him that she would hear the names of Mark or Robert Lyddon spoken. To provoke indiscretion in others was his delight but he was incapable of being himself indiscreet. A man to be relied upon, and she was half sorry he was so very much Miss Lyddon's man. She could, had it been otherwise, have found a use for his sagacity and good counsel, and felt it possible that she might one day have serious need of them, but they were not at her command. There was no man anywhere to whom she could take her problems. Her two male relatives, her father and Harold, were hardly in this category.

Late though it was when Mr. Fullerton returned her to her door in a taxi, she sat down to write a letter to her father so that it could go by the early post in the morning. She was tempted to write a very angry letter, so easy is it to write a good, angry, letter, the pen seeming to charge forward on this errand of its own accord. But whatever she might and did think of her father's behaviour she could not bring herself to write angrily to her mother's husband, so chose instead to write coldly. She thought, on reading it over, that it was not unduly cold.

"My dear Father—

"Mrs. Gresham has just told me about your quite unjustifiable visit to her last week. She felt she had to tell me and I am thankful she did for it must on no account happen again. It was something you should not, of course, have dreamt of doing and I am deeply distressed and ashamed. I look upon the two hundred pounds as a charitable donation to a member of my family, and that I cannot endure the thought of. I shall therefore pay it back, little by little, until it is wiped off the slate. You must please give me your promise never to ask her for money again, or attempt to see either her or Miss Lyddon without first telling me of your intention. Otherwise you will make my position here intolerable and jeopardize the good relations between my employers and myself.

"Your much distressed and humiliated daughter,

"Medwin."

His reply came two days later.

"My dear Daughter—

"Perhaps I should have told you I intended to see Mrs. Gresham. Otherwise I admit to no action of which either you or I need feel ashamed. I went to see her purely in the way of business. I could have gone to a hundred other people, but I chose her because of her late husband's connection with the Gresham Investment Trust Co. I assumed that she must have considerable business understanding and experience. We had a most agreeable little talk and she strikes me as being a thoroughly practical and sensible person. At any rate she had wit enough to see the possibilities in my scrubbing invention and to invest a small sum in it. I am now trying to find a good name for it. I think of calling it 'Char-phast' or possibly 'Char-joy,' but you might hit upon something better if you put your mind to it. The name, as I hardly need to point out to you, is of great importance. What do you think of 'Char-eeze?'

"I went to see your mother on Sunday—I waited until I saw that woman go out for her afternoon walk—and found her quite cheerful and making good progress. Dr. Tenby says she can go back to her wheel chair in a couple of days, and then after a short while to crutches.

"I am going up to London tomorrow for two weeks at least and will be staying at the Tennyson Hotel in Great Russell Street. You will find it in the telephone book if you want to get in touch with me. I have a long list of people I propose seeing, and I am feeling very well and very optimistic.

"Your affectionate
"Father."

"P.S. I complimented Mrs. Gresham on her delightful house and on her good taste. We got on very well indeed.

"Mr. Schlemmer keeps dropping in on your mother. I can't understand why she doesn't send him about his business."

She did not know what to say to her mother. She had not been to the lodge very recently, spending her Sundays with Sarah at Wimbledon instead, but she had written regularly and now wrote her usual bi-weekly letter avoiding all reference to her father. She did not want to distress her mother by telling her of his call on Mrs. Gresham, and thought it best to let him tell his own story in whatever way he pleased. A few days later she received a letter from her mother.

"Darling—

"Do you know what's happened? I had a hurried note from your father, from the farm, to say that he was just off to London to stay for two or three weeks. He said that someone he'd seen in London the last time he went there had invested some money in the scrubbing-machine, and that now he could go ahead and make arrangements for launching it. Have you any idea who put up the money, and how much it was? I don't know why, but I feel worried. He seemed jubilant but also quite unnecessarily mysterious. It's not like him not to have told me who the 'someone' is. Poor dear, he's been so desperately depressed and gloomy, and now he's alarmingly the opposite. Do you think it's all right? He's given me his address—the Tennyson Hotel, Great Russell Street. Don't keep bad news from me if you know of any. I'm feeling very much better, and will soon be getting about again, and I can bear anything but being kept in the dark.

"Louise is awfully funny and I have a great many private laughs. She's quite fascinated by Mr. Schlemmer, who calls regularly. I think she feels he'd be a wonderful vehicle for propagating truth, if he could only be made to see it. But my dear, I ought to tell you that she is pining to get home. It seems that Mr. Beedle is not at all well and is tired of 'doing' for himself. In a week or two I believe I could manage perfectly well alone, with just a little occasional help from Mrs. Briggs.

"Your very loving

"Mother."

"P.S. Charlotte and the children, as you know, are planning to occupy 'The Willows' in two weeks. Then they can all come over to see me, and that will be wonderful. She's been able to let the Wimbledon house she tells me, for the summer, which is lucky. Harold is going off to Sandwich to play golf. He seems to neglect stock-jobbing for golf without a twinge of conscience. Poor Charlotte. I'm awfully afraid he's bored with 'that woman' now. Anyway, he is becoming very proprietary about Charlotte and the children, as if he couldn't see with half an eye how magnificently she's managed without him all these years! However one must of course be on the side of virtue, and if he does return entirely, as seems likely, we must try our hardest to rejoice.

"She's just written to tell me about having become a Quaker. She was shy about speaking of it, she said. I don't know why she should be. I think it's an excellent thing and I think she'll be much happier.

"How like me to make the postscript such an important part of the letter!

"Bless you, darling, and take good care of yourself.

"M."

Yes, thought Medwin, her father was certainly 'jubilant.' He was as pleased and gratified as if the money had descended upon him from heaven in a golden shower. He had got it, and that was enough. She knew that at least he would not spend it foolishly. He would stay quietly and decorously at a quiet and decorous hotel, and he would spend his evenings poring over the 'Directory of Directors' and making out lists and crossing off the names of the people he'd seen or written to with no result. A certain amount of money would necessarily be spent on taxi fares, and some on underclothes, shoes, shirts, ties and a new hat. If he went out at all for pleasure he would only go to the cinema, of which he was both contemptuous and fond. He would make one or two friends in the hotel, perhaps; most probably lonely women with whom he would converse with great politeness, even a certain amount of innocuous gallantry. If he saw opportunities for compliments, he would pay them and pride himself on doing it well. He would get his lunches very cheaply at an A.B.C., or at Lyons. No, he would certainly not spend the money foolishly, there was no danger of that. Too much was at stake. He would spin it out because its main value to him was that it might enable him to obtain more. She knew that he was happy, perhaps for the first time in many years. Now he was a business man again, and his chief sorrow would be that he had not a business address to put on his card. He would long for an office, and if anyone could be persuaded to advance him further funds, probably he would obtain one. She thought that if he could form a company again before he died he would die a not unhappy man.

Her mother's letter came by the afternoon post, and she had no time to read it until the evening, when she was alone in her flat. She sat thinking how she could pay off the two hundred pounds without cutting down the money for Sarah, without depriving her mother of things she needed, without diminishing her payments to hospital and doctors, and without going shabby herself. It was something of a mathematical problem, and she soon wearied of it and put her head down on her arms.

If only Mrs. Gresham, usually so shrewd and cautious, had said to her father, "I can advance you money only with your daughter's knowledge and approval," or "I never make investments of any kind without first consulting my business adviser." Either would have ended it. But her difficulties, she thought, showed more readiness to begin than to end, and it seemed of small use to try to keep her life in order.

She would say nothing to Charlotte about the money. Charlotte would certainly see no kindness in Mrs. Gresham's act, and much dishonour in their father's. To Charlotte, white was whiter and black blacker than to most people. Besides, if Charlotte learnt that she intended to repay Mrs. Gresham she would refuse to take money for Sarah's keep, and she took little enough as it was.

She wondered if she would ever again hear the voice of Robert Lyddon on the telephone, for there, she thought, was a man she could have talked to in the way that it is comfortable for a woman to talk to a man. She feared not; no, not ever again. And this she now counted not only her fault, but her misfortune. And yet, how easy a thing for him to do! The hand lifting the receiver, the finger dialling the familiar number—nothing else was needed. Where was he? Somewhere within reach of a telephone no doubt. Even if there were no telephone in his room or flat, there would be a telephone booth within two minutes' walk. And she said aloud, very slowly, at least half a dozen times, leaning her forehead on her palms and not caring how strange her voice might sound to the listening walls and furniture. "Robert Lyddon, go to the telephone and ring up Grosvenor 0099." But nothing happened and yawning and feeling drained of vitality she went to her room and undressed. She was putting her nightdress over her head when the willed thing happened. The telephone rang. She slipped into bed and took up the receiver. And now she wondered that she had ever doubted that he would telephone. He had said he would.

She saw no reason to postpone a meeting. She agreed to be in, expecting him, at a quarter to seven the following evening, and she added that as she was not going out they could talk at their leisure.

"What made you decide to ring me up tonight?" she wanted to know.

"I decided to wait three weeks," he said, "and the three weeks is up."

It was as simple as that. Her willing had achieved nothing at all. He was not, in any case, a man who vacillated, or whom the receiving of a chance thought, if one were on its way to him, would influence. He had his reasons, and one of them might be that he had now shortened by three weeks the painful time of waiting, had brought nearer the day when he would be able to tell her of his wife's decision. Yes, he had his reasons, and she was glad to know it.

There he was, and it seemed natural enough, and his presence seemed to have about it a calming inevitability. There he was, where she had thought he would never be again, and there was the gin and Dubonnet and the ice, and on the mantelpiece some wallflowers that she had bought at lunch time. It was impossible not to feel glad that he was there. When he first came into the room, he picked up the photograph of Sarah, giving it, this second time, a closer, more interested scrutiny, but saying nothing. Then he walked to the window and looked across at the back of the house, which the late sun gilded. The crocuses that were in the garden when Medwin saw it for the first time had long since been replaced by daffodils and hyacinths, and these in their turn had given way to red and yellow Dutch tulips, which, past their prime now, were presently to be followed by scarlet geraniums and salvia. The tulips still made a show and he smiled at the sight of them. He sat down in the chair in which he had sat before and took out his cigarette case, and Medwin mixed the cocktails as she had seen him do.

"And Gwen!" she asked.

"I've seen her twice."

"Quite recovered, I hope."

"Well, yes. Only I got the feeling that there's a spring broken. Tell me if you think I'm wrong, but could it be"—he bent his head to light a cigarette—"that she was punished—God knows in what subtle ways—for being connected with my family?" And he shook out the flame of the match.

"I had thought of that," Medwin said slowly.

"You'd say it was not outside the bounds of possibility?"

"I should think, not entirely," she said, "though it might well have been a quite unconscious cruelty, I suppose." But the idea was no sooner expressed than discarded. Miss Lyddon did nothing unconsciously.

"That," he said, "I cannot believe. There has been too much harm done. A special cause of suffering has been that they insisted, against her wishes, on paying her expenses in the sanatorium, though half was paid by the other one, for whom Gwen, I think, feels gratitude and some affection. The point is that she has suffered too much and in too many ways. I was shocked when I saw her. You see, in all her life she has loved —really loved—only two people—myself and her. And I was away."

"I wish I could have seen Gwen," said Medwin.

"It might have been good for her to see you. You are so completely uncaptivated, so completely free. Good God!" he exclaimed, "how I know that woman! Through my father, through Gwen, and now through you, though you've said little enough. I know her as I know no one else. She's in my bones."

"And must we talk about her?" Medwin asked. "Must we?"

"You're afraid of saying more than you should?"

"You see," she explained, "I know more than I did when you were here last."

He was silent for a moment, taking in her meaning.

"And what view do you take, now, of my father?"

She looked at him and smiled. He had said, "The whole thing concerns me very little," but still, he wanted to hear from her what kind of picture Miss Lyddon had drawn of his father. That did concern him. But it concerned him, she thought, only because of the image that might have been left with her of someone he loved and would protect if he could, and this was defensible and proper. She answered, choosing her words:

"I think he probably acted as a great many emotional people would have acted in the same circumstances. I don't think more blame attaches to him than to her, or to any of the four. There they were, as she put it, all bottled up at Hartsdown together. And no one could have foreseen the tragedy—or if anyone could and should have foreseen it, it was she."

"That," he said, "is fair I think, and true." And then he smiled. "The more I think and read about those days and those people—and I read a good many biographies of the period—the more I realize what a lot of passion was burnt up by two tremendous and exhausting wars. What takes its place is cooler, more reasonable. There's less poetry in it, and," he added, "more grey ash," and for the first time there was a trace of bitterness in his voice.

"Did we think so when we were younger ourselves?" she asked.

He answered, "It isn't the same brew. There was something Russian about their way of living and feeling. I mean of course the clever, not the stupid ones. These people my father was born among were a class apart, their realities were certainly not ours. The parties in those great houses with all the strolling and the talking and the loving, how they must have heightened temperatures. They were intensely self-conscious people, and they must have been highly attractive, I suppose, with their easily got, freely displayed culture. Attractive to each other—possibly not to those on the outside. I'm not speaking particularly of my grandfather. He had a job to do and did it supremely well. But because of his connections and his wealth and his charm, he happened to be very much one of them."

"Would you have liked," she asked him, "to be one of them yourself?"

"No. The air they breathed seems to me vitiated. How endlessly they must have talked about themselves and about one another, never leaving anything unsaid. It was well for Haverford, I think, that he got away. It was no milieu for him."

"But surely he would have taken her away."

"I wonder. Could he?" He shook his head. "No, he was well out of it."

For a moment there was silence. She wanted to drop a curtain between them and that house, and she wanted to keep from telling him more than she should, for the temptation to tell him was strong.

"There is one problem at least that has been cleared up since I saw you last," he said. "I am not going to Nairobi. Or not unless the alternative I spoke of turns out to be made up entirely of false hopes."

"You refrain from telling me what it is," she said, "and I won't ask because obviously if you wanted to tell me you would."

"No," he said. "I'm deliberately holding back. I want to tell you so much that once launched on the subject I might not stop."

"I'll let you know," she promised, smiling, "when I'm bored."

He thoughtfully revolved the ice in his glass before he spoke again.

"First," he said, "I want to tell you this. I know more about you than when I was here last. You see, she wrote sometimes to Gwen. Twice I think. In one of these letters, which Gwen showed me, she spoke of you. She took pleasure in speaking of you, it seemed to me. She said you were a war widow with a child, and that you had previously been working at a hospital in the country. She said you were a very charming person, that you had taken hold of the work quickly, that you made no mistakes, and that they were greatly pleased with you. Even before Gwen had recovered she planted this barb in her quivering flesh. All she pined to hear, poor devoted soul, was that she was missed. Not one word of that from either. The conclusions that were to be drawn from that, Gwen drew."

"So I have contributed to Gwen's misery."

"She's incapable of malice or envy. I told her I'd seen you and how it came about, and she questioned me about you with nothing but friendliness. However, I only tell you this because I want you to know that I know more than you think I know."

She smiled at this.

"You're welcome to it," she said. "It was only that I'm not good at talking about myself, except to a very few."

"No, no," he said, with a touch of impatience, "it was far more than that, and you were right. You knew nothing about me. I understood that and approved it."

"Very well," she said. "Whatever it was, and you may interpret it as you please, it's a thing of the past now."

"So is your saying what you have just said," he answered quickly. "I hope it's equally irrevocable."

"If what you mean is that I trust you now, I do."

"Then," he said, and raised his glass to his lips, "we may go on from here."

"For a while," she said, "I would like to." Their eyes met with understanding and with a calm promise. A promise of being able to retrace their steps, if turning back should be asked of them. A promise that the ground would be mapped, that there would be no question whatever of their losing their way or getting too far from their base. Reasonable people do not run head on into danger when they have been so clearly warned. They would know precisely at what points mines had been laid, and these points they would scrupulously avoid.

She was now observing more and more details of his appearance and manner. The first impression of solidity, of firmness, of masculine self-assurance, remained. The face was square rather than long like Miss Lyddon's, the eyes lacked the startling cold grey brilliance of hers and had more warmth and shadow Had indeed much warmth and shadow, though his glances occasionally stabbed her with their resemblance to those she already knew. It was a face, she thought, that would wake easily in quick response to another day. This could have been his sailor's training, and however uncongenial he might have found it, the life had put its preservative and salty touch upon him. His hands moved without clumsiness or self-consciousness. They were hands that knew practical and ingenious things.

"Then if we go on from here," she said, breaking a silence, "tell me what you now propose to do."

He took out another cigarette.

"When I have gone," he said, "I would like you to open up the hiding place. You will find a square brown paper parcel there and inside it some books. These are presentation copies of my one published work—a kind of novel I wrote during the war when I was at sea. It's a story of a ship and some of the men in it. It was published nearly two years ago by Hare and Botwood and it did pretty well. Upon that small achievement I propose to build a literary career. But I'm not such an optimistic fool that I dare count on that to keep me seaworthy and afloat. I'm taking a dull and humble post with a shipping company as insurance against shipwreck. One of my friends embarked on a literary career without any such insurance, and he's now running a filling station on the Portsmouth Road. I don't propose to take that risk. I shall write at night and at week-ends, and we shall see. But I want you, if you will, to read that book and give me your honest opinion on it. I've made a rapid inspection of your books," he said, "and I think highly of your judgment."

"Well," she said, "you may have been led astray by them. Most of them are your aunt's, an overflow from the house. But my own wouldn't be so very different, though there'd be more poetry. Books have been a good half of my life. I've had to educate myself. I've made a beginning, I hope, but not much more than that. And of course," she added, "I'll read your book immediately. Tonight. I imagine you wrote it under some other name."

"R. L. Marriner," he said. "I took Marriner because it was my mother's name, not to make a bad pun. It sold eight thousand copies."

"Which is good, isn't it?" she asked. "For a first book?"

"Goodish," he said. "At any rate, encouraging. And now I want to write *that* story. The story of the tragedy at Hartsdown."

He looked across at her and waited for her response.

"With suitable changes, naturally," he said. "Come, come,

you look doubtful, or worse. Tell me why I should not write it."

"Isn't it," she asked, "just keeping the whole thing alive? Aren't you in danger of—well, wallowing in it, as you put it yourself?"

"No," he said. "Certainly not. It's a story with which the good God saw fit to launch me into this world, so to speak. I was born to a man who was broken by it. When I said it didn't concern me, I meant that I don't give a single damn that not one penny of the Lyddon or the Devenny money ever came my way. And that, believe me, is the truth. I've never wanted to be a rich man. I never shall be. Neither would I write the story with any ideas of justifying my father, or accusing *her*. It's a story, like any other, but it happens to interest me more than any other. That is all. And I would give it," he added, "a different ending. I planned it all when we were on the China Station, after that leave when I came home to find my wife dreading my return. I needed something to think about."

"I see. And what ending would you give it?"

"There's the death, of course. That has to be. But instead of leaving my aunt's letters unopened, as he actually did, Haverford, or the character who takes his place, does open them and in time answers them. She goes to him in Germany or wherever he may be, and they marry. And the marriage is disastrous."

"You are assuming, I see, that I now know the full story," Medwin said. "Well, I do."

"I guessed as much. She would be sure, I think, to want you to know it. Well, the marriage goes on the rocks. Alive or dead, the girl comes between them. They can't exorcise her. In real life the real Haverford knew that. His prototype in the book is less intelligent. It proves a long agony for both. She leaves him at last, and becomes the woman she now is and would have been," he said with certainty, "in any circumstances whatever, though she herself may think not. 'Haverford' proves the stronger character of the two, and she cannot live with a stronger character. She must mould the people she lives with, or break them. She could neither mould nor break 'Haverford,' and he is forever on the watch for what he has come to see and to hate in her. I mean, of course, the fictionized 'Haverford.' The other, as we know, happily escaped. So she leaves him and continues to exercise her power in her own disastrous way. Did she speak to you of Meg Sullivan? No, I'm sure she didn't. There was another escape."

"Tell me," she said.

"She was Catherine Harrington's successor. A young woman married to a playwright. It faded out quietly enough, and ended, at last, in a convent. Perhaps happily, who knows?"

"It's all a long time ago," she said. "She's changed. She's suffered."

"I could believe it," he said, "but for Gwen. She was such very, very small game. Why need she have bothered to twist her up in her fingers as she did? And do you think, do you believe for one moment that she didn't know what that girl, Catherine Harrington, was going through? Do you believe that she didn't deliberately refrain from going to her and telling her the truth? It was a cold and cruel struggle for power. Catherine Harrington had tried to keep her from doing something she had set her heart on doing. It was a trial of strength. Don't ask me who won in the end. I couldn't tell you."

"I think you're wrong, there," Medwin said. "I think you're wrong about her attitude towards Catherine Harrington. I'm sure you are."

He shook his head. "I know her too well," he said.

There was a pause and then she said:

"Write the story then, and be rid of it for ever. Explore them all and wring every drop out of them and of it, and then forget it. Otherwise it may do you harm."

"Me?" he laughed. "Never. Not for an instant. To me it's a theme, a plot, a knot to be untied. I can hardly wait to tackle it."

"And I shan't see the novelist in you," she asked, "overwhelming the rest? I shouldn't like to see that."

"Why should you even fear it? There would be malice towards none, and as much charity as the theme will allow. I can't hate her. I have never succeeded in hating anyone, whatever the provocation." Then, abruptly, he asked, "Did she tell you of the aftermath? Did she speak of the coroner's verdict?"

"No. She never mentioned that. Why?"

He got up and put his empty glass on the table.

"She gave the coroner to understand that my father was directly responsible for the tragedy. His part in it, or her story of his part in it, was heavily underlined, and not only that, but widely broadcast in the newspapers. He had to live that down. It was not agreeable for him."

"I don't know what to say," she told him.

"May I suggest that you ask me to have another drink?" And he smiled down at her.

She laughed and said, "Oh, please help yourself. You're more skilled than I am. And fill mine too."

"And then," he said, looking at his wrist-watch, "I ought to go."

"I suppose," she said, "you have a dinner engagement."

"No. I was going to a restaurant. Would you come with me?"

"Yes," she said, "I would." Then she laughed again. "I might have asked you to stay here and dine or sup with me, but the only thing in the flat is a small tin of ham that your aunt gave me. It was sent by your Uncle Luke from America. And I could have made a salad."

His eyes were full of amusement.

"Let's be sensible about this," he said, settling down again. "I have no hesitation at all in saying that I'll share the ham with pleasure. Neither my appetite nor my conscience rebels at the thought. I'm sick of restaurant food, though I hope you'll come with me next time. But I'd like best to stay here, if I may choose. We're not in London here. I don't quite know where we are, and that's pleasant in itself."

"Good, then, we stay," she said. "I'm sure your attitude towards the ham is the right one. I'm growing morbid, I think. But why is it pleasant not to be in London? London is my birthplace and my city. Do you hate it?"

"I'm homeless in it, and once was not," he told her.

"That," she said, "I can understand. Even my own feelings towards it have changed, and I don't think it has anything to do with the war. Once I walked these streets feeling that they were my own. As a child, and as a young girl. My sister and I owned London. We owned every bus and shop and street-crossing and tree. What has happened to me, or to it?"

"Then," he said, "you walked in London. Now you walk in the precarious world, as we all do, or should do, after thirty."

"After thirty?" she repeated, surprised and amused.

"I put your age as more than thirty."

"I've just passed thirty-three."

"I drew the conclusion from other sources than your face," he said. "And that," he added, smiling, "I say without the smallest wish to pay a compliment, but merely to state a fact."

"I much prefer that," she told him. "And now that you're staying and we have time, here's a bit of recent autobiography. I've lately been realizing how much I needed a friend and an adviser. Perhaps it's premature to say what I'm going to say, but I don't feel that it is." She went on, not waiting for him to speak. "Your aunt has a solicitor, Mr. Fullerton, a bachelor of sixty or so. A charming, stout person, light as a feather. One feels he could go bounding over woods and hedges by just now and then putting his toe to the ground. We like each other, and sometimes we go to the theatre together."

"And she doesn't mind?"

"Oddly enough, it seems to please her. I thought, the last time I saw him, how right he was for my confidences, if only he hadn't been who and what he was. I could have told him about meeting you, and longed to tell him. I could have asked him if I was being shockingly, wickedly disloyal. But as I can make no such use of him whatever, I had to decide the matter for myself in the end."

"Much better so. But how can you lack what you say you lack? People to turn to—friends, advisers?"

"Because," she said, "my life was spent in a series of boarding-houses. At seventeen I began to earn my living. When the war came I lived as other girls did, sharing a room, going out with this person or that, taking the best that came my way. But nothing was built up, nothing was established. Do you know what I longed for, more than anything else? To know families. Even one family. Father, mother, brothers and sisters, cousins. A family whose home I could go in and out of, where I'd be made welcome, so that I could share in their little affectionate world of fun and jokes and nicknames. My friends—the girls I worked with—lived alone, as I mostly did. Their families were always somewhere else. And the men I used to go about with—they're dead or married or have gone back to where they came from. I hardly remember them, except the one I married—so much the best of them all. That was my life. And the families I might have known—I shall mourn for them all my days."

"I once knew such a family," he said, "as you had in mind. There were eight of them. I loved them all so much that I married one of the daughters because she was a part of the whole. I wanted to be even more one of them than I already was. As a young man they had for me all the glamour in the world. And now they've scattered, and it turned out as it did turn out, and there's nothing left. Nothing but memories, whose validity I sometimes doubt."

"I see," she said, "that you won't allow me my regrets."

And she got up and switched on the lamps, for the sunlight had long since gone from the back of the big house, and lights now shone from the windows.

"I suppose," she was about to say, "I had better draw the curtains," but she stopped herself, leaving the words unsaid, though she did draw the curtains and he watched her, knowing why.

"I can't picture her," he said, smiling, "training a pair of opera glasses on her secretary's windows, somehow. Can you?"

She smiled too but did not answer. They both knew the curtains were drawn to help her to forget that she was guilty of deceit, though she was not sure how guilty, or if it really mattered. She hoped she could forget it for as long as the evening lasted, and after.

CHAPTER 10

ON THE WALLS OF MISS LYDDON'S BEDROOM, WHICH WAS painted a dusty pink, were drawings by Degas, Daumier, Constantin Guys, Derain and many others, and there were more recent ones by Augustus John, Rex Whistler and John Piper. She came home to lunch one day in some excitement and announced that she had bought a drawing by Ingres, and as soon as it was hung, invited Medwin and Mrs. Gresham to look at it. It was a beautiful room, and the needlework curtains, the bed-spread and the tester which ran around the top of the narrow four-poster bed were all from her bedroom at Hartsdown and had been worked by an industrious ancestress in the beginning of the eighteenth century.

The drawing was of a plump young girl in a simple, high-waisted dress, her hands touching the strings of a harp, and her head turned to face the artist. Medwin's eyes returned to it again and again, and as the two women were presently discussing something which did not concern her, she looked her fill at it and the other drawings. Then Mrs. Gresham presently left the room saying that she must dress to go out, and Miss Lyddon, with a glance, kept Medwin, who was moving to the door, from following her.

"Wait," Miss Lyddon said, "I want to show you something." And she went to her cupboard, took a dress from a hanger and brought it out. It was a printed crepe with poodles jumping through hoops making a small, amusing pattern. "Now," she said sternly, "I don't want a lot of fuss and nonsense and protests. The warm weather is upon us and I notice that you don't possess a single cool print dress. Here's one I ordered in a weak moment from Louise Dupin and it doesn't suit me. It's far too frivolous. Take it and let me see you wear it. Edith's never set eyes on it so far as I know. And I shall be very grateful if you'll accept it with no more than a polite thank you." She laid the dress over Medwin's shoulder and looked at her with eyes half-closed and head tilted back. "It will suit you perfectly."

Medwin looked at her with a troubled face.

"Oh," she said, "you know how much I'd rather not take it. Why do you do it?"

"Why? Because I don't want to throw it away and it's too good for any of my poor protégées. It was a mistake to buy it and I don't often make mistakes. At least save me from regrets and remorse by taking it, and let's hear no more about it."

"You make it very hard for me to refuse," Medwin said.

"I should be very much hurt if you did refuse. I haven't forgiven you yet for not taking that old fur coat of mine. Now, while you're here I want to show you some photographs. They'll serve to illustrate the story of Catherine, Giles, Mark and myself. In fact the whole family are here, and endless other people, but you needn't look at them all." As she spoke she went to the drawer of a tall secretaire and took out two morocco-covered albums. She sat down on a chaise-longue at the foot of the bed and motioned to Medwin to sit beside her. Medwin laid the dress over a chair and did so.

"I've often wondered," she said, "why I haven't been shown any pictures of Hartsdown."

"There are plenty here," Miss Lyddon said. "You know, of course, why I never go there. The sight of the lake still turns my stomach over. And as the house looks out on the lake, I'm perpetually reminded of that horror. James and Fanny understand, of course. First, look at these photographs. They were taken for 'Country Life' some twenty years ago. Isn't it a perfect house? Thank heaven it was not built by Vanbrugh, but just before he became the fashion. I wish you could see it. You could, of course, but I think you'd find staying there something of a bore. Dear Fanny's a deplorable hostess and is interested in nothing but her hobbies, but luckily James asks for nothing better than to be left in peace. By the way, I saw Fanny take you off into a corner the other day at lunch. Did she suggest your going there?"

"I don't remember being taken into a corner," said Medwin, "but she did speak of my paying them a visit some time. She didn't mention a date, and I told her how my week-ends were usually spent."

"I'm afraid I interrupted the talk at that point," Miss Lyddon said. "What a pity. But I really wouldn't advise you to go. James could never be rude, of course, but he doesn't suffer visitors gladly. He has a way of regimenting his guests which would have shocked and horrified my father. Instead of breakfast being from eight-thirty to ten, as it used to be, with fresh coffee and toast and scones arriving at intervals, James insists on everyone's being at the table at eight-thirty precisely. And to keep dinner waiting, whatever the excuse, is the sin of sins."

"But it's a house that ought to be full of people," said Medwin, looking at the photographs.

"Well, on four days a week when it's open to the public, it is," Miss Lyddon said, with irony. "However, it's no good under our present planned economy to try to entertain as my father did. No, James and Fanny never attempt to give parties and I'm glad they don't. They'd be mere travesties. Now I want you to look at these snapshots. Here's one of Catherine standing in the rose-garden. Look at that profile. Did you ever see anything more perfect? And the way she stands, the grace of the whole figure. Even in those ugly clothes we wore then, her beauty can't be hidden. And look at this group. Luke took it, I remember it so well. That's Mark with his hand on Giles's shoulder. It was just after Giles first came to stay with us, and I was already falling in love with him. And Catherine and myself, arm in arm. We were just about to play croquet, the four of us. All unconscious of our doom, I suppose. And there's Mark, by himself, in tennis flannels. He was good-looking enough and knew it."

Medwin looked closely. She did not want to take her eyes from the face of Robert Lyddon's father, the laughing young man to whom the world just then must have seemed so full of promise.

"I'm glad," she said, "that you haven't torn it up."

"Oh, why bother? It's pasted in and I should only spoil the album. And there are so many groups in which he appears. Here's another of Catherine, lying in a punt, reading. On that very lake. Do you see a resemblance to any other face you know?"

"No," said Medwin. "Should I? Whose?"

"Yours, of course. The forehead particularly, and the general shape of the face, and something in the expression, too. I noticed it the first time I saw you. Oh, you haven't her mysterious and fatal beauty, and you may thank heaven for it, but a resemblance there certainly is."

"I can't see it at all," Medwin said.

"I assure you it's there. Here's one of Giles and myself about to step into my car. It's an early Daimler. Isn't it amusing? And look at my headgear. A sort of yachting cap with a veil attached."

"I think you look charming," said Medwin smiling, touched by the happiness that seemed to radiate from the two. "The whole of an epoch's in that picture. And he's exactly as you described him. What a fascinating face! And the dog?"

"My little Mimi. She never left me." She took the photograph from Medwin and studied it herself. "If I could go back to that place and that moment, I would crawl every inch of the way on my hands and knees." She smiled. "If time were reversible, what a lot of people would not be at home! How few offices would be filled, how few trains would run, how few people one would see in the streets. Millions of us," she said, bitterly, "would return to our mother's wombs."

"But would our mothers be there either?" Medwin asked lightly. "It's lucky we're all fixed in this river of glue called time, I think. Now show me some pictures of your father."

Miss Lyddon turned some pages.

"Here he is, the darling, talking to Mr. Asquith. I took that picture, and it's one of the best in the book."

Half an hour went by in this way, half an hour of working time, and then Miss Lyddon put away the albums. "It's all gay and delightful and happy to look back upon," she said, "up to the moment when I told Catherine I wanted to marry Giles. But I still had control over events, or I believe I had, until Mark went to her and said the abominable things he did say. In five minutes he utterly destroyed three worlds. I never feel he has suffered enough for it. Has he suffered at all? He married happily, he made a congenial life for himself and brought up a family. And I, at one blow, lost everything that to me made life worth living. However, self-pity is supposed to be one of the viler emotions, though I think one has a better right to pity oneself than to pity others. Pitying others is often a waste of time or insulting. Don't you pity yourself?"

"No," said Medwin. "And if time were reversible I'd still be one of those present."

"Why don't you pity yourself? You have a perfect right to. You've been poor and handicapped all your life."

"I've never been poor," said Medwin. "I've always had clean sheets and I've never been hungry. That's not poverty, as you well know."

"Don't be priggish," Miss Lyddon said, with one of her ironic smiles, "and don't trouble to talk to me as if you thought the Almighty or Mr. Bevan were listening in. You've been damnably poor."

"I meant exactly what I said."

"Rubbish, my dear girl. However, let's change the subject. I've something far more agreeable to say. During the small hours of the night I had a brilliant idea. We'll go to France this summer for a three weeks' holiday, and we'll take Sarah, and Antonia can come with us to look after her. It's as easy as winking. I can't imagine why I didn't think of it before."

Medwin stood looking at Miss Lyddon and summoning all her wits to meet this contingency. She slowly shook her head.

"Sarah's too young. She'd get over-tired and cry and be troublesome. And this summer I can't leave my mother. Couldn't we think about it next year."

"Next year?" cried Miss Lyddon. "Next year I may be dead. Don't you realize that at my age we count our summers over like misers? You say no to everything. Is it just the spirit of contrariness in you or do you dislike me?"

She picked up the dress from the chair and tossed it over Medwin's shoulder again, and her face looked stormier than Medwin had yet seen it. She stood her ground and looked steadily back at Miss Lyddon, holding her elbows in her hands.

"Are you going to say no to that, too?" Miss Lyddon demanded, "because it comes from me? If you do, I warn you I shall be angry and deeply hurt. Only Edith, it seems, has your confidence and affection."

"Now why," Medwin asked, "do you say that? Please tell me why you say such an unfair thing."

"Oh, I heard you laughing together this morning like a couple of schoolgirls as I passed the door. It's only with me that you're unnatural and on your guard. Don't deny it. I can feel that you are."

"She was reading me that letter from her grandson," Medwin answered quietly. "I think it amused you too."

"Not to that extent, I can assure you. I'm not likely to go into wild peals of mirth over the sayings of the toddlers. You're infinitely more anxious to please her than to please me. Hence that exaggerated laughter. Why are you so on your guard with me? Tell me. I think I have a right to know."

Her hands were on her narrow hips, and her face was now haggard with suspicion.

"If it's true that I'm on my guard with you," Medwin said, "it must be because I feel that you won't allow me to be friends with you on my terms but only on your terms. Do you remember the promise you made me driving down to the Home that day?"

"Perfectly. But you have an odd idea of the meaning of friendship. To me it means confidence. I look for friendship from you, and find only cold caution and distrust."

"I really think Sarah is too young to go," Medwin insisted, "and my mother too delicate to be left. How can you suppose that to me three weeks' motoring in France would be anything but a delight?"

"Then throw caution to the winds for once in your life and come. We could even stay at some quiet place in Brittany where Sarah could play all day on the sands. I'm tired of being frustrated at every turn. I'm too young to travel with my contemporaries. They bore me; heavens, how they bore me! They *bore* me, do you understand?"

Medwin smiled.

"You're the most imperious creature I have ever met," she said.

"Then don't thwart me. Your sister will be near your mother this summer, you told me so. Either you dislike me, or there's some man you don't want to leave. It would be like you not to tell me."

She went to the mirror and nervously touched her crisp, grey curls. Then she turned.

"Well?" she demanded fiercely as Medwin was silent.

I cannot, I cannot, Medwin was thinking. What way out is there?"

"I'm not happy about my mother," she said. "She isn't making the progress she ought to be making."

"Look," said Miss Lyddon, flinging out her arms, "Edith can put her hands on a dozen excellent women, retired nurses, any one of whom would gladly stay with your mother for a few weeks. It would be a little holiday for them."

"Not this year," said Medwin, unyielding. "Please not this year. I have too many things on my mind. There are things I haven't told you, and though they don't concern a man, unless that man is my father, I should have no peace from them. Please not this year."

Miss Lyddon shrugged her shoulders.

"You pass my comprehension. For each obstacle I knock down, you find two to set up in its place. I don't know why I bother about you. I'll ask Helen Murchison and that dull husband of hers to go with me. Come, let's get to work. I've wasted enough time."

She went quickly out of the room and down the stairs, leaving Medwin to fold up the dress and follow. On her way across the hall Mrs. Gresham came out of her bedroom, ready to go out, and stopped to speak to her.

"I just wanted to say," she said, "that you needn't bother with that letter to the Matron of the Holiday Home. I've decided not to send it. I'll speak to her about the mattresses the next time I go down there."

"Very well," Medwin said. "I hadn't actually written it yet." Mrs. Gresham's eyes travelled downwards to the folded dress under Medwin's arm.

"What pretty stuff!" she exclaimed. "How amusing! Dogs jumping through hoops. Is it something new?"

"It's new to me," Medwin answered. She had no lie ready, and in any case did not feel disposed to tell one even if there had been a plausible one at hand. "It's a dress Miss Lyddon doesn't like herself in. She wants me to try it on and see if I can alter it."

Mrs. Gresham said, "She usually asks my advice about such things. She's never even shown it to me. It's charming material." She fingered it. "French, of course. Probably from Louise Dupin."

"She's been scolding me," Medwin said, "for not having a summer print. The truth is you both spoil me disgracefully. I could quite well do without one." And she made a little move in the direction of the staircase.

The smile had gone from Mrs. Gresham's face. "I should think twice if I were you," she said, "before taking it. Are you sure she hasn't worn it? I haven't seen her in it but others may have. You don't want people to see you wearing cast-off clothes. Or I shouldn't if I were in your place. Of course you must do as you like about it."

"Well, probably it won't suit me, or can't be made to fit me," Medwin said. "In which case, I'll give it back." She waited for Mrs. Gresham to go down the wide staircase ahead of her, which she did with dignity and carrying her head—adorned with a hat of burnt straw trimmed with green roses—a little higher than usual. In the hall, Wilson was already waiting for her and went to open the front door. She turned and looked at Medwin, and the expression on her face was as if it had just been slapped and she were pretending it had not been.

"I'm just off to that Charity Matinée for Arab Refugees," she said. "I'm going to be rather late, I'm afraid, but I don't suppose it matters. Good-bye."

Medwin went into Miss Lyddon's room and sat down at the writing-table. Miss Lyddon after walking about the room for a moment with her hands in the skirt pockets of her black and white checked dress, came and sat down beside her.

"Am I forgiven," she asked pleasantly, "for my bad temper?"

Medwin gave her a cool little smile.

"I wasn't really intimidated," she said. "It seemed to me mostly sound and fury, signifying nothing. If you were really angry I imagine you'd be ice-cold and every word would cut like a whip."

"That's one stage further," Miss Lyddon said, with her quick grey glance. "I was angry, but as you've guessed, I can be angrier."

Medwin opened her pad, for there was a pile of letters to be answered.

"Mrs. Gresham saw the dress," she said, "and asked me what

it was. She liked the pattern. I told her the simple truth. I'm sure she thinks you're far too generous and of course you are." And she added, "Both of you."

Miss Lyddon gave a laugh. "Whatever she thinks," she said, "it's not that and you know it. I'm glad you didn't fib, though." And then she smiled her ironic smile. "You poor wretch, you must sometimes feel you're being ground between the upper and nether millstones, don't you?

"Sometimes," agreed Medwin. "I shall call you U.M. and Mrs. Gresham N.M."

"Thanks, anyway, for making me the upper one," Miss Lyddon said. She seemed now to have entirely recovered her good humour. "Well, it's all your fault for being young and pleasing and empty-handed. We have too much, and get too little pleasure from it and are too near our end." She shuddered. "I would like never to see anyone over forty. Now to work."

And then the telephone rang, cutting Medwin off from the necessity of saying any more.

"Yes, Mrs. Debenham? Of course, I always know your voice. Yes, she's just here. About the Costume Ball? I'm sure she wants to talk to you about that. Here she is."

It was the next morning during a pause for coffee that Mrs. Gresham told Medwin about her childhood in Leicester. It began by her asking about Mr. Fosdick, to which Medwin replied that she had spoken to him on the telephone, but beyond the fact that he had applied for a preliminary patent, there was no progress to report. Then Mrs. Gresham talked about her own father and how he had patiently and steadily built up a fortune as a boot manufacturer from very humble beginnings.

"I don't know how much you knew about me," she said, "but of course my background and Miss Lyddon's were very different. She comes from the leisured, moneyed class, but actually I can't see that my father is in any way inferior to Admiral Lyddon. My father had his way to make, while Admiral Lyddon got everything by inheritance—except of course, his brilliant career in the Navy. Both in their different ways, were of great service to their country and their community. If you ever go to Leicester you must visit the Art Gallery and see the pictures my father presented to it. They aren't perhaps to everyone's taste today, and I suppose you young people turn up your noses at them, but some day they'll come back into favour. My father was a great admirer of the paintings of Lord Leighton and Burne-Jones and

Holman Hunt and Millais. Of course I don't pretend to be a connoisseur of art. These pictures," she said glancing about the room, "were bought for me by one of the most reliable art dealers in London. Some day they'll belong to my grandson, and I bought them with an eye to their future value. Personally I don't like Sickert, and James Pryde is too gloomy for my taste, and as for Augustus John, I only like his drawings. Everybody of course likes Canaletto and Guardi. They're easy to like. Miss Lyddon says I haven't really got beyond Landseer, but if Landseer's pictures give me pleasure why should I be so snobbish as to pretend they don't? I've no use for that sort of thing." She stroked her bosom and went on, "But when it comes to future values, I take the best advice I can get, just as I would about any other investment. And if my grandson chooses to present my collection some day to an art gallery in Toronto or Montreal, he'll only be doing what my father did a hundred years or so earlier." And she repeated the familiar gesture.

Just before they resumed their work Mrs. Gresham asked:

"Well, what about the dress? Did you decide to give it back?"

"I couldn't," Medwin said, "without offending Miss Lyddon. She made such a point of it. And as a matter of fact, it fitted me very well."

"For a very good reason," Mrs. Gresham said coldly. "It was made for you."

"Oh no," Medwin exclaimed, "I don't think so. In fact I feel sure it wasn't. Miss Lyddon said——"

"Never mind," Mrs. Gresham interrupted. "Only I wish you had let me get you a dress from Bertha Mollnar's. You remember I spoke of it a long time ago. You wouldn't hear of it, and now Miss Lyddon has tricked you into accepting one from Louise Dupin. I'm quite sure she had it made from your measurements."

"Well," Medwin said, appealing to her, "what do you advise me to do? She said she didn't like to throw it away and that it was too frivolous for her. And I don't want to hurt her feelings. I wish very much that you were both less generous. You put me under obligations to you at every turn."

Mrs. Gresham was silent for a moment.

"No, you'd better keep it now. The harm's been done."

"Frankly," said Medwin, "I find it all very embarrassing. I

don't want anything from anyone." And she went to the writing-table.

Mrs. Gresham said slowly:

"Miss Lyddon is my oldest and dearest friend. She's part of my life—a very great part of it. But she has a way of binding people hand and foot. You don't realize"—and she got up and stood beside Medwin's chair—"I'm quite sure you don't realize how skilfully she does this."

"I'm far too independent ever to let that happen," Medwin said. "And certainly I'm no more bound to her than I am to you. Rather less in fact. There's the matter of my father."

"Oh, that," Mrs. Gresham said, with a nervous little gesture, "I asked you to forget about that. It's exactly as though I'd put the money on the tables at Monte Carlo." Then suddenly, totally unexpectedly, tears came into her eyes and her face altered. "I know I have a jealous nature," she said. "I always have had. It was lucky I was an only child, and lucky I married the sort of man I did marry. No one knows how I suffer from it. And she makes me suffer, quite deliberately, she enjoys doing it. Oh," she exclaimed, putting a handkerchief to her eyes, "I ought not to talk to you like this. I'm ashamed of myself. Ashamed. Please forget what I said, Mrs. Blair."

"Of course," said Medwin, looking away from the broken and twitching face. "And I wish, Mrs. Gresham, you'd call me Medwin. I'd be so pleased and flattered if you would. Will you? I'd feel more certain then that you felt you could trust me."

"I'm run down, I think," Mrs. Gresham said, sitting in her usual place at the end of the writing-table, and blowing her nose. "I'm not often like this." And she added, "Thank you, I'll try to remember to call you Medwin, but I've got so used to Mrs. Blair now. If I forget, sometimes, you'll understand, won't you?"

And she composed herself and picked up a letter from the top of the pile, but the room seemed full of her tears and her emotion, and it was some time before either of them could shake off a feeling of awkwardness and discomfort.

Then, later, when they had finished their work, Mrs. Gresham said:

"There's just one thing more." She hesitated, coloured, and then went on, "When you asked me to call you Medwin I think I spoke as if I didn't want to. That's not true. I've wanted to for a long time. Only *she* slipped into it so easily and after that

I couldn't. It would have looked as if I were just doing it because she did. Will you . . . do you see what I mean?"

"Yes," said Medwin, trying not to show pity or embarrassment. "Of course. It's my fault. I should have asked you long ago."

Then to her relief, Wilson came in to say that lunch was served.

CHAPTER 11

MEDWIN HAD READ THE BOOK TWICE, GOING THROUGH IT rapidly the first time and slowly and critically the second. She knew she would read it again. There was roughness in the writing that she thought not unintended, for it suited the subject. The characters in it were a queerly assorted group of men each exemplifying some human quality distilled by war and danger. The death of one of them moved her and seemed to her particularly well and truthfully done. She thought she recognized bits of autobiography here and there—a game much to her taste—but they were not confined to any one character; he seemed to have seen himself in all of them. The plot, if it could be called that, lay in the performance of the difficult act of renunciation. In the attainment of the state of mind necessary for this, in the temporary loss of it and the finding of it again, and at last in the hard and anguished fulfilment of it against a background of alternating boredom and peril, lay the drama. Two of the men loved the same woman, the middle-aged wife of one of them, and in the way the oddly attractive and unusual character of this woman emerged lay not only the book's chief promise and achievement, but also, in Medwin's opinion, Robert Lyddon's justification for his belief that he could write the Hartsdown story. She not only now felt certain that he could write it, she also felt certain that his choice of a career was the right one for him. The relief of this was great; it was also deeply exciting. She could not wait to tell him of her certainty.

She could not wait to tell him, yet wait she did and had to, for he did not telephone again for a week. She wondered for a brief second if he liked to make her wait, liked to think of her as alert for the sound of the telephone, but put the thought from her with a smile. He was no male coquette. The answer was that he had other things to do.

It was in vain that she warned herself of the possible folly of allowing herself to become too deeply interested in him. She had been from the first moment. And now that a month, a single month remained, perhaps, for the enjoyment of this encounter—she would not call it more—she proposed to enjoy it to the full. From some quarter, it might be a good quarter or a bad, a wind was blowing upon it that was ripening it fast, and his silence during that week, and his silence during the three weeks that he had previously allowed to pass, did nothing at all to check this ripening. It was, she now felt certain, looking back, a pregnant silence, full of restraint, and this restraint was, to her, not only significant but revealing. Impetuosity she mistrusted, both in herself and others. Few of us, she had often thought, are either good enough or wise enough to be able to indulge it freely without storing up regrets. As for Robert Lyddon's wife, she did not put her from her mind but thought about her a great deal, and felt sure that some of the character he had given the unseen woman in the book was hers. She was undoubtedly imposing upon two men a vast amount of uncertainty and strain—and doubtless upon herself as well—and if she further prolonged it, she ran the risk, surely, of having the choice taken out of her hands by the defection of one or the other. No woman would wish to invite this danger unnecessarily. If she were making it a test—and this was not likely—of endurance and devotion, it would be the lover, surely, who would flag first.

Well, she had only to wait another month, and Robert Lyddon might vanish from her life again. It seemed to her highly probable that he would vanish, and, knowing the man, she knew he would be as fully prepared for one eventuality as for the other. He would not allow himself to be caught unawares. It was not his nature.

When he came, the dark blue, plainly bound book, its end bristling with slips of paper put in by her to mark things she wanted to comment on, lay ready for him on the table. She could feel, the air around him was thick with it, his pleasure at being there. It was, by a great deal, better than the time before. What might come, if a woman's painful choice did not prevent it, had come in great strides closer. She admitted this, but was not alarmed by it, because it was accompanied by its dampening, restraining opposite. Hope was perfectly matched here by its anonym; yes by no; a roadway by its checkmate—a wall without a gate. She would become fully acquainted with both before the end. She was prepared to accept either. She thought tonight that what was to come was already there, had entered with him, so that they were three. But the third awaited the shape the future and a debating woman would give it. Or was it already shaped? Who could say?

She wore the print dress she had not been able not to accept, and was unashamed. She had shared the ham with him; after that, nothing else mattered. She could tell him about the dress and would tell him—to confess to it would mean absolution—but first there was the book. And already the delight of being able to be both honest and warm in praise, animated her face.

"Yes," she said, "of course you must write. Of course, of course! You must know it as well as I know it, and better. Write the Hartsdown story. I know now that it's safe with you. This"—and she held up the book—"is real. It's the real thing. I could almost have cried with relief and pleasure. Have you ever felt that? Do you know what a delight it is?"

"I do know," he said. "In one breath you've told me everything I want to hear."

"I've been bursting with it," she answered.

He smiled, took out a cigarette and walked over to the window. The summer rain had just begun to fall on the geraniums and salvia in the garden, and through the open window came the sound of it, lightly pattering on leaves and paving, and a fresh odour came up from the wet stones and wet earth. On that side of the flat sounds were muffled by the backs of houses, and London seemed a rumour of itself, and could be believed to be not there at all, immensely absent. She wanted to say "Come back from the window," but let him stand there looking out. He turned away soon, back into the room again with her, and she was glad.

"I wanted to come sooner," he said, "but for various reasons, I waited. One reason was that I intended to anticipate your verdict, whatever it might be, by beginning the Hartsdown story. I have the first chapter in my pocket." And he touched his coat.

This made her laugh, and she thought, how like him, and was pleased because it seemed to her so perfectly in character.

"So that's what you think of my opinion?" she asked, lightly. "You discounted it from the start."

"Let's say that I have enough conceit to think it might be favourable. Also, the longing to launch myself upon my new career was too strong for me." He took some folded pages out of his pocket. "Here you are. Chapter One. I'll leave it here for you to look at when you have time."

"Which will be tonight, of course," she said. "As soon as you've gone. And now let's drink to your new career." And she added, with a new note in her voice, "I shall pretend to myself in later years that I had at least a finger in it."

He looked at her in such a way that she turned her head and went towards the tray and the glasses. He followed her and said as quietly as if he were speaking of the softly falling rain:

"You will be in everything I do and think from this time onwards. Whichever way it goes."

Her arms dropped to her sides. Her face altered as he watched it, grew soft and ripe with truth, as though protective layers had fallen away and a moment of sun had brough it to quick maturity.

"Oh," she said, "this has been with us from the very beginning. Since that night when I first heard your voice."

So drawn to each other were they, so shaken, so alight with feeling, so dangerously poised for coming together, that it seemed as if any small, light breath of air might blow them into each other's arms. But the debating, unhurried woman, present to him, and present to her through him, stepped between them. The too-great tension relaxed. With heavy, down-cast eyelids they moved further apart, without contact or any touch even that of a sleeve, which, in spite of the woman who had her choice still to make, might have been too much for them.

"So that is said now," she told him, speaking at last, and she held her arms tightly folded across her breast.

"And cannot be unsaid," he answered. "Not to speak the truth to each other would be the one unforgivable sin. I'm not ashamed of having spoken, even though there is another month of waiting."

"I know," she said, and looked at him serenely and steadily.

"It can do you no harm," he said, "and it is the best thing that has happened to me since I was born."

It could do neither of them harm, they were sure of it, but to remain apart was now no easy thing. Their looks were embraces. The neat, compact, assured man with the recognizably Lyddon face was hers, and she knew she could not have enough of him. She did not see how she could ever have enough of him, now that she had waited so long and was still to wait. Their aloneness was a siren song, the private walls of the flat with their urge and blessing, folded them in and the rain falling past the windows was lovers' rain, dividing them from everything but themselves. But while there was the woman who was motionless between two roads, she would not have him nearer to her. Nor did he come nearer. He had come all the way in heart and mind and spirit, and that was, for a little while, enough. It might have to be enough for ever, and she told herself that she must be content, for a miracle had happened.

So much had the rain darkened the day that she drew the curtains now and turned on the lamps. While she did this, and each was conscious of every movement of the other, he went to the tray and busied himself with the cocktails that she had been about to make before what had been said had been said.

"Our nerves," he said, "are as tight as fiddle-strings. These will do us good. Talk to me. Tell me about *her*, what she has done and said. I feel you're standing in a thicket that grows higher every day."

"I can find a way out," she said, coming back to the sofa. "I'm not afraid of that. It might be wise if I were to go now, for the relations between those two are worsening and I am partly the cause, I suppose. But then—" and she looked about her—"good-bye to all this, and good-bye to much more besides. I can't go now. Or can I? Should I?"

"Don't think of going now," he said. "You're in no way to blame. If you're the cause, you're the perfectly innocent cause. Let's keep this," he said, "a little longer. It's the only home either of us have."

"I don't know where you live," she told him. "Tell me, so that I won't be wholly cut off from you when you leave here." He told her the address. He was living in a furnished bed-sitting-room in a house in Eaton Square. He lunched and dined out in restaurants or at his club.

"The owners of the house," he said, "are a retired Naval officer and his wife. Like most people they find it hard to make ends meet, and take in two lodgers, myself and a civil servant. The arrangement gives them the maximum of privacy, and the other man and myself the minimum of comfort. However, it serves, as far as I'm concerned, and at night I go back to my room and write. The telephone is downstairs in the hall, and if you should ever want to ring me up, Mrs. Persons will come up three flights of stairs breathing heavily and recover herself outside my door. Then she will tell me I'm wanted on the telephone in a voice that's dulcet with martyrdom."

"I'd rather you rang me up," she said, "in that case. But now that we've said what we've said, there is no reason why you shouldn't ring me up oftener."

He got up and moved about the room. Now and again while he talked he paused to look at the photograph of Sarah, or to smell the wallflowers, or to drop the ash from his cigarette into an ash tray.

"We have a month," he said, "and I can no more tell you what will come after that than I can tell you what the weather will be like this time next year. I have no clue. I have given a promise which I would not have given if I had foreseen this, but having made this promise, I believe I must abide by it. Do you agree?"

"Yes," she said.

"I have said that I would accept her decision and wait for it. On the other hand, I could go to her now and tell her that for me the situation is changed. In your opinion, have I the right to do that?"

She leaned her forehead on her palm.

"I wish I knew," she said, "but I think you have no right."

"I forgave her and said that the choice should be hers. I knew she would not make it lightly and that it would be no easy choice for her. At that time I had absolutely no reason to suppose that I would be involving the happiness of someone else, to say nothing of my own. I was perfectly free, then, to dispose of my life as I, or as she, pleased. It was a matter of some indifference, by that time, and I gave her the choice not at all quixotically, but because I was entirely willing to accept either fate. I think it right to make this quite clear."

"Yes," she said. "I understand that."

"Now, in these last few weeks, the situation has entirely altered for me, but it remains the same for her. It might, of course, greatly assist her to make her choice. On the other hand, when I offered her the choice, I offered it without reservations. I had not even the faintest tremor of apprehension or anticipation, and considering the magnitude, to me, of what has happened, this seems to me extraordinary. I ought to have felt the nearness of it. I only felt a faint premonition of it when I heard your voice that night."

"While we were speaking," she said, "it all seemed to me

queerly familiar, as if it had happened precisely so before. I can't explain this, but the feeling was very strong. All the same," she added, smiling, "I nearly refused to let you come. That was my sense of caution trying to interfere, I suppose."

"On such threads our fates hang, alas!" he answered. "Well, I have posed the problem. I gave her her choice, gave it of my own free will, absolutely. She has to choose between, on the one hand, lover—and I have no doubt that she loves him—and on the other hand, son and husband. I put the son first, because it is he, really, who makes the decision cruelly hard for her. I think," he added, "that not only has she the feeling that a divided loyalty would be bad for the boy, but also that she must make the sacrifice in order to keep the balance even. To have the boy and the lover, would be, she feels, to have everything, to take too much from me."

"But what about her feeling," Medwin asked, "for you?"

He stood in front of the mantelpiece considering his answer.

"I think the truth of the matter is," he said, "that we both know, and have always known, that I married her brothers and sisters, her parents and her home as well as herself. Their family life was ideal. As a unit, it was the best thing I knew, or have ever known. It was a musical family; among themselves they made up an accomplished little group of players, a sextette that performed admirably. What I didn't then stop to realize was that once this was broken up, the music departed; that the family, as a unit, was superior to any of its individual members. She was one of the violins; she never touched her violin after we were married. I could never persuade her to. I wouldn't say, it wouldn't be fair to say, that she did not love me, and does not love me now. I believe she does. And it would not be fair or true to say that I did not and do not love her. I do love her; enough to want her to be happy, even though not necessarily with me. Now, I have gone much further than that. I want her to find her happiness apart from me. Altogether apart. And when I say I love her, you will understand what I mean by this. It is an old friendship, and it is mixed with a great deal of respect. And one of her brothers, killed in the Narvik landing, was my best friend. Her mother writes to me regularly, and calls me 'My dear son.' Can you understand now, why I promised her her free and uninhibited choice?"

"Yes," Medwin said, "I can."

"And if she chooses to stay with me?"

"Then," Medwin said, "stay with her you must. It would be better for your son. You have not said so but I am sure he loves his mother."

"He adores his mother."

"He is the crux of the whole thing, as I see it," she said, "and it is his fate and future that hang in the balance more than yours or mine or hers. What I cannot understand," she said, "is how she can contemplate leaving you and him, but it's folly, of course, to attempt to put oneself in the place of another person in these matters."

"Quite simply," he told her, "I think it comes down to this. For the first time she feels she is being loved entirely for herself. That makes so powerful an appeal that all the rest becomes comprehensible."

"Yes," she agreed. "Comprehensible, at any rate."

"I understand it myself better now than I did," he said, "because for the first time in my life I know what it is to love. And I know what was lacking before."

She lowered her eyes.

"Dare we take this month?" she asked, tensely.

"That's what I want you to tell me."

She leaned her head against the back of the sofa.

"Do you remember the choice of the lovers in 'Hassan?' Their lives apart for ever; or one night together and then dreadful death. It was the woman, I remember, who made the choice. She chose the second alternative."

He smiled.

"All the same, I would like you to choose."

"Then unhesitatingly," she said, "I ask for that month. And I would like to see you every day. And when it's impossible for me to see you, I would like to hear your voice on the telephone."

"Thank God," he said, "that you have chosen as you have. You would have let me choose for you, and you'd have accepted my choice, but you did the braver thing." He went to the window and looked out. "It's still raining," he said, and now all the tension had gone from his voice. "Will you come out to dinner somewhere, or would you rather stay here?"

"This time," she said, smiling, "you must make the choice."

"Then we stay here, of course. Besides," he said, "that's far too pretty a dress to risk getting wet in, though you could change it, I suppose. No, I love this place, and we're alone here as nowhere else."

"I'll make an omelette," she said, "with some eggs my mother sent me from the country. And," she added, with a laugh, "there's a story there, and it brings in my father and Mrs. Gresham. As for the dress, you'll have to hear about that, too. She gave it to me, and there were some unfortunate repercussions. There's so much to tell you. But I'll tell you about the dress first."

He sat down in the chair again, she on the sofa. We'll talk and talk and talk, she thought, and all the time we are talking we'll be wondering how much longer we can keep from flying into each other's arms. But I will not raise a finger or an eyebrow to bring it about. Nor will he; but there is no need to, for the moment is inevitable. And when it comes, then we'll pack into this month as much as it is capable of holding, for both of us, in our hearts, believe that it will have no successors.

CHAPTER 12

THEY SEE NO CHANGE IN ME, MEDWIN SAID TO HERSELF THE next day, and marvelled. She was lunching with both women and there were no visitors. They see no change, she thought, where everything is changed. What a clever mask the face is, resuming all its old habits so cunningly, and without even a second's rehearsal.

But if they saw no change in her, she at least was aware of a change in them. She could feel between them that strain, that tension, like that of a bow bent too far, that she had felt on the night of the first dinner party and occasionally since. But this time it was more intense and nearer the surface. It was Mrs. Gresham who showed it most. If there had been a quarrel, and she felt sure there had been, Mrs. Gresham, as might have been expected, had had the worst of it and had suffered the most from it. Miss Lyddon must have sucked up vitality from many such emotional battles. She lived on them, she refreshed and renewed herself by them. Perhaps, Medwin thought, unable to endure defeat by her, when she had said she would not go to

France, she had sought a victory elsewhere and had gorged herself on the blood of the slain.

Yes, she was sure Mrs. Gresham had suffered a defeat and a painful one. Her nerves were in a poor state, her mouth, with its wide, thin lips, was ready to tremble and the lids of her slightly prominent brown eyes to redden. To offset all this, perhaps, she had put on a new and charming dress of grey silk with white spots, a material that was much in fashion that spring. She turned to Medwin during lunch, and with a touch of defiance, said that she did not intend to keep any of her engagements that afternoon; that she was going to spend it instead with Lady Sprague, who had asked her to go and see her.

"So will you please cancel any engagements I may have after lunch?" she said. "I don't think there was anything particularly important." And Medwin promised to do so, remembering something Miss Lyddon had recently said; "Poor Edith! Whenever she feels down-trodden or depressed she always runs off to see that fountain of pious platitudes, Beryl Sprague."

Now Miss Lyddon's lips twitched, amusement hovered in the corners of her mouth and about her nostrils. On the whole she was discreet and unprovocative, but enjoyment was present, and triumph.

"Why trouble," she seemed to say, "to quarrel with me? My antagonists invariably have the worst of it. Is it worth while?"

She was weary, no doubt, with half a century and more of a friendship that was dogged and unflagging, and now, perhaps, no more than useful and a habit. But far, far too useful to be dispensed with yet, and to break it completely would be to break too much else beside. And with whom would she live, and where? This great house, the expenses of which could only be borne nowadays if divided between two large separate incomes, was her home and her background. Hartsdown, even if she had wished to go there, was her brother's and her sister-in-law's; and a woman who spends her life travelling, even if this were possible today, was a snail without its shell. To live alone would be to be diminished, perhaps even to be pitied, and Miss Lyddon had no wish for the pity of others. No, Medwin believed, whatever happened, those two would go on to the end—the end for one or both. But in the cold amusement in Miss Lyddon's eyes there was much to puzzle her. She thought she saw in it something new, and this and the delicate irony which all through lunch kept up its flicker was, she felt certain, partly for her. She was conscious of deliberate aloofness, as if Miss Lyddon had chosen to remove herself a little from both of them in order to plan some new attack from some entrenched position.

She would soon learn, she thought, what it was all about; doubtless during the afternoon when they broke off for a cup of tea, for it was then that Miss Lyddon became, as a rule, most expansive and confidential and dropped even the little she used of the way of employer to employed.

But the time went by without any of her usual playfulness showing itself. The light jocosity that so often accompanied their working hours was absent, though not too markedly so, and when they broke off for tea they discussed the new Insurance Act and the working of the Health Services, and how these recent changes would effect Medwin and her family. But these things Miss Lyddon might have discussed in the same way with a stranger and Medwin could not get rid of the feeling that something was held back, postponed, in abeyance. They got through a great deal of correspondence, roughed out a letter Miss Lyddon intended to send to everyone who had helped at a recent "Bring and Buy" bazaar in aid of the Crippled Boys' Home, and then planned a dinner of twenty people for a certain recently returned Governor who had once been a protégé of the Admiral's. The invitations were to be written and sent by Medwin that evening.

"Edith has decided not to come to this dinner," Miss Lyddon said. "She refuses on the grounds that she has never met the guest of honour and that most of the other people are my friends rather than hers. She's planning to go to the theatre instead with old General Palliser." She paused for an instant, her chair pushed back, her long fine hands pressed against the edge of the table, and then said, getting up, "I propose to let you off too."

Medwin looked up at her and asked, with a smile:

"And am I to say thank you for that?"

It was the way in which Miss Lyddon liked her to reply; the to and fro of their talk had required this easy and friendly character, with something in it, now and again, of amiable sparring. And now Miss Lyddon said, without any change in voice or expression:

"It is immaterial to me whether you thank me or not. It was merely an intimation that you would not be wanted."

And she gathered up some letters and put them unhurriedly

into her big crocodile-skin writing case and then, in a silence that could hardly have been more complete in the upper stratosphere, left the room.

So that is how she strikes, thought Medwin, and sat inert in her chair, halted at this point. So that is how she has struck at Gwen and others. I have never seen a snake strike, but surely that is how it is done. Perhaps a slight swaying of the head as warning and then the lightning-quick dart; the moment, so perfectly chosen, the fang so cleverly planted, making its tiny, fatal incision.

Ah, but dear, dear Miss Lyddon, she thought, I am not Gwen. I do not love you, though there is much I could love about you. You have shocked me but you have not hurt me. You have only made me angry. I am armoured from hurt, and chiefly armoured, it would delight me to tell you, by your nephew's love. But it was a well-directed hit.

She stirred and straightened herself and put out her hand for the list of guests which Miss Lyddon had written down in her neat, masculine hand. If she were quick she could get the invitations written and posted before Robert Lyddon came. She saw that one of the men to be asked was a man Miss Lyddon had often spoken to her about, with approval, and she remembered something she had said only a few days before.

"You're the sort of young woman," she had remarked with one of her bright, ironic looks, "who can't keep clear of matrimony, I suppose. I'm no matchmaker, I detest the odious game, but if I were, I'd throw you in Tom Ackerman's way. Well, all the same, I think I will. You shall meet, and as soon as possible."

What had happened to cause this slap in the face? And one so obviously planned and neatly timed. Miss Lyddon had guessed how she would reply when told she was to be 'let off.' She had had her answer ready. Was it because she had refused to go to France? But yesterday afternoon Miss Lyddon had been perfectly friendly; the air, stormy earlier, had completely cleared. She did not think she would punish retrospectively. No, there had been a quarrel, and about her. The dress—and Mrs. Gresham had been right about it—had probably begun it. And Miss Lyddon perhaps knew, now, about the two hundred pounds. Mrs. Gresham, in the hope, it might be, of winning a victory over her friend, had told her about it; had even perhaps, allowed Miss Lyddon to think that her help had been sought in the matter. Well, she could not speak of it to either. She must simply await events. Meanwhile if Miss Lyddon thought she would run to her, asking what she had done to deserve this rebuff, she knew little of the material she was attempting to work upon.

Then the rebuff must be ignored. How could she deal with it? If she did not choose to ignore it, then she must go, and she was not prepared to go. No doubt there were other jobs to be had, but none so superlatively convenient and desirable. Also, she was deeply in Mrs. Gresham's debt. A slap in the face was no more than a slap in the face, and it had been dealt, she knew, not out of irritation or dislike but out of jealousy and wounded pride. And so, in a sense, out of affection, out of misconceived and misbegotten love. She would wait and see how Miss Lyddon proposed to deal with the situation she had herself created. As for her own attitude, she would try to convey, when next they met, a philosophical shrug of the shoulders for a friendship of so brief a duration. So this, she would suggest, is what your protestations of affection amount to. I suspected it from the first. Now you see why I have done my best to hold you off. You will not have the opportunity again of so insultingly taking back something that was never asked for and never wanted.

The invitations were written and sent, and she changed quickly into the trouble-making dress and then in the half-hour before she could expect that longed-for sound, the doorbell's ring—that point in time from which so much delight would flow—she re-read the first chapter of the Hartsdown story.

He had called the place Mullinscourt and laid the scene in Hertfordshire at the close of the nineteenth century. It was to be, she saw, a period piece. He had gone back a little in time to show his younger characters growing up, and the setting was so vividly presented, it was so little a faded past and so perfectly a living and unselfconscious present that she was for the second time enchanted. How much and how visually he must have read, how often he must have wandered back like an inquiring child, into his father's youth, touching everything, accustoming himself, like an Alice Through the Looking Glass, to this lost fabled world. He had made the final years of that long reign his own, and she guessed how he looked forward to picturing, too, the altering moods and values of the time in which his drama would presently take place.

These people fascinated him; that was clear. He had made the head of the family a well-known soldier and he had given him that curious combination of gentleness, shyness, military prowess and devotion to the army and to God occasionally found in one skin and most often in a British skin. His derivation was chiefly the Old Testament, but in his personal and private life he was a humble seeker after Christ. To make his character still more paradoxical, he had married an heiress, and the great seventeenth century house had come down through her family, not through his. She was a cold, handsome, imperious woman who ruled her husband and had handed on more of her qualities to her only daughter than to her sons. Theresa, the daughter, fourteen when the book opened, was clever, desirous, passionate in the pursuit of her own wishes. What she wanted she wanted extremely; what she had was exclusively her own. With two of her brothers she was on fairly happy terms, though they mistrusted her tongue and her brusque needs; with the third brother she was perpetually at cross purposes. Three worlds were displayed within one house, existing side by side but seldom overlapping; the world of the grown-ups with their huge house-parties, their London seasons when they fanatically pursued whatever the rest of their world pursued, their vast circle of acquaintances, their endless political discussions; and the intense and equally self-centred world of Theresa, who lived privily, and of the boys, who, when they were not at school were kept at a distance and guided by remote control.

Well, she thought, putting it down, there is no doubt he has it all in his pocket. It will be a big book, and there is some danger that he will overload it with the wealth of his material. I must warn him of that. And her mind went back to a remark of his at their first meeting. "The whole thing concerns me very little." She understood now, what he had meant. He was not concerned in the quarrel and especially he was not concerned in any material way. He was aloof and apart in so far as the break touched upon his fortunes. He had not said, "The whole thing interests me very little." It interested him extremely and must always have done so, from his earliest youth. Loving his father, he had worked himself back into his ruined youth as one works a hand into a glove.

And Miss Lyddon, whom he had seen once or perhaps twice from a window was, as he had said, in his bones. He did not need or want to see her again; he preferred not to see her again for fear that the sight of her might blur that clear image. He knew her as no one else knew her, and she was barely aware of his existence.

When he came he had under his arm a bottle of whisky and one of gin wrapped up in brown paper, and this made her laugh and broke the tension she had half dreaded. When she reproached him for extravagance he said he did not want their supplies to run low. It was only there, with her, that a drink meant anything to him. "Comparatively speaking," he added, with a smile. Later they were going out to dinner. They did not want to place too great a strain upon themselves, and though this was not spoken of, both knew it.

They talked over the first chapter and she praised it warmly, adding a warning that he was in danger of crowding his scene and his stage.

"All right," he said, "but first let me pour it all out and get it down on paper. Then you can cut to your heart's content—or we both can—later. I'm too full of it to be selective now."

She took note of the fact that he was assuming a future for them but made no comment.

He asked her how high the thicket had grown, and she said: "Higher than ever. Higher than my head," and told him what had occurred that afternoon. But surely, he said that was to have been expected. Felines large and small, human and animal, were bound to use their claws and he had been wondering when it would come.

"And if I don't play?" she asked. "If I don't go to her and ask what I've done to displease her—as of course I shall not do—what then?"

"Oh, then," he said, "if you've guessed the cause of it rightly, and I suspect you have, it will all come out soon enough. If you don't go to her, she'll come to you. What you're to say if she accuses you of asking Mrs. Gresham for help instead of her is a hard question to answer. I think you'd better tell her the truth."

"And prove poor Mrs. Gresham a liar? I'd hate to do that."

"Better than adding one lie to another," he said. He went and poured himself out a drink. "If only," he said, "they didn't both love you in their different ways. It's just that that may set off the whole ammunition dump."

"Don't," she pleaded, "make me think it worse than it is."

"The harm's done," he told her. "We'd better face it. The

time will come when you'll have to make your exit, but I trust it won't be yet."

"I think I understand their characters pretty well," she said, "but what I don't and can't understand is how they became what they are. But living with them has taught me one thing. It's taught me that old age can be a cruel fraud; it can be the tenderest lamb dressed up as old mutton. The years change us too little. I only pray I'll be like my mother."

"Has she the secret of growing old?" he asked.

"She's learnt, I think, to relinquish everything but love."

He was silent a moment, and then he said:

"When shall I see her?"

"Oh," she cried, "I want you to see her! Whatever happens. She's always wanted so much for me, and I long for her to know that I have it now—everything that I could have hoped for and more."

"For God's sake," he said, "don't say such things to me and expect me not to take you in my arms."

She covered her face with her hands, as if ashamed, but he pulled her hands away and holding her by the wrists, drew her to her feet. They faced each other, beseeching each other with their eyes not to wait any longer, not a moment longer. And then with a cry they were together. To be near enough was now impossible, now that nothing separated them. But for the flesh they could have merged and become one, she thought, and yet it was the flesh, too, that urged it. Her hands caressed his head, grasped his hair, her palms pressed his cheeks, her fingers touched his forehead, his eyes, his lips, as if she were blind and must learn him through touch, or locked themselves behind his head and drew it down again and again to hers.

No, she could not have enough of him, nor he of her. The knowledge of the implacable cruelty of time and of the goodness, of the thing it terminates is the knowledge that gives depth and pathos to every love that is aware of its own quality, and this knowledge was already deeply in their bones as it was in their embraces and in their delight.

"But this is terrible!" she cried at last. "Now we are lost, and all our caution blown to the four winds. Heaven help us, we meant to be strong and wise."

They had sunk down together on the sofa, and he released her gently and stood up. He took a cigarette and lit it with hands that she had not seen fumble until now. Then he turned to her.

"This has changed too much," he said.

"Yes," she said. "It has changed everything." And she raised her hand as a drunken woman might and looked at it and let it fall again.

"Tomorrow," he said, "I'm going to tell her. She must be told. She imagines she is choosing, debating, in a sort of vacuum. That's no longer so. This is life or death for us. I was a fool to imagine I could still leave her to make the choice."

She got slowly up from the sofa and going to the mirror over the mantelpiece she smoothed her hair and shook it back into place. The happy, lost look that had been on her face a moment ago had gone.

"Before our happiness," she said, "there's your son's. Has any thought of a break between you and his mother ever entered his mind?"

"No," he answered.

"Robert," she said, "if she chooses this other man and a new life, then your son will be all yours and it would be as if his mother had died. Children have to bear that, often enough. But if you and I . . . if we took the decisive step ourselves . . . are you willing to give him up entirely?"

"No," he said quietly. "Never. Never. For one thing, he'd have a worse father. I've nothing against this man as a man; I don't doubt his sincerity or his love for Sybil, but as a father, no, and as a stepfather still more no. He fears the boy might come between them, and that, I think, is the crux of the whole matter. Whatever happens, I would keep my share of him and a large one."

"But this sharing," she said, "it was never mentioned before. It was never in the bargain. Never even discussed between you, or thought of, was it?"

"No. But she might consider it now. She might modify her views."

"But she would have the better right to him if you and I . . ."

"Would she? It was not I who thought of breaking up our marriage. Oh, don't think I blame her. I have never blamed her. But we're civilized people, I hope. We respect each other. All this could be settled amicably."

"There was never a me, before," she said. "Might that not change her feelings?"

"I think too well of her to think so," he answered.

She was silent, and turned to rearrange some flowers in a small bowl on the mantelpiece while her mind busied itself with what he had said. Then she faced him again.

"No," she said. "Sharing your son, dividing his life and his love was never contemplated by either of you before. She rejected it, and I think bravely. Either he was to be yours, or he was to continue to be as he thinks he is now—the son of parents who live together and love each other."

"You mean," he asked, "you want me not to tell her?"

She nodded. "Not to tell her. If you go back to her, if you come together again, then you can tell her, when it no longer matters. If it were the dread of hurting you that was making her hesitate, it would be different. But it's not that, or not chiefly that. It's the boy." And she put her elbows on the mantelpiece and leaned her head on her hands. "Robert, that's why she must fight it out as it stands. Whv should she, perhaps be asked to sacrifice herself if we are unwilling to sacrifice ourselves?"

"It might be the deciding factor," he argued, "where one is badly needed. If there's anything worse than what she is going through, I don't know what it is. That's why I've given her all the time she asked for, and all the consideration I could give."

"I could love you for that alone," she told him. "But suppose it should happen that you went to her and told her at the moment when she's decided that she cannot give up the boy and you? For I don't believe she can be indifferent to you. I find that impossible to believe. Then everything would be confused and muddied. Oh, Robert, I'm like the woman in Hassan. I'll take as much as remains of this month, and then I'll abide by her decision."

She went to him and put her arms about him and he pressed his cheek hard against hers, and it was wet.

"Are we to love each other as we can love each other, and then tamely take what may come?" he asked. "Do you know what you're asking of me?"

"Nothing has ever yet come to me the easy way," she told him. "Death ended my marriage. I got my child in mental distress. And having her, I can't have her, but must keep her somewhere else. What I have had I've paid for in some way. I can't believe that anything as perfect and as lovely as this has been handed to me as a free gift, and something tells me you are not for me, or not for long."

"Hush," he said, "hush. I am for you. Always and for ever."

She smiled through her tears at the human, foolish words.

"Don't you realize," she said, "what it would mean not to have had this? Never to have had it at all? But it's here, it's true, it's happened, and it can't be taken away. Oh, my darling, I'm going to love you so much that it will make up for the time when perhaps I won't have you. I swear it."

He closed her mouth with his kiss, and as they stood there a rising wind moaned at the corner of the house and rain was flung against the window, as if in derision.

CHAPTER 13

SHE HEARD THE POSTMAN'S SHARP RAP THE NEXT MORNING and went down to the front door to get her letters. There was one from her mother and one from Sarah, whose hand had been guided by Charlotte. It said:

"I am well and love you best of all. I like it here. I have seen Grannie. 100 kisses from Sarah."

Her mother's letter was a long one.

"I think, darling," she wrote, "I ought to tell you that Louise is packing up to go. I told her I would warn you. She wants to leave, unless you tell her she mustn't, the day after tomorrow, and as she only has a suitcase and a small handbag, I really don't know why she is packing now, except that she is like that, and besides, is anxious to be off. I gather that Mr. Beedle has reached the end of his patience, and also that the friend who is taking her place at the library is suffering from rheumatism. All this need not worry you in the least because I have said everything I have to say to Louise and also I am quite able now to manage alone. Mrs. Briggs will continue to come as usual, and also promises to 'pop in' at odd moments to see if I am all right.

"It's lovely having Charlotte and the children so comparatively near. Charlotte begged me to go to her, but their small house is already overcrowded and she has her hands far too full as it is. Besides I cling to this little place. I love it. I was never able to give you a home and I can never thank you enough for giving me one. Nowever, we have thought of a happy compromise. Charlotte is going to leave Richard with me for two weeks. After that, we shall see.

"Do you know how your father is really getting on? He writes such odd letters, and talks about people I never heard of as if they were great friends of his. I hope it's all right. I do wish he were back. I miss him dreadfully even though so much of the time he just sits and plays patience. This has nothing to do with my wanting him back, but he seems to have become quite attached to some Countess or other. He keeps spelling her name differently, but I imagine it's Bulgarian or Rumanian. I'm sure it's all right, but he's like a tired old horse who suddenly finds himself in a lush green meadow. I don't really think he's kicking up his heels in any tiresome way, but he can be very credulous at times and I feel you ought to look into it. Could you go to see him? I know how busy you are, and that you talk to him on the telephone, but if you were to see him you could give me a better idea of how he is and what he is up to. I wish I knew who gave him the money, he's now spending. It couldn't have been the Countess, because he hadn't met her when he went to the hotel. It's all very puzzling.

"Mr. Schlemmer calls once or twice a week. He wants to make a film of 'Pilgrim's Progress' which he only read the other day for the first time. He seems to think he's discovered an unknown masterpiece. I find him very refreshing. He calls me Mrs. Greatheart now.

"As Louise will be gone before you can come down again I expect you'll ring her up to say good-bye. She's been very good to me and I'm deeply grateful. Of course your father won't come near me until she's gone, so it's as well, perhaps, that she's going.

"I'm really feeling much better and only need one crutch now. It will be very pleasant to be on my own, with just Richard. I hadn't seen him for a long time and it was a joy to find how much he resembled Charlotte."

Medwin had no opportunity of seeing her father until the middle of the following week, for when she rang him up and said that she wanted to pay him a visit and suggested a date, he said he had arranged to go to the cinema with a friend that evening, and again that he was about to run up to Manchester for a night to see a man on business, and later that he had caught a cold in the train—and this was true enough, for he could hardly speak—and that he thought she would be wise to keep away from him until he was better. It was finally arranged that she was to come to his hotel at nine o'clock on a Thursday. She did not ask him to her flat because she did not want him so near to the scene of his deplorable act. He said he would look forward to her visit and that he would like her to meet a friend of his, a Countess So and So—she could not catch the name—a very charming woman.

"But I'm coming to talk to you," she pointed out.

"That's all right," he said. "She lives here, at this hotel. That's how I met her."

"Well," said Medwin, "if I must. But I'd much rather see you alone."

It was no good sighing for the father who had come home so confidently and gaily to the house in Kensington every evening and had caught her up in his arms when she ran out to meet him. That father was as real, as valid as this one, and there was no reason, she told herself, why her mind should dwell more on one than on the other. His life had slipped, somehow, out of his control and who could say how far he was to blame?

Meanwhile there was no improvement in the relations between Miss Lyddon and Mrs. Gresham; and as to the continuing coldness between Miss Lyddon and herself, neither made any reference to it. Miss Lyddon's attitude was strictly and narrowly that of employer to employed; they might never have laughed and joked together and it was difficult to imagine, now, that Miss Lyddon had ever made her her friend and confidante. If Miss Lyddon expected daily, hourly, that Medwin would go to her and ask the cause of this alteration, she gave no sign of it. Each vied with the other in being coolly polite, correctly formal, and not by word or look did either betray what was in her thoughts. And Medwin, whose whole emotional life was now centred upon Robert Lyddon, who felt so deeply and engrossingly and personally what was happening to herself and him, was hardly touched by all this. If you only knew, she thought, looking at Miss Lyddon, how little this matters to me! I have only to walk across the garden and into my flat to find love and warmth; to pass from winter to summer. I am so unspeakably rich and happy that you cannot touch me. So enchanted and like a dream were the hours that she passed with Robert Lyddon that she was disposed to shrug her shoulders at what was happening in the big house and to discount the possibility that she might be, however innocently, the cause of it. No doubt, she often assured herself, this had happened before and would again. It would pass. At the same time she knew, in her less absorbed and self-centred moments, that things must either mend or break, for such tension could not be maintained indefinitely.

Between herself and Mrs. Gresham, everything was much as usual, but with an added warmth and affection on Mrs. Gresham's part, as if, aware of the coolness between Medwin and Miss Lyddon she had chosen to show them that she, at least, could be relied on to be unchanged and unchangeable.

It seemed the aim of both women never to be alone together and if there were no visitors—and when there were any an appearance of friendship was more or less kept up—Mr. Fullerton or Mrs. Debenham were in great demand. But if they knew that they were there as buffer states between hostile neighbours, they gave no sign of it, and it seemed to Medwin that of all the people in the house, Wilson was the most disturbed. His face wore an added gravity as he went about his business, and now and again she saw him looking at Mrs. Gresham with an expression of real anxiety. If there should be a break, she thought, there was no doubt which way Wilson would go.

On the morning of the Thursday on which she was to see her father, she went across to the house and, as usual, Maria let her in. Just before she knocked she heard Maria and Antonia laughing and talking together, but as she opened the door Maria's face quickly assumed a look of vivid concern.

"The Signora Gresham," she said. "Not good." And she leaned her head to one side with her cheek against her open palm.

"Ill?" Medwin asked. "In bed?" And she asked it in her sparse and lately learned Italian.

Maria's Italian at once began to flow but it flowed too fast and Medwin shook her head. But she understood that Mrs. Gresham was in her bedroom and wanted to see her and she ran up the stairs. She knocked, and Mrs. Gresham faintly said, "Come in."

She was in bed and she was wearing a coral pink, lace-trimmed bed-jacket, and her face looked utterly forlorn. It was an elaborate, chintz-upholstered bed, padded and quilted and curved and suggestive of amorous encounters, and the contrast between it and the woman who lay in it was touching and a little grotesque. Mrs. Gresham looked vanquished, totally depleted, and she turned upon Medwin eyes that might have been made up for tragedy.

"Maria told me you were in bed," Medwin said, and sat down close beside her in obedience to Mrs. Gresham's gesture. "I do hope you aren't ill."

Mrs. Gresham moved her head from side to side, keeping her stricken eyes on Medwin.

"No, not ill," she said. "Only worn out and thrown aside."

"But what has happened?" Medwin asked, and remembered what Robert Lyddon had said about the ammunition dump blowing up.

"Everything has happened. The very worst has happened." And Mrs. Gresham put a handkerchief to her eyes, which brimmed over. "All this," she said, and made a semi-circle with her hand, "is breaking up. I'm a dreadfully unhappy woman. I don't know which way to turn."

It was hard to believe that this was the same woman who had conducted her multitudinous affairs with such complacency. Moments of humility and doubt she occasionally had, and lately these had been intensified, but to see her so reduced was shocking.

"Won't you tell me what it's all about?" Medwin asked, gently. "I've known, of course, that things haven't been going well. I suppose that even between the oldest friends this may sometimes happen."

"She's leaving here," Mrs. Gresham told her in a breaking voice. "She says she's been with me too long. I can't bear it. I thought we could go on to the end, together, making a success of it—and most of the time, until lately anyway, it has been a success—and now she wants to ruin everything, my life and even her own life, for what will she do alone, without me? It's a tragedy, a tragedy."

Medwin said quietly, though with a growing anxiety:

"Don't you think, Mrs. Gresham, that it will all blow over?" But she was thinking, and am I the cause? What can I do? What ought I to do?

Mrs. Gresham shook her head. "It's gone too far this time," and tears ran down her cheeks. "She's spoken to Maria and Antonia. She means to find a flat somewhere and take them with her. And what would I do? It means selling this house. It's been my home for over thirty-five years. This is where I belong and where I hoped to die. Everything in it speaks to me of my married life and my husband. My son was born here."

"I know," said Medwin. "All that makes it doubly hard for you. But surely it needn't happen. Surely it's just some misunderstanding."

"And all the talk there'll be," Mrs. Gresham sobbed. "The questions. The unkind things people will say about us. I can't bear it!"

"But I don't believe this is really the end," Medwin told her. "I can't believe it. Won't you tell me what caused it all?"

Mrs. Gresham wiped her eyes, but her tears continued to come and sobbing made it difficult for her to speak.

"I'll try to tell you one day. I can't now. It's too dreadful, too shocking. I'm not a quarrelsome woman; I'm easily hurt and jealous, I know, though I try not to be. But I couldn't say the things she says, I couldn't. I couldn't hurt anyone as she hurts me." And she suddenly laid her hand, palm upwards, on the lace bedspread, close to Medwin, and with such an obvious though silent appeal to her to put her hand in it that she did so. And still struggling with her tears, Mrs. Gresham went on:

"I've grown very fond of you. You came here as our secretary, but you've become more than that. You've become a friend, and I don't make friends easily. If Miss Lyddon goes, and she will go, would you stay with me? Perhaps in some smaller house in London. You could have Sarah with you. And of course I'd go on with my work. I couldn't give that up, though she says it's only to keep my name in the papers." She withdrew her hand to wipe away her tears which at the memory of this insult flowed afresh. "Yes, she could say that to me, after all these years." She paused a moment, then went on, "You'd find plenty to do. And forgive me for speaking of it, but your salary would be just what it is now, or even more if you liked. I think Wilson would come with me and perhaps Davis. Couldn't you? I think perhaps I could face the future if you said you could?"

"Oh, Mrs. Gresham," Medwin said, "I'm very grateful and very deeply touched at your wanting me, but surely it won't come to that. I feel so certain that it's just a misunderstanding and that it will all blow over."

"I'm afraid it's final," Mrs. Gresham said. "You don't know the cruel things she's said to me. Things I shall never forget. My oldest and dearest friend. And now, who is there left? My other friends have their own lives, and even if they hadn't there aren't any I'd care to live with. I'm terrified of being alone and lonely. I always have been. The mere thought of it is a nightmare. I've always wanted to feel necessary to someone. I suppose that's partly why I took up this charitable work, though of course I wanted to help too. But it isn't enough. One wants something closer and more personal. If only I had my son."

"But you have," said Medwin.

"Oh, I know I'm luckier than millions of mothers. I tell myself every day. But he's there, I'm here. He doesn't need me. And besides," she added, "I don't think I'd like living in Toronto."

Medwin kept back a smile.

"Well," she said, "I can't believe that this is really the end. It seems too sad and too unnecessary. Shall I try to talk to Miss Lyddon about it? I will, gladly, if you think it will help. Even though she isn't disposed to be very friendly to me at the moment, and even though outsiders often do more harm than good."

"I don't feel that you're an outsider," Mrs. Gresham said. Then she drew herself up a little on her pillows and said with all the desperate appeal of which she was capable, "Will you at least promise me one thing? Will you promise me that if she asks you to go and live with her, that you won't go? Will you promise me?" And then, mistaking Medwin's brief hesitation, she cried, "She's asked you already and you've said you would!" And she turned over with a sudden movement and buried her face in the pillow, sobbing, "I think I'll kill myself. I'd be better dead!"

This was not far from hysteria, and Medwin quickly pushed back her chair and got up.

"Mrs. Gresham," she said, firmly, "you must not talk like that. I'm going to ring up Dr. Radnytz and ask him to come and see you. You're overtired, and this disagreement with Miss Lyddon has been too much for you. Will you see him? I'm sure it's the wisest thing to do."

"Oh, if you like," Mrs. Gresham said between her sobs. "I don't care. I'm broken and tired and old. He's helped me before, perhaps he can again. I don't care."

Medwin put her hand on her shoulder and bent over her. Grief was grief, whatever its cause, sorrow and misery were themselves, and she could not withhold pity.

"As for that promise," she said, "of course I give it, gladly."

There was silence. Even Mrs. Gresham's breathing seemed

to have stopped as this balm fell on her. She shifted herself and put out her hand.

"Thank you. You can tell Dr. Radnytz I'd like to see him. Only don't go far away. Don't leave me. I've taken a sleeping tablet, and perhaps I'll sleep now until he comes. I never closed my eyes all night."

Medwin lingered for a moment but there seemed nothing more she could do or say so she went down to Mrs. Gresham's sitting-room and telephoned for Dr. Radnytz. His secretary answered and said he was in London and would call at three o'clock. That done, Medwin sat down at the writing-table to see what the morning's post had brought to Mrs. Gresham and busied herself sorting it out, putting on one side papers and circulars and separating business letters from private ones.

Then the door opened and Miss Lyddon looked in. Seeing Medwin there she came in further and closed the door and stood with her back against it, tall, rigid and hostile. In her eyes there was such a look as a dog might wear who wonders whether or not he will bite and wants just another final smell to make quite certain. Medwin noticed for the first time that her cheeks were fairly heavily rouged. She sometimes put on a faint touch of colour in the evening, but this morning she had put it on boldly, even carelessly.

"Well?" Miss Lyddon said.

"Well?" Medwin returned. And then made uncomfortable by Miss Lyddon's fixed, accusing stare, she asked, "Is there anything I can do for you? I'm just attending to Mrs. Gresham's letters."

"They can wait," Miss Lyddon said. "If I know her, and I ought to, she's taken to her bed for the best part of a week. You can give me your attention for the moment."

Medwin dropped her hands into her lap.

"Very well," she said, and her face looked as blank as she could make it look.

"I can't talk to you here," Miss Lyddon said. "I must talk to you in my own room. Will you please come downstairs?"

"I'm here to obey my employer's instructions," said Medwin. "If you wish me to come downstairs I will, of course."

"I hoped at least that we could dispense with this sort of nonsense," Miss Lyddon said caustically. She opened the door and led the way downstairs without speaking, and when they were both in her room and Medwin stood waiting for her to speak she said, "I can't talk to a monument. Please sit down." And she closed the door.

Medwin looked at her pleasantly and said, "Perhaps you'll tell me which chair you would like me to sit in."

Miss Lyddon gave a harsh and unamused laugh.

"It's my misfortune, I suppose, to like almost everything about you. Even your stupidity. The one thing I cannot bear and will not endure is your duplicity. Sit where you like. Yes, sit on the sofa. I prefer to stand. I'll come straight to the point. Why did you go to Edith and ask for help for your father? Why didn't you come to me, as I repeatedly asked you to do if you were in need of help?"

Here it is, thought Medwin, and I have no answer ready. But surely, she told herself, Robert is right. There's safety and sanity in truth. It's medicinal. Lies tie knots; truth unties them. Beryl Sprague again.

"Well?" Miss Lyddon said as she made no reply. "Why don't you answer me?"

"It isn't easy to answer you," Medwin said, "because as you know, the answer involves someone else. I suppose misery and torment can make most of us take refuge in untruths sometimes, and I suppose Mrs. Gresham is no exception."

"So she lied to me, did she? Don't let us mince words. And remember, I'm prepared to believe everything you say. She lied, did she?"

"Oh, why do you two torture each other so?" Medwin cried. "Why do you do it?"

"Probably as an outlet for our emotions," Miss Lyddon replied. "You're a woman; you ought to know."

It was not the moment to attempt to refute this implied calumny against their sex and Medwin let it pass.

"You continually work on her feelings," she said. "You're the cleverer of the two and you take delight in twisting her this way and that until to protect herself she takes refuge in a lie, if you choose to call it a lie."

"If it was a lie, then for heaven's sake let us call it a lie," Miss Lyddon said, but there was relief in her face and it was plainly visible. "It was a vile lie, a colossal lie, a contemptible lie, capable of doing untold harm. But if you had taken me into your confidence at once, if you had been candid with me, none of this need have happened. How did your father get in touch with her? Did he write to her! And why to her? Tell me."

"Hasn't it occurred to you," Medwin asked, "that all this is very humiliating indeed for me?"

"Nothing need be humiliating between friends," said Miss Lyddon. "Nothing. Good heavens, am I supposed to be so devoid of intelligence as to be unable to understand? Clearly the poor man was driven to do what he did. But what made him go to *her* and how did he go about it? Let's have the whole story."

There was nothing else to do but to tell her the facts, and Medwin told them, taking care to explain that for years her father had known about the investment house of Gresham and Protheroe. "And I want to say," she told Miss Lyddon at the end of it, "that never before in his life, to the best of my knowledge, has he done such a thing." And she added, "Such a disgraceful thing."

"Come, come," Miss Lyddon said. "Don't exaggerate. It was no crime. Have some pity on him."

Medwin was silent.

"Well, well," Miss Lyddon said. " 'Oh, what a tangled web we weave,' and all the rest of it. For this, Edith and I are to part company. You see the harm you have done by keeping everything to yourself. You could so easily have been frank with me."

"I don't consider myself responsible for what has happened," Medwin answered coldly. "And when I agreed to come here, I didn't know that I was to be allowed no private life."

"All the same, I'm afraid the responsibility is yours," Miss Lyddon said, and she began walking up and down the room with nervous movements. "The confidence and the friendship I offered you was not returned, and this is the result. You discussed the whole thing with her. Why keep it from me? As for what you just said about your private life, that's childish and absurd. Do you realize that I have never so much as rung your doorbell since you've been here. Is that showing no respect for your privacy? So much did I want you to feel mistress of your own home that I have never so much as crossed the garden to your door. Edith may have intruded on you; I don't know and have never asked, but I certainly have not."

"That was not the sort of privacy," Medwin said. "that I meant."

"I'm not in the mood for quibbling," Miss Lyddon said. "You made an accusation and I have refuted it." And then she paused in front of Medwin and fixed her with one of her shrewdest and most penetrating looks. "I suppose," she said, "she has asked you to go and live with her when our present arrangement ends. Has she?"

"She has," Medwin answered quietly. "And I suppose you will ask me too, and let me say here and now that I've no intention of going with either of you."

"Ah!" cried Miss Lyddon. "A little daylight, a little honesty at last. How refreshing it is! More of this in the past might have been an excellent thing. Well, as you only knew of our decision less than an hour ago, it's hardly likely that you've made other plans."

"I could always go back to the Ministry of Food," Medwin told her, "and work with men again."

"I hope you don't imagine," Miss Lyddon answered unexpectedly, "that all women employers are like us. I should think we were probably unique. Singly you might perhaps match us, though I doubt it, but certainly not as a pair. Dr. Radnytz should have warned you. He knows us pretty well." And she smiled ironically.

"He's coming to see Mrs. Gresham at three this afternoon," Medwin told her. "She's desperately miserable, and perhaps he can help her, if you won't."

"I have no pity for her," Miss Lyddon said. "None. And you needn't ask me to have pity on her. She must come to me and ask my forgiveness and admit that she lied. And even that won't alter my decision. We have been together too long."

"You'll neither of you be happier or more contented apart," Medwin said.

"You think not? She's a most difficult woman. She almost drove poor, placid Ernest mad with her jealousy."

"You're both jealous," said Medwin, "and both difficult. Why can't you make allowances for each other?"

"Why?" Miss Lyddon asked, continuing her walking. "Because we happen to be imperfect human beings. Frail vessels. And damnably unhappy."

"I have no patience with you," Medwin said, and she looked Miss Lyddon full in the face. "And now tell me to go."

Miss Lyddon paused to take a cigarette from a box and light it.

"I'm taking more and more to smoking," she said, and shook out the flame of the match. "I wonder when you'll come to it? One of these days, no doubt, when your youthful complacency has departed and you see your life behind you instead of ahead of you, and you see it for what it is—a pretty poor thing. My dear," she said, "Edith and I are two despicable women, let us admit it, and that is why you have no patience with us. Why should you have? I doubt if we do a single thing, either of us, *pour le bon motif*. But I forget you know no French. Let us say, for a respectable reason. We are as hungry for personal success as a couple of debutantes at their first ball. I am an extremely arrogant woman, but at the same time I can never be assured often enough that I am not insignificant and futile. I have moments of cruelty that would make me loathe myself if I weren't so aware of their cause. I have got little happiness from life, and yet I want to live for ever. The thought of death, of ending, appals me. And the opiate of religion, remember, has never been one that I could swallow. I picture the whole panorama of living going on before my eyes and I under the ground, forgotten. And if you tell me that the dead see nothing, I can only answer that that is an even better reason for hating the thought of it."

She walked to the window, stared out of it for a few seconds and then returned and resumed her pacings.

"Of course I have been spoilt from my youth. My parents adored me, my brothers—or two of them—were afraid of me and gave in to me. I grew up a sort of goddess in my father's house. I lived in the midst of flattery and admiration, but it was never enough. I knew all the important and interesting people within my reach and they told me I was brilliant or fascinating or in some way remarkable, and I never believed a word of it and hungered for proof of it. What would have happened if I'd married Giles, I don't know. Perhaps I'd have tormented him into his grave just to keep myself continually assured that I had power over him, but at least I wouldn't have been what I am now, but something different. You see, you can tell me nothing I don't know about myself, and in that way Edith and I live at opposite poles. She poor creature, has no idea what goes on in her own mind, or why. People still puzzle themselves over Hitler and his ways. Good heavens! I understand the man perfectly. So would millions of us if we looked closely enough into ourselves. They say 'All power corrupts,' but that's by no means invariably true. It should have been, 'Desire for power corrupts,' and of course it does. Anyone who desires power over other lives of even another life is potentially criminal, and

I've always wanted power over every life I've come close to. I want power over your life, and if you're wise you'll say good-bye and go, and never see me again, though I pray you won't. You see, I like you as I haven't liked anyone for years. The mere sight of you gives me pleasure and banishes thoughts of death. I don't know what you have—a sort of bloom, perhaps. You haven't even come to full maturity yet. You're gentle and adaptable and uncannily understanding; and you have a kind of moral tranquillity, though God knows how you got it. You make me think of a young Spartan woman, though I never saw one. You seem to stand so firmly and resolutely on your own feet. And you're empty-handed and I have too much and she has too much and we'd like to fill your hands but you turn from us as if everything we possessed were tainted. Well, perhaps it is and perhaps you're right. And you're right to think me a despicable woman with few redeeming qualities, though something tells me that in a pinch I might have courage. But so has any cornered animal; there's no flattering unction in that. So now," she said, coming to a halt in front of Medwin, "what have you to say?"

"You've disarmed me," said Medwin, "as you meant to do. But will you go to her and put her mind at rest? She's in a pitiable state."

"No," said Miss Lyddon. "Nothing can excuse or condone those lies. We had better part. I shall not alter my decision even to please you. I must end my days in peace, away from her. Time is too precious to me now."

Medwin looked quickly at her and saw that under the rouge her skin looked dry and yellow. She's not well, she thought, and her mind hovered between pity and contempt. Like a disordered compass with a wavering needle that could not find its north, her mind swung between comprehending love and comprehending aversion. She got up.

"So it must all end," she said, "in disaster, because of me?"

"Take what share of blame you think right and just," Miss Lyddon said. "I shan't attempt to apportion it. At least you have the satisfaction of knowing that you could have averted it. It will take time, of course, to bring it to an end. Perhaps two or three months. I'm seeing Archie Fullerton this afternoon and we'll discuss the whole matter. If you choose to stay with us until the end, I trust you will. I have given up the idea of going abroad."

Medwin hesitated, looked out of the window, looked back at Miss Lyddon and then said:

"I still can't believe that it will end like this, but if it must, and you both want me to stay, then I will."

"Don't expect me to answer for her," Miss Lyddon said. "I want you to stay, naturally, especially now that you seem inclined to be frank and open with me. Just one thing more, before you go upstairs. It's ridiculous, of course, for you to think of repaying her that two hundred pounds. It means nothing to her."

"It means something to me," Medwin said.

Miss Lyddon flashed her one of her most typical and most ironic looks.

"One of the things I suppose I like most about you," she said, "is the fact that you're a sort of gold-digger in reverse. Well, ruin yourself if you like. The time isn't far off when it will cease to concern me."

CHAPTER 14

ROBERT CAME BEFORE SEVEN AND AFTER THEY HAD HAD A drink and she had told him the news of the day and they had discussed it fully, they went out to get dinner somewhere. She suggested that they walk a little and as they went out into the bright, long-lived day he said he wished things had not come to a head so soon, so inconveniently soon. He agreed with Medwin that Mrs. Gresham was greatly to be pitied, but it was her folly that had precipitated the whole disaster. Yes, Medwin said, but there was no knowing how she had been goaded into it, or what abominable things Miss Lyddon had said to make her take refuge, in defence of her pride, in preposterous invention.

"Well," he said, "if it had not been for that, my aunt's ferocity might have slumbered a little longer. Now let's forget them for a while, if we can. Outrageous though they are, they brought us together and nothing else matters."

The low sun, seeming to have lost none of its warmth and brilliance and to have gained in golden splendour, shone in their faces as they turned into Park Lane and entered the Park. It drove long shadows across the grass under the trees, and the trees were languid with it and with their great burden of foliage. And everywhere it glanced or fell it enriched and glorified, and the whole scene was miraculous for colour and every person and thing was deliciously imprisoned in amber light. It was the setting, Medwin thought, for God knew what, but for something that should be truer, more real, more meaningful than human hearts could compass or human words describe. They walked in a glory to which they felt unequal, they were brought to a banquet to which no appetite, attuned to poorer fare, could do justice. It was too lovely, serene and triumphant an evening for those caught up in the complicated web of living, and in addition to that, so little accustomed to each other. Fog, eyelessly enclosing them, would have suited them far better. Mist or rain would have been more in their element. Now that they found themselves for the first time walking, self-acknowledged lovers, upon a public stage, they were unprepared for all this blaze and beauty and were diminished by it. All the ease and freedom they had felt when enclosed between four small, familiar walls had vanished now that they had this extravagantly sunlit world to move in. Their words seemed to return to their own lips, their tongues seemed to falter.

"Now you see," he said, reading her thoughts, which matched his own, "why I like best to be in the flat. Out here we lose something. You feel it too. Something of us is vanishing into all this space. I want you to myself and for myself, and this defeats me."

"But I'm here," she said, and touched his sleeve, "and I'm the same."

"And I'm the same," he said, "but together, like this, we make something less real."

"We're putting on a show," she said, smiling, "for all the neighbours."

"I'm longing for the restaurant," he said, "and for our knees under the same table and our elbows on it. Then we can talk again."

"It's the newness," she said. "It's all so new to us. Where are we going?"

"We could go along Oxford Street," he suggested, "to Soho and some restaurant there."

"Yes, I like Soho. We could take a bus along Oxford Street."

"A bus?" he said. "The only conveyance for lovers is a taxi, which I'll gladly take as soon as you've walked enough. On a bus we'd look at people and people would look at us and our joint identity would evaporate like steam."

"It's all been too much like a dream so far," she said, "but lovelier and more private. We're not yet used to common day; though," she added, lifting her face, "this is no common day."

"It's only that I grudge every moment that we're not close," he said, "so that I can talk to you as I can talk only to you."

"It's because," she told him, "we're not yet lovers."

He looked at her with one of his quick, comprehending looks, but made no reply. Then he hailed a passing taxi.

"Come," he said, "enough of this. Either there's all the time in the world or there's far too little to waste." And he gave the driver the name of a restaurant and they got in, overpowered by the day and the too much that was not themselves. Not caring that they might be seen he took her into his corner and drew her head down to his shoulder, and they sighed with relief and the easing of tension and apartness.

After they had dined he took her to her father's hotel, and they were late. He left her there and said that he would go to a news theatre and come back for her at half-past ten.

It was a shabby hotel, and old, but smugly respectable. She went into the lobby and saw her father waiting for her with the evening paper in his hands, and sitting in a chair that seemed to be upholstered in Turkish carpet. Seated in a similar chair with her back to him and also reading a paper was a woman with bright red hair. She could only see the hair and the black velvet bow that was poised in it but she guessed at once that this was the Countess and that the chance of escaping a meeting with her were small.

Her father saw her, got up and came towards her. He was wearing his new suit and looked a good many years younger than when she had seen him last. His hair had been neatly trimmed and he had grown a military-looking, closely cut moustache which became him. She had not seen him since that day in the Chartley's kitchen when he had been peeling the potatoes for supper.

"Hello, father," she said, kissing him. "You look exceedingly well, I'm glad to see."

"So do you," he said, "so do you," but even as he spoke his eyes were turning towards the woman in the chair.

"Shall we go up to your room?" she asked, still hoping to avoid or postpone the encounter.

"Well," he said, "it isn't much of a room. Wait a minute. I'd like you to meet the friend I spoke to you about, Countess Radulescu. She's just over there. She's a very cultured woman and speaks I forget how many languages." And there was a gentle and foolish pride on his face such as can be seen sometimes on the faces of parents of young and talented children, and as he was speaking he was moving over towards the woman with red hair. "Countess," he said, and she promptly got up and turned towards them. "Countess, I want you to meet my daughter, Mrs. Blair. Countess Radulescu."

She was quite shapeless and rather stout; she had let her figure go, it seemed, with reckless indifference, but her face had once been handsome and the features were classic and regular. Her carrot-red hair showed a half-inch of grey at the roots, and she wore large turquoises in her ears and on her hands, the knuckles of which were much distorted and enlarged by rheumatism or arthritis. She had on some very strong perfume, and it was not a perfume for the fastidious. She had, in all probability, a long trail of conquests behind her, but they would have been the sort of conquests, Medwin unkindly surmised, which, in retrospect, would mean little more than notches in a stick.

Medwin said, "How do you do?" and they shook hands.

"It is a great pleasure to meet you," said the Countess. "Mr. Fosdick has spoken so much of his clever daughter. Shall we all sit down? I ordered coffee but as you were not here I sent it back to be kept hot." She snapped her fingers at a passing waiter and he nodded and retired from view.

"I've already had coffee, thank you," Medwin said, but the Countess ignored this and the three seated themselves. The Countess offered Medwin a cigarette, and when Medwin said she did not smoke, took one herself and fitted it into a long black holder. Mr. Fosdick took a paper-wrapped cigar out of his pocket, undid the wrapping respectfully and with the air of performing a rite, and lit a cigar. It was not, Medwin judged by the smell, a very good cigar, but she thought that the Countess's perfume perhaps interfered with it somewhat.

"I suppose you had dinner with Mrs. Gresham," her father said.

"No," Medwin answered, "I had dinner in Soho with a friend."

"I've been telling the Countess," Mr. Fosdick said, "about Mrs. Gresham and her delightful house. What was that picture over the mantelpiece in her room? Mrs. Gresham did tell me the name, but it has slipped my mind."

"Do you mean the Canaletto?" Medwin asked.

"That was it. It was a Canaletto," Mr. Fosdick told the Countess, impressively. "A most beautiful picture. I wish the Countess could see that house, Medwin, and the lovely things in it. She knows a great deal about pictures and furniture."

"My home," said the Countess, "was a castle thirty miles from Bucharest. They have taken it away from me now. It was full of art treasures. My husband was a great collector, especially of weapons and armour. He had more than five hundred daggers, many with jewelled handles. Very beautiful. He is of course dead now. He was a very remarkable man of noble, Magyar blood. And handsome!" She lifted her eyes to the ceiling and raised both hands. "So handsome!" She turned to Medwin and laying a finger on her knee, said, "My child, the story of my life would make a most wonderful novel. Most wonderful. I have been telling your father some—only a few—of the strange, terrible and exciting things that have happened to me. Things you cannot imagine. Things you would find it hard to believe."

"I can't visualize Rumania at all," Medwin told her. "But that, I suppose, is hardly surprising as I've never been out of England."

"Never been out of England? Then," said the Countess, "you are now probably too late. There is no telling how soon the Iron Curtain may advance to the shores of Calais. I want coffee. Why are they so slow bringing the coffee?" And she turned rather heavily in her chair, but there was no sign of the waiter.

"It'll come," said Mr. Fosdick. "No use being impatient. You have to wait for everything nowadays. It's almost as good as travelling," he said to Medwin, "to listen to the Countess's stories. She makes me think of the lady in the Arabian Nights. What was her name now?"

Medwin told him.

"That's it. Scheherezade," he repeated, smiling. "She's a regular Scheherezade."

And Medwin thought, this is escape for him. Escape from a long nightmare of disappointment and frustration, escape from looking after the hens, and seeing no one, and being shabby and ashamed. I must be patient with him.

"And how do you like this hotel?" she asked the Countess. "Is it fairly comfortable?"

"It is not the Ritz," the Countess said judicially.

Mr. Fosdick chuckled.

"Not the Ritz!" he said. "I should rather think not. Never mind, if all goes well we may find ourselves at the Ritz yet." And his face wore a look of happiness as if even the sound of the words gave him pleasure.

"How are things going?" Medwin asked. She thought she had better find out what she could, for she saw that it was going to be difficult to get her father alone.

"Oh," he said, almost gaily, "I have great hopes and great expectations. Great expectations, thanks to the Countess."

"But nothing more concrete?" Medwin inquired.

"I wouldn't say that," Mr. Fosdick answered. "I've seen a number of people who are definitely interested. But it's no good trying to do this thing in a small way. I've learnt that much. We must put it over in a big way or not at all. Make a real splash with it. The trouble is, it's going to require a lot of money to launch it as it ought to be launched. The cost of advertising and manufacturing," he said, looking very serious, "will be tremendous. But I don't think that's necessarily a disadvantage. I never could see it succeeding in a small way."

"There is absolutely no reason," said the Countess very slowly and impressively, "why this invention of yours—and by the way—" she told Medwin, "I have named it 'Scrub-Joy'—should not be in every office, every hotel and every home. I am bringing it to the notice of my friends in the City. I believe in it, and if I believe in it, they will believe in it. We must all believe in it. That is of the first importance." And she blew a smoke-ring and watched it from under her wrinkled eyelids.

"You ought to have taken one of my cigars," said Mr. Fosdick, looking at her indulgently. "Medwin, you wouldn't have been surprised to see the Countess smoking a cigar, would you? She's a great cigar smoker. Many Roumanian ladies are."

"Yes, so I've always understood," Medwin said, smiling at the Countess. "I hope you didn't refrain on my account."

The Countess shook her head. "It makes these foolish people stare," she said. "Ah, here is the coffee, at last. Sugar?" she said to the waiter. "I don't see any sugar. You know I always must have sugar."

The waiter pointed at the tray, and looking more closely the

Countess saw that there was in fact a portion of a lump on each saucer. "Ridiculous!" she said. "Go away and bring me more sugar or I will complain to the management. Don't tell me sugar is rationed. I am aware of that. Go away and bring more."

Mr. Fosdick chuckled again. "There ought to be more people like you about," he said, and added, turning to Medwin, "she always gets what she wants. She'll get the sugar. You'll see."

The coffee was served in a teapot which bore the name of some other hotel, and the cups were very thick and had chipped rims, but Medwin took some, though she guessed it would be bad. It was very bad indeed.

"How long do you think you'll be here, father?" she asked, knowing that it was a foolish question but feeling at a loss for something to say.

"Oh," he said, "it's a little difficult to tell you exactly. Perhaps another two weeks—three weeks. It depends on the progress I make."

"He must not be hurried," the Countess said. "He must have plenty of time. Too much is at stake."

Medwin thought she was taking a good deal upon herself. She turned to her father and said, "I suppose mother has told you that Louise is going home tomorrow. I must ring her up in the morning to say good-bye. Forgive me," she said to the Countess, "for speaking of family matters, but the truth is I'm so busy I don't see my father very often."

"But of course, of course," the Countess said, brushing some ash from the front of her black dress. "Naturally he must have news of his family. Poor man, until we met I'm afraid he was very lonely."

At this point Mr. Fosdick half rose from his chair to bow to a tall gaunt woman who looked at him and smiled a little coldly as she passed by on her way to the lift.

"That's Mrs. Gaullfry," he said to Medwin. "Her husband was a bishop in Australia for many years. Quite a distinguished man, I believe."

"And when he was alive he was married to a fool," the Countess said with unexpected savageness.

Mr. Fosdick laughed.

"Well," he said, "she isn't as well endowed with brains as someone else I could mention, but she's been kind, very kind. She has a daughter here too," he told Medwin. "A Mrs. Tomlinson, whose husband is in Hong-Kong. She's very nice indeed."

"Nice," said the Countess. "I shall never understand what that word 'nice' means."

When the waiter finally returned he bore three small and broken lumps of sugar in a saucer. By that time the coffee was finished. The Countess, without a word, took the lumps of sugar and dropped them into her handbag.

"I told you she'd get them," Mr. Fosdick observed, with satisfaction.

The Countess showed no sign of moving, so Medwin finally got up and said, to her father:

"Won't you take me up to your room for a few minutes? Mother particularly wants to know if you're comfortable, and I said I'd report. And then I think I'd better be getting home." She turned to the Countess and held out her hand. "I hope you'll excuse us," she said, "and many thanks for the coffee. Good night."

Mr. Fosdick took out his watch. It was a watch Medwin could remember from her childhood.

"Wait a little," he said. "We'll go up in a quarter of an hour. I just want you to hear the Countess's story of how she escaped from the Gestapo."

"Oh," said Medwin, but after a second's hesitation she sat down again, saying, "Of course, I should like to hear it."

It was late when they finally went upstairs. It was an inside room and looked out on a well, but the evening sky was plainly visible if one craned one's neck. On the table by his bed were the "Directory of Directors" and his inkstained copy of "Who's Who?" There were a few papers and magazines about, and a cheap edition of a detective novel. The room was stuffy and smelt of stale cigar smoke and apples, a plate of which were on the table. He had washed out some of his handkerchiefs and these were drying over the backs of chairs. There was a cracked hand basin and running water. It was just the sort of room she had pictured, and she was not surprised by anything. She had not even been surprised by the Countess.

"Father," she said, feeling that she must warn him, "I hope you won't mind my saying this, but if I were you I wouldn't place too much confidence in the Countess or in anything she may tell you. Candidly, I don't trust her. I hope you'll be careful and that you won't let her have any money."

He stared at her and she saw that he was genuinely amazed.

"You say you don't trust her?" he asked. "But you simply don't know what you're talking about. She's a lady. A clever, cultured woman. You mustn't think, just because she's a foreigner——"

"Oh, father," she interrupted him, "you know it isn't that. Please be careful, and above all, don't let her have any of that money. Make it last as long as you possibly can, won't you?"

He gnawed at his moustache for a second, then he shook his head.

"You don't know her, that's all. I trust her absolutely. She's a lady and she wants to help me."

"Have you given her money already?" she asked. "Please don't say it's none of my business, father, because you know I'm going to repay Mrs. Gresham, though it will take a long time. Have you given her money?"

"Given?" he repeated. "No, I haven't given her any. She's earned it. She's introduced me to some useful people. And anyway it wasn't much."

"I suppose it's no good asking how much," she said.

He made no answer to this. "It'll be all right," he said. "You'll see. And I'm not spending a great deal. This place isn't expensive."

She saw that she had not succeeded in planting even a small seed of doubt about the Countess in his mind.

"Well, father," she said, "if this doesn't succeed, we'll manage. We managed before. Only please don't incur any more debts, or I don't know what I shall do." And she added, "Mother says she misses you very badly."

"I suppose she does," he said, looking down at the carpet. "I miss her. But this is more important than anything else. Some people think there's a fortune in it. Just at the moment I'm waiting to hear from one of the Countess's friends. He's looking into the whole business of manufacture. Nowadays, of course, with all these controls and permits, it's going to be quite a complicated matter. If I could only lay my hands on some more money I'd be all right. It's just a question of time."

She thought of Robert walking up and down in front of the hotel.

"I've told you what I think, father. There's nothing more I can say except to beg you again not to trust the Countess too far."

"Well," he said, "thank you for coming, and I'm glad to

see you looking so well. Give my kind regards to Mrs. Gresham if you think of it. She's a fine woman and it was a pleasure to meet her."

There was nothing more to say and it was like talking to some-one who was behind thick, sound-proof glass. She offered him her cheek and ran down the stairs without waiting for the rumbling, palpitating lift which was on its way to a higher floor. On her way through the lobby she caught a glimpse of the Countess, who was leaning both elbows on the reception desk chatting with the hall porter. Her back was turned and Medwin got out without being seen by her. She found Robert walking up and down outside, smoking, and she put her arm through his.

"Let's walk a little," she said, and the touch of his arm seemed to dissipate all her troubles. "Were you bored at the cinema? Was it a wasted evening?"

The reluctant dark had not quite come, the sky was still light but the street lamps and electric signs were hurrying the lingering twilight on its way. London seemed theirs as the brightly coloured city of less than two hours before had not done. They were themselves again. He put her hand against his lips.

"I wish I could tell you," he said, "how happy I was just walking up and down watching the door and knowing that at any moment you would come running out of it. I think you're too time-conscious to keep me waiting much, but if you did it wouldn't matter, unless I thought you might not be coming. Never, never keep me waiting, though, and then not come."

She pressed nearer to him. Now that it was almost dark they walked arm in arm with clasped hands, and in step. She told him about her father and about the Countess.

"She seems a stock character," he said, "lifted straight out of innumerable works of fiction. Surely he's come across her before, either in real life or in novels."

"You'd think not," she said, and sighed, but it all mattered less now that they were together.

"Don't worry about it," he said. "You can do nothing more. He must take what comes, and if he incurs any further debts they need not concern you. If he can't borrow more he'll come home and that will be the end of it. He's living on borrowed money; we're living on borrowed time. We have a little more than two weeks, and for part of that time we are going to be together. The question is where."

"Anywhere," she said. "Anywhere."

And in front of a lighted shop they paused and looked at each other, and she knew that this was one of those moments that her memory would never tire of releasing for her, and that looking back, whether it were from some happy landscape that she would not change for any other, or from some dusty wasteland that she had to cross, it would always be there.

CHAPTER 15

LOUISE'S MANNER, WHEN MEDWIN RANG HER UP TO SAY GOOD-bye, was more than usually dry and restrained. Medwin was made aware of things that could not be spoken of on the telephone, of things hinted at and darkly withheld. No, Louise said in answer to her puzzled inquiries, there was nothing wrong with Mr. Beedle, no, there was nothing wrong with the house. When asked if she looked forward to being at home again, Louise said it would not be as agreeable as she had hoped, but would say no more. She promised to write.

"I am just off now," she said, "to catch the bus. Mrs. Briggs is coming with me to carry my suitcase. There was no need of a taxi."

Medwin glanced over her shoulder at the clock.

"But you needn't go for half an hour yet," she said.

"You know I like to be on time," Louise replied. "I am anxious to be off. I can wait at the bus stop."

It was easy to picture her wearing her battered hat, her umbrella hooked over her arm, impatient to take up her old life again. The months she had lost would never be regained; she had done what she could for a sister with whom she had nothing in common, for a niece whom she loved almost unwillingly, and in whose flesh she fancifully clothed herself, to taste a youth such as she had never known. If only I could tell you, Medwin thought, aware of the shamed envy in Louise's heart, how wrong you are. Rejoice in your narrow, fading, virgin body. It cannot betray you now.

But soon she put Louise out of her mind. Too much was happening, and most of it distressing. The life of the great house was slowing down, though this slowing-down was gradual, like that of a huge and well-oiled wheel which continues to revolve after the driving-engine has ceased to work. To Medwin who watched and even assisted at the process, this slowing-down was accompanied by sharp pangs and regrets. How much had she been to blame? And then she would ask herself, driven to angry impatience by the folly of the whole business, how much did it all really matter? Let them ruin their lives if they chose; let them revenge themselves on each other to their mutual hurt. She felt only disgust that two women of more than mature years could act so childishly and with such monstrous selfishness. Then she would swing sharply from this mood to one of remorse again. If she had only told Miss Lyddon of her father's visit and what had come of it, if she had only given confidence for confidence——

She was not greatly surprised when Mr. Fullerton rang her up and asked if he might come and see her at half-past six. She had guessed that he might do this sooner or later, and she hastily rang up Robert at his office and warned him not to come till half-past seven. Mr. Fullerton, she said, might stay for an hour or more, there was no knowing, and she advised him to telephone before coming, to find out if she were alone.

Mr. Fullerton seemed, on the surface, much as usual, but underneath it she detected anxiety and concern. He presently abandoned some of his usual caution and asked her to tell him, if she could do so without betraying confidences, what had happened to cause the impending break between the two women.

"I never expected it," he said, "never, and I am greatly distressed by it. Mrs. Gresham has already put the house in the hands of agents. The two seem bent on destroying everything that they've built up over so many years. I would do anything I could to stop it."

"So would I," Medwin said sadly.

He looked at her speculatively and went on:

"It's highly improper, of course, for me to come here and discuss my client with you, but she is also an old friend, and as she chooses to keep me in the dark, what can I do? No other course is open to me." He examined her face again, as if he hoped, by reading it, to gain knowledge from it rather than from her words. Then he went on, his small eyes alight now with sagacity, as if he had read all that he needed to read, "I rather suspect, my dear Mrs. Blair, that it's you who have upset the apple cart." And without waiting for her reply, feeling perhaps that her reply would only have embarrassed him, he hurried on. "There's no need for you to answer. I see my guess is correct. I was reasonably certain of it."

"I suppose you're right," she said, and then she echoed his own words. "But what can I do?"

"Ought we not at once to remove the cause of the upset?" he asked. "In short, your charming self? Isn't there a possibility that once the bone of contention is out of the way—forgive the unflattering simile—they might come together again?"

Medwin looked at him and shook her head.

"I'm afraid it's too late," she said. "I suppose I ought to have gone long ago, but it all came to a head so suddenly. And how could I believe that I was really the cause of the trouble? It seemed to me—and still seems—fantastic."

"Fantastic?" he repeated. "Fantastic? I wonder. You have charmed them both. Charmed them utterly. I do not say this to flatter. And I think I can understand. And so, I think, could you, if you tried to put yourself in their place. I don't know how well they realize it, but they are two exceedingly lonely women; both are hungry for affection. As indeed"—and he smiled—"few of us are not. Well, we must accept that fact and go on from there."

"I wish," she told him, "that I could have talked to you before. I often wanted to. Now it seems to me too late. They have begged me," she said, looking at him with candid eyes, "to stay to the end. There will be mountains of work to do. So I've said I would."

For a moment he was silent. Then he said:

"You think then that nothing could be gained by your immediate departure, and," he added, looking about him at the charming room, "much would be lost?"

She felt the indignant colour rush to her cheeks.

"You're not suggesting, I hope——" she began, but he quickly interrupted her, holding up his hands.

"My dear, dear Mrs. Blair, forgive me if I expressed myself badly. I know you too well for that, and I have the highest opinion of your integrity. I was thinking for one moment, and most regretfully, of your happiness and comfort. Who could wish to leave all this—and for such improbable reasons? You were too modest to persuade yourself easily that you were the cause of the trouble. That is natural. On the other hand, if you were no longer here I can't help thinking that the story of my two friends might have a happier ending."

"But Miss Lyddon is determined to end it in this way," she said, and a little of her liking for him had now, she realized, been dissipated. "Mrs. Gresham hates and dreads the thought of it, and it it weren't that Miss Lyddon's mind is made up, I think it could be patched up tomorrow."

He ruminated, pulling at his chin.

"Knowing Miss Lyddon as I do, I'm surprised that she didn't leave at once and go to a hotel if she intended the break to be final. That would be in keeping with her character, as she dislikes half-measures. The fact that she is still there makes me wonder."

"It would have caused more talk," Medwin suggested. "As it is they can simply say that the expenses of that great house have been too heavy."

He shook his head.

"I'm afraid the truth is that neither will risk leaving you to the other. So you see," he said with a rueful smile, "you are at the same time keeping them together and keeping them apart. You will take my meaning." He paused and sank the flesh of his lower chin into his collar. Then he looked up again. "I would like to tell them you have decided to go, and name a day and keep to it. I can't tell you how much I, personally, shall regret it. I have liked to think of you in this place. Poor Miss Jones seemed, somehow, not quite right here. And you have been most kind and indulgent. We have had some delightful evenings together, though not as many of late as I should have liked." He flashed her a mischievous smile. "You seemed perpetually engaged. But first of all I must think of the happiness and welfare of my client. You must be offered up, dear Mrs. Blair, like a sacrificial lamb. Do you agree?"

"I am quite ready to go," she said, and her voice was without emphasis or expression.

"What an excellent thing it would be," he said, with a return of his customary playfulness, "if you could say you were leaving to be married. Then neither could blame the other for your going."

She looked at him quickly and then away.

"Unfortunately I can't promise that. I wish I could."

He sighed and brought both plump, cushioned hands down upon his knees.

"There are moments when I wish I were twenty years younger and a very great deal handsomer," he said, and got lightly to his feet.

"I don't like handsome men," she said, forcing a gayer note as she too stood up, "and time seems to ignore your existence. The truth is," she added, on an impulse that surprised herself, "I'm in love, but he's not mine for the taking, and perhaps will never be."

"My dear child," he said, and the round face became instantly grave, "my dear child. I understand. How sad! I am infinitely sorry."

"Oh," she said, "it's what might have been expected. Things come to me like that. Rather than not have had it, I welcome it as it is. But please," she told him, "what I have said is only for your ears."

"That is understood. I wish it sounded more happily in them."

"I'll do what you say," she told him. "I'll take back my promise to stay with them till the end and say that I'm leaving at once. But don't blame me if it does no good at all. I suspect that it won't."

"I think," he said, "we must at least try it."

She watched him go down the stairs and heard his light foot-steps along the hall to the front door. Toe-steps, rather, she thought, buoyant and imponderable. And now he would go floating down the mews and into a taxi, and for all she knew she might have seen him for the last time.

So everything was coming to an end, and so quickly. She put her hands to her face and stood for a moment motionless. She had the sensation of being nowhere, now that Mr. Fullerton had so quickly and cleanly cut the remaining bit of ground from under her feet. She felt that in his playful and unserious way he had virtually accused her of acting less honourably than she should have done. Had she been more forthright, he had seemed to suggest, had she acted with less thought for her own convenience, all this might not have happened. She dropped her hands and looked about her, and thought that the little place which had become so dear to her, cried out to her not to leave it. It had enclosed so much happiness, and now she must turn her back on it as if it had not been, since Robert came, the very birthplace of love.

And what am I to do now, she asked herself? What am I to do now?

The telephone rang and she went to it knowing that it would be Robert and comforted by the thought. He said that if the coast was clear he would be with her in five minutes.

She spent an hour the next morning in Mrs. Gresham's bedroom. Dr. Radnytz had ordered his patient to leave all work until she was better able to cope with it, but she must have guessed that it was piling up alarmingly for she sent for Medwin and they dealt with the most pressing matters. Her nerves, it was all too evident, were in a wretched state. Her eyes would suddenly redden, it was difficult for her to concentrate, and she seemed continually on the edge of some emotional outburst. But for her promise to Mr. Fullerton, Medwin would have postponed what she had to say, but by this time she hardly knew what her own motives were, and when she thought, no, I cannot tell her, she seemed to hear Mr. Fullerton's suave voice saying, "Who would wish to leave all this?" So when Mrs. Gresham said she had done enough she went close to the bed and took one of her hands. She had guessed, she told her gently, that she was the cause of much of the trouble and that therefore the sooner she went the better. She had intended asking for leave from Thursday to Monday, but now she thought it would be the wiser course to leave on Thursday and not come back at all. Without her, the quarrel might heal itself.

Mrs. Gresham gripped her hand tightly.

"Then she's told you, has she? She's told you what happened, and why she's turned against me?"

Medwin shook her head.

"I can't help knowing that I'm concerned in it, and that's all I need to know. I'll find a temporary secretary for you, someone who can at least help you through the next few weeks. I'm sure, dear Mrs. Gresham, that it's the right thing to do."

Mrs. Gresham began to cry. No, she wouldn't hear of it, she couldn't bear it. She needed Medwin now as she had never needed her before. There were the papers of over twenty years to be cleared up, to say nothing of the work that was daily accumulating.

"If you go," Mrs. Gresham said, "I won't even try to get well. I can't face the atmosphere of this house alone. I can't face the break alone. No, oh no! You mustn't go. I ask you, I beg of you to stay with me!"

She pressed her handkerchief to her eyes with both hands, and bending forward, cried into it hopelessly and disconsolately. Her sobs became so uncontrolled that Medwin was afraid they could be heard beyond the room. She saw that she was doing more harm than good and she had known from the beginning that it would not work.

"Don't," she begged, "oh, please don't cry! If it really matters to you, if it helps you, I'll stay. It was only that I seem to have caused so much trouble by being here, I thought I had better go. Please don't cry, Mrs. Gresham. It makes me feel more and more that I'm to blame."

"I'm so ashamed," Mrs. Gresham said, "but I can't help it. Everything is slipping away from me. I feel so utterly lost. I've devoted so much of my life to her, and now she says she never wants to see me again. I've had so little in my life—you don't know how little. My husband was never an affectionate man, and my son married so young and left me and went away—it seems that I have no place in the world at all. One can't turn to one's friends—they're too busy and have their own lives to live—and she was all I had. Then when you came I saw she didn't want you to like me, that she wanted you for herself, and I felt I couldn't bear it. I didn't want to be shut out again, and she wanted to shut me out. She was determined to shut me out. Every day she seemed to find new ways of hurting me. You don't know what I've had to bear—and in my own house—though of course she pays her share—" She blew her nose. "I don't know why it is but nowadays she brings out the very worst in me. I'm not really a stupid woman, but she makes me feel I am because she's so much cleverer and knows it. She makes me feel stupid and common and a bore. She wants you to think of me like that. And you will, you do! Oh, Medwin, all my confidence in myself is going. And if you leave me, just when things are at their worst, I don't know how I can bear it!"

"Well," Medwin said quietly, "I shan't leave you then. I'll stay. And my opinion of you isn't going to be influenced by Miss Lyddon or anyone else. I'll stay because I'm fond of you—too fond of you to leave you. I'll stay till you've got so used to the idea of doing without her that perhaps you'll even begin to like it." And she smiled down at her. "I'll help you in every way I can, and I'll stay until the end."

Mrs. Gresham wiped her eyes and gave a great, final sob. Then she tried to smile, and Medwin was reminded of the white smile of the sun looking out briefly from behind dark, piled-up clouds full of hail.

"Bless you!" Mrs. Gresham said. "Bless you and thank you!" She caught one of Medwin's hands and quickly pressed it and let it go. "You don't know what it means to me just to feel you're near. If I've said things I ought not to have said, please forget them. If I've been disloyal to her, I mean. I try not to be. She's nearer to me than anyone now, nearer than a sister. Though I never had a sister. That's why it hurts me so terribly that she's turned against me. Sometimes I wish I'd never known her; that we'd never met."

Medwin presently left her after making her promise that she would try to sleep. She then went down to Mrs. Gresham's sitting-room where she worked till one. She lunched at her flat and was ashamed of the pleasure it gave her to handle the very pots and dishes and feel that they were hers again; hers for as long as she and Robert might need them. She went back to the house at half-past two wondering what the afternoon with Miss Lyddon would be like. She could not predict what mood she might find her in, but she had planned what she herself was going to say and how she would say it and that gave her confidence.

She found Miss Lyddon, who had lunched out with Mr. Fullerton, waiting for her, and they got to work at once, with few words, and were brisk and matter-of-fact and far apart. When Wilson brought in the tea and Miss Lyddon's chocolate, Medwin said:

"Miss Lyddon, I very much want and need a few days' holiday, say from Thursday to Monday. Would that be at all possible?"

"Of course," Miss Lyddon said. "Why not?"

"Thank you," said Medwin, and then went on, before Miss Lyddon could speak again, "and now I want your advice, please. I feel I ought not to come back. I feel that if I weren't here there might be at least a chance that you and Mrs. Gresham might settle your differences."

"Rubbish!" interrupted Miss Lyddon. "If ever we needed you we need you now. Of course you can't go. Has *she* put this idea into your head?"

Medwin gave her a reproachful look. "I told her I felt I ought to go, and she was so distressed at the idea that I wished I hadn't spoken of it. But isn't it what I *ought* to do? Please tell me. I could go on Thursday and go for good—and perhaps it would be for everyone's good."

Miss Lyddon began to pace up and down the room. She could never argue and sit still.

"Has Archie put you up to it, then? It would be like him. Why can't he mind his own business? He'll continue to be my solicitor whether I'm here or not. I won't have him interfering." She came to a halt in front of Medwin, and giving her one of her penetrating looks, said "All right, I won't plague you to tell me, but I know he's at the bottom of this. Well, I ask you not to go. If you have any affection or gratitude for either of us, and I like to think you have, in spite of everything, please stay. Archie's a fool. Of course you must stay."

Medwin looked into the fierce, brilliant grey eyes and said, with a sigh, "I don't know what to do. You're so fiendishly clever and it's hard to say not to you."

Miss Lyddon gave a short laugh, like a bark.

"You've had practice enough, heaven knows! You see, Medwin," she said, with a sudden change of manner, "if all this time you hadn't been swinging like a wretched pendulum between myself and her, you and I could have been friends. In time you would have understood and trusted me. But her being here has spoilt everything. It's made you two-faced, in spite of your natural honesty. She's at one pole, I'm at the other, and you've tried to face both ways. An impossible attitude. You've been like the proverbial donkey between the two bundles of hay."

"I've tried to be loyal to both of you, if that's what you mean," Medwin said. "And I've never known anyone who mixed their metaphors as you do."

Miss Lyddon gave her a quick smile and resumed her pacing.

"As long as I'm in this house," she said, "I insist on your being here too. If you leave, I'll go straight to a hotel, and leave Edith to crawl out from under as best she may. I'll have no mercy on her."

"Mercy?" said Medwin. "I've seen few signs of that."

Miss Lyddon ignored this. "Just wait," she said, "till I tell Archie what I think of him. Well, what do you say? Stay, or I go to a hotel, tomorrow. I have a separate inventory of my furniture and pictures and so on, and Archie can see to it all. It would serve him right."

Medwin got up and faced her.

"Very well," she said, "if it's come to ultimatums, I have one for you. Make it up with Mrs. Gresham, at least temporarily, or I go on Thursday for good."

"I was expecting that," Miss Lyddon said. "How can I 'make it up' with Edith, as you call it? I've done with her. She's a liar and a fool. She's bored me long enough."

"You can make it up perfectly well," Medwin said, seeing that this was a line she must pursue. "She's just what she's always been, and you've been friends for over fifty years. She's in a pitiable state. I don't know how you can be so cruel. And at least put off the final break for six months. If you do, I'll stay, but please, there must be no more quarrels."

"Talk to Edith about that, not to me," Miss Lyddon said, but she was not angry. "Well, if I go to her and say, 'Let's stop being a couple of fools, let's call a truce,' will you promise to stay?"

"Yes," Medwin said. "But I want to go away on Thursday until Monday. I need a holiday." And her voice sounded such a note of weariness that Miss Lyddon darted a quick look at her.

"I've no objection if she has none," she said. "I won't even ask what it's for. I hope it's to be with Sarah, but somehow I doubt it."

"I want to get away from everything for a while," Medwin said, and passed a hand across her forehead.

"Heavens, you looked like Catherine then!" Miss Lyddon exclaimed. "I suppose that faint, elusive resemblance to her accounts for half your charm for me. You help me to live in the only place I want to live—the past."

Medwin turned away without comment. She did not want to feel herself touched or beguiled or warmed by anything Miss Lyddon might say. She wanted winter between them, and no thaw—or no thaw yet.

"Thank you," she said, "for letting me go. I'll come back on Monday, and then I'll stay, and I hope you'll see Mrs. Gresham as soon as possible because I'm really worried about her."

"You needn't be," Miss Lyddon said. "You haven't seen her putting on this act as often as I have. However, I'll do it, I'll humble myself, though I'm not looking forward to it. I know what it will cost me to keep you here, and I'm prepared to pay the price, but let me tell you I wouldn't do it for anyone but you. As for Archie I can't wait to deal with him. He's like a cat who's afraid he's going to lose his favourite place by the hearth. And I won't even flatter him by calling him a tom-cat."

Medwin paid this bit of sarcasm the tribute of a faint smile.

"And is there any hope that the truce will be permanent?" she asked.

"It's a contradiction in terms," Miss Lyddon said. "No, the truce will be a truce. I shall end it when I see fit, but meanwhile, hostilities will cease. Will that suit you?"

"If that's the best you can offer," Medwin said. She sat down at the writing-table and in a moment Miss Lyddon joined her. The fact that she had not taken to her bed like Mrs. Gresham was no proof, Medwin thought, that the happenings of the past few weeks had not told on her. Facing the light she looked years older.

CHAPTER 16

Once they were on their way together, the tension relaxed. Now they could be themselves and there was none of that self-consciousness that had made their walk in the park that evening something to take refuge from. They were like bees storing up too little honey for a winter that might be endless. For a while they were going to cut themselves off from past and future, and so intensify and magnify the present that it would be timeless, and would provide for them a private world to which they could perpetually return. To live now, and to live in this now for ever was their aim. And when she told herself, in a doubting moment, that time itself would dim and dwarf it, reversing the telescope through which they looked, so that one day they would ask themselves, "Was it from Lymington we went? And did we go to Yarmouth or to Ryde?" She put the thought from her as absurd.

It was magical to be together and lovelier than they had known it could be. Lovely and magical to see their suitcases carried by the same porter, to begin their little joint life by discovering what the other would choose from the bookstall to read—things they made no pretence of reading. Their mutual delight in finding out how it all would be, smiled upon their lips. When he needed change for the porter it gave her a sharp, foolish, housewifely pleasure to find it in her purse and give it to him. In the train they were as ready for delight as children setting off on long-anticipated holidays. She made him sit by the window and sat next to him, hemming him in from strangers, and by turning half-way in her seat made a little corner where they could talk and know that their voices were lost in the noise of the train. Whenever he turned his face to glance out of the window her insatiable eyes flew to his profile and fastened and fed on it in secret. She could not have enough of him. Whether time cut them off next week or in fifty years, she knew it would be too soon. The triumph, the accomplishment of this present cancelled past and future pain, so loud was it in their ears. They could hear nothing else but each other's unspoken pronouncements that this was the best, the highest; their mutual Everest, worth the ascent, worth even the cruel descent, if that were to be.

No one who had chosen to watch them could have thought them anything but in love, eager as each was to hear every word spoken by the other; two people who were alight with awareness, who had shed all grosser, duller matters, stripped themselves of everything that might have cumbered them, so that at a touch or glance they kindled. They seemed and were aloof and dedicated, and as lonely, with a precious, cherished loneliness, as if they travelled supersonically, with some planet as their destination. So different was their being together now, now that nothing was to be withheld, that lovely though their hours in the flat had been, they knew that they had been taut with inhibition, and that Miss Lyddon had never been wholly absent. They had had to take this journey to escape her. Now they had crossed a border into a free territory, and her jurisdiction, however lightly they had tried to regard it in the past, was at an end.

They changed presently into a smaller, humbler train which took them to Lymington, where soon the ferry sidled in and they and a crowd of others went on board. They made their way to the front and stood leaning shoulder to shoulder against the rail as they nosed down the narrow estuary and out into the Solent. It was a warm and cloudy day and the greys and greens of calm water and calm sky, marsh and thick, clumped, motionless trees were soothing to their eyes. Seagulls cried and dipped into the water, or, with beating wings, snatched up morsels from the mud along the banks, and when they were out in the open water a warm and gentle breeze blew in their faces. The Isle of Wight lay before them with the invitation and charm and appeal of all islands, and Medwin said, smiling:

"This is the nearest I've ever come to a trip abroad. I'm glad you thought of it. It's like going to another country."

He looked at her and said, "One day——" but his lips closed on that. They were as superstitious sometimes as jungle folk, feeling that something lay in wait for the words they dropped, something that might use them to tease and torture them with later.

Now, while people pressed around them and they had no privacy, and a baby cried peevishly, and the world intruded, she took out of her bag a letter received that morning from Louise, and opened it. If she stood in a thicket that grew ever higher above her head, Louise and her father were like little bushmen shooting poisoned arrows through it; and seeing her face change its expression, he asked, "What now?" and she gave him the letter to read. It was written on cheap lined paper and Louise had not troubled to write the address, only the date.

"My dear Medwin:

"I believe I hinted before I left the lodge that I did not anticipate a pleasant homecoming and now that it is all over I will tell you why. Your father had written to our head Librarian making certain accusations against me. You will doubtless guess what they were. Among other things he said I was a public danger and a corrupter of the young. He also mentioned the names of the books he had found in my suitcase. When I returned, therefore, I had to face a group of officials who interrogated me for some time, though I am glad to say, in a quite kindly way. I think I succeeded in clearing myself of most of the charges made against me, though I did not deny my interest in certain political theories. They have warned me however, that should there be any further complaints against me they would be obliged to remove me. In other words, I would lose my job. As you know I have no resources beyond the annuity which brings me in fifty pounds a year and my pension, which I hope to retire on. Should I lose this I would not be able to live. In fact I might easily become a charge upon you for the rest of my life. So you see the harm your father might have done. I will leave it to you to decide what steps you ought to take to prevent any further persecution on his part.

"I found Mr. Beedle very well and the house quite clean and tidy, but he is glad to have me home again. I think he found the shopping rather tedious. There is no more news. I hope your mother continues to make progress.

"Affectionately,

"Louise."

It was tragic and it was shocking, and it had also a faintly humorous side which did not miss them. It was no one's fault unless it were Louise's, who had chosen such a slippery path to walk upon, knowing that she was likely to be elbowed off, and yet expecting to be safeguarded and protected. Mr. Fosdick had perhaps persuaded himself that he ought to do what he did, or he had done it in anger and indignation; but whatever it was, he had no business to do it, and it was on a par with his visit to Mrs. Gresham.

"Take a strong line with him," Robert advised, "and show him the letter. My poor darling, when will you be free of these troubles? You are so upright yourself that I think fate delights in hurling missiles at you. It's time it ended, but when will it end?" And he bent his head and touched her hand with his lips, sure that no one could see, they stood so close together, and not much caring if anyone saw.

They had chosen a hotel not far from the pretty little town of Yarmouth, and drove there in a taxi. It lay in pleasant grounds close to the water and had once been a large country house, much added on to. The long corridors were at different levels, and the rooms were high-ceilinged and spacious. Theirs had a wide view of the Solent, and on the far side of it they could see the mainland softly screened in haze. When their suitcases had been brought in and the door closed, they clung to each other in wordless ecstacy and triumph. Never a thing so longed for had worn such a shining face. Their eyes were dazzled. They could not believe they had been so fortunate as to trap this joy, this golden span of four days that, from where they stood, seemed both stationary and limitless. It was all theirs, and they could play with the minutes as if they were separate gems, and run them through their fingers which before had played only with coloured glass.

"No parting," she said, when he released her. "Four days and nights and every moment of them together. I shan't hear your footsteps go down the stairs."

He looked at her with an entreating look.

"Don't speak," he said, "as if you felt this was all there would ever be. You seem to run to adversity with open arms. Give fate at least a chance to be on our side."

"Perhaps I embrace adversity," she said, "because I feel I can be sure of it. One must be sure of something."

He put his arm about her and drew her over to the window.

The water was satin smooth, and the sun looked palely out through light cloud on which his nimbus was printed, advertising rain. Robert took this in with a sailor's eye. Rain or fine, it made no difference to him. Their world would be happily bounded by four walls.

"As far as I'm concerned," he said, choosing to speak boldly, whatever might be listening, "these four days are the beginning of our life together. I can't think of them in any other way. I love you too much."

"I love you too much," she said, "to dare to think of them as anything but four days torn from a calendar. Where we now are seems to me a brightly lighted little stage, with everything around in darkness. I shan't take my eyes from it for an instant. When the curtain's rung down, don't let me be afraid. That's all I ask."

He held her tightly, and leaned his head against hers.

"With you," he said, "I could love God and be happy, and perhaps even good. Everything seems possible, when we're together."

"That's happiness, I suppose," she said. "A stretching and expanding of the spirit. One's soul has growing pains, but desirable ones. A delicious, immortal ache."

"And you've never felt it before?" he asked, smiling, but half jealous to hear that she had not.

"Never so much as now, my dearest."

They stood looking out, tasting their aloneness and exulting in it.

"I don't want much," he said, "in the way of material things. I've never wanted to be rich, though I don't want poverty either. But I'm a glutton for some other things—peace of mind, enlightenment, what I suppose you might call grace with a capital G. Some people find it in solitude, but I'll find it with you or never at all."

"But you must look for it," she said tenderly, "with or without me. What are we here for?"

"Are you so sure of that?' he asked.

"That we're here to find Grace? Yes."

"Then don't tell me you think we can only find it through pain and loss."

"Perhaps," she said, "if we're capable of getting it through happiness, we'll get it that way, but few are."

"Then first," he said, "let's try it out with happiness." He pushed her gently from him and held her at arms' length, looking into her face, as if, she thought, he were on a ship that might sink under him, and he searched her eyes for land. "Before coming here," he told her, "I wrote a letter, telling her about you. No, don't speak for a moment, I didn't post it. It didn't seem fair to you to post it without telling you. I couldn't do that. It's in my pocket now. I ask you, my dearest, I beg you to come out with me and let me post it now."

She looked back at him steadily.

"That's impossible, Robert. I couldn't do it. I can't unsay what I've said, I can't feel now what I didn't feel before. I've felt everything I could feel, and said everything I could say. Now I can only say: no! And I mean it."

The healthy colour had left his face. His eyes implored hers; his whole being and all his love was in them.

"I beg you to let me send it."

"I'd never forgive myself," she said, "if I did." And then, with a break in her voice she cried, "Oh, my darling, we must be strong about this. We agreed. Must one of us go back alone?"

He still searched her face for some sign of wavering, but found none. Then he took the letter out of his pocket.

"If it has to be destroyed, you'd better do it. I can't."

She took it from him and quickly tore it in half, and in her quickness he thought he saw a sign of fear, as if the moment had almost been too much for her. Then she tore it again and again, and threw the pieces in the waste paper basket. (Later she disposed of them, unable to endure their mute reminder.) He took her in his arms again and she could feel how his heart beat She pitied him and herself, but there was a path she could not take. If she had taken it she would have said to herself, "That was my father in me. Now I shall never know how to trust myself again." And how she could explain this, even to him; that she feared to press the advantage, to use the weapon placed in her hand, to reach out too far and too blindly for what she wanted, to indulge and excuse in herself the self-same weaknesses she deplored in another? No, she could not tell him, or not yet; she could tell no one how she was made cautious and watchful by something she was not even sure she had any cause to fear. A girl she had once known had lost her mother through tuberculosis, and could never cough without looking into her handkerchief. We were the children of our parents, and some alertness, she often thought, if we knew the truth, might be expected of us. To take the course she would have liked to take was not to be permitted. He, wondering, half in despair, half in admiration, could not know where she got her strength; she could not tell him why she feared her weakness.

At last, reconciled, if they could ever have been said to be apart, they kissed each other, gently and wildly and gently again, and they thought it would be good to settle in, to make themselves at home for this stay that was to stretch so far and include so much. She asked if she might unpack for him, but he would not hear of it. She'd forgotten, he said, that he'd been a sailor. He was the tidiest man alive. So they apportioned space, so much for him, so much for her, his clothes to hang here, hers there, and crossed and recrossed each other's paths till it was done. She thought she had never liked anything better than to see her toilet things and his within inches of each other. It broke down such flimsy, gauzy barriers as remained, and they took up domesticity like a banner. Here, privately, deliciously, they were; away, away together, out of any sight or mind but their own, and their own now, for most purposes, identical. The warmth of his coat to her cheek, the softness of her hair to his, the hands that slipped under his arms to meet behind his back, seeming to say they would never let him go; the warm, living eager body that at every turn was hers to delight in, these things were more real to them than any events they had ever known before. And tempted to remain in and too easily give themselves up to loving, they went out and walked hand in hand through a small beech wood down to the water. Their hands found they could not bear to be long apart, loneliness drove them together, and the firm warmth of his she knew she needed for every day of her life.

They hardly thought where they were. It might have been France, or they might have been by some Swiss lake; it did not matter, and it would have been the same wherever they were. It was a meeting-place of longitude and latitude, and both of these connived to make their position; from them, lines were drawn to the poles and the North Star and Arcturus, and lines returned from these to them, unerringly. They noticed no one, it seemed that no one noticed them, but they were too blind to see. They did not live aloud when they were where others were, but ghost-like were hardly there, and then gone. Dinner in the dining-rooms was scarcely a fact. It was only a fact that they had regained their room again, and the drawbridges were up. No one could disturb or reach them; they were aloof upon a star, and their eyelids were heavy with love. To have waited for this was heaven; to have waited a moment longer would have been hell.

They left the hotel after an early lunch on Monday with many a backward look. The first two days seemed beautifully spun out, amazingly distendable and spacious, with room for everything and even some to spare. Then, when their stay was half over, the tempo abruptly and wickedly changed without warning, as a storm blows up on a calm day and everything is quickened, and hurry is in every ragged, flying cloud. Then there was suddenly not time at all, no space left in which they could pack anything they wanted to do or say. Their time of departure, that moment they had deliberately not looked at, was upon them, and it wore an inexorable face, and they could cheat it a little only by finely drawing out the night; by not sleeping or caring to sleep before the dawn came, and then slipping, unwilling, into deep unconsciousness out of an extremity of fatigue. The cruel way they had been cheated of half their time, amazed them. It was as if a hurricane blew them towards the closing minutes, hurled them on to boat and train, unready and holding to each receding thing, like children pulled to bed. The hours were telescoped into minutes, the minutes into dying seconds. Even their train journey, their last hope and stand, betrayed and failed them. It seemed as if one end of the train were on the shores of the Solent, the other in Waterloo Station, and it but wrinkled its skin and they were there.

And now, fearfully, she thought, Oh, where has it all gone? It's as if we had spilled these days out upon the thirsty sand. Was it a dream? No, because they were so different, so magically changed. He seemed different to her, she to him. They were so much, much more what they had been. Now he was her circumference, bounding her on all sides, inclusive and total. She had come to a full stop in him. He was her other dimension. That man, close beside her in the hurrying taxi, still brown of face, blue of living eye, taut, swift to grasp her hand and fold it and hold it, assured, neat, masculine, was terribly hers; there was no other world for her but him. She lightly kissed his cheekbone, and when he said, "I'll tell him to drive to my house and I'll collect my letters," simply kissed him again and said, "Yes," only not liking the moment when he should get out of the taxi and leave her for that brief time. He had said he would report at his office on Tuesday morning, and until that time they were to be together in the flat. She watched him go up the steps and unlock the front door and from her seat in the taxi, mentally followed him in. His letters must have been on the hall table, for he was quickly out again, pushing them into his pocket as he came. He caught her smiling eye, which seemed to draw him back into the taxi as if he were on the end of a hook. And there he took her hand again and they drove along Buckingham Gate and past the Palace and down the Mall, and then up into Pall Mall and St. James's Street and so to Berkeley Street, and now they were nearly home. He released her hand to fish the letters out of his pocket again and look at them, and then she felt him stiffen.

"That's a queer thing," he said, and she answered:

"What is?"

"It's from her mother. Why is she writing to me now?"

"But she sometimes does, doesn't she?"

"She hasn't since the separation. Somehow I don't want to open it. It's got an ominous look. Wouldn't you say so? Look. Shall I open it now?"

She said, "Louise's letter had that look too. They can slay us, if they choose. Well, I suppose you'd better open it."

"I'd keep wondering," he said, "if I didn't. It may be nothing at all." And he tore it open brusquely, a finger under the flap, and took it out of its crisp envelope. It seemed to be a letter of some length, and as the taxi turned sharply into Charles Street it threw them close together and she saw, "My dear son." He kept one of her hands now as he read it, and she felt his grasp tighten. Then he laid the letter on his knee and turned away his head.

"Tell me, darling," she said, slipping her arm through his. "Tell me."

"A thing has happened," he said, slowly, "that I never thought of. Never for one moment anticipated. He's left her. He's cleared out. He's marrying some girl in Washington."

His grip on her hand tightened again till she could have cried out in pain. The taxi was passing the house now, and then it turned down into the side street and turned left again into the mews. There, everything was as usual. The narrow cobbled street was full of vans and cars, and the taxi had to pull up before reaching Medwin's green-painted door because the doors of the garage were wide open, and Miss Lyddon's car was just being backed in. After using it, it was her habit to leave it in front of the house for Stevens to put away, and it was unfortunate that it was being put away at this moment, for she did not want Stevens to see her entering the flat accompanied by a man with a suitcase, or, worse, with two suitcases, her own and his.

The awkward moment served to set aside, briefly, the news he had told her.

"Quick, darling," she said, "pay the driver and let's get into the flat if we can before Stevens sees us."

She picked up her own suitcase and got out, and hurried to put her key into the door and open it, stooping as she did so to pick up the bottle of milk which had been left for her that morning. She waited just inside the door until Robert joined her, then shut it and bolted it, as if the whole world pressed against it.

"Do you think Stevens saw you?" she asked.

His face, as her eyes flew to it, looked different. He looked as if he had just had some vivid and surprising experience that he had not yet had time to take in, or not completely. It seemed to be still in his eyes, upon his forehead, and he stood for a moment in silence in the hall.

"It wasn't Stevens," he said, and looked at her.

She knew at once. She could almost see upon the surface of his eyeballs the imprint of what he had just seen.

"You mean it was Miss Lyddon?"

He nodded. "I saw her and turned my head away. But even if she didn't know who I was, she saw me follow you in. She was all in black, with some white here——" and he touched his breast. "Like a lean Inquisitor," he said, "ready with rack and thumbscrew."

She looked at him in wide-eyed pain.

"Then ought you to go, do you think?" she asked.

"Go? With all we have to talk about? Good God, no! You say she never comes here."

"Never, so far," Medwin said, and thought for an instant, and then went on, "and if she did come, she'd come by way of the garden, and you could go out the other way into the mews, though I pray it doesn't happen."

"Pray your hardest then," he said. "Should we get holy water and sprinkle it at the door? Would that keep her away?"

She smiled wanly.

"Anyway," she said, "let's go up."

He took both suitcases and followed her up the stairs.

"What an astounding face," he said. "A face for Dürer to draw. A medieval face. I never saw her so close before. And you live near it. You see it every day. What courage you have!"

He set the suitcases down beside the door into the bedroom. Medwin sank down on the sofa and pulling off her hat, let her head drop back. She did not want to talk about the letter yet. It was too new and too enormous for her to grasp. The bare facts, all she had yet been given, stopped her thinking. It was easier to speak of Miss Lyddon's face as he had just seen it.

"Believe it if you can," she said, "I've grown fond of it."

"I could have done without that vision of it," he told her. "Somehow it turned a knife on me. But don't let's talk about her to avoid talking about the letter."

"It seems," she said, "that this is not our day." And she closed her eyes wearily.

"The only thing that matters," he said, "is this. Will you read it?"

She opened her eyes again and sat upright.

"Do you want me to read it? Must I read it?"

"I think you must."

She took it with a prayer. It might be that this was their final disaster. She could not touch it without an inner cry, knowing or guessing it to be a cry itself, equally as loud as hers, or his, or louder.

It was in the writing of a woman who took thought for the appearance and neatness of a letter, and who chose not to betray her inner turmoil by hurried penmanship, crossings out and re-writings. Whatever her state of mind, only the words themselves were to be allowed to reveal it, and in this she at once captured respect. She had sat down to her task only after thought, honest thought that she would bring to anything she did. At some desk, in the bedroom, perhaps in the small country house she was known to live in, just over the Sussex borders in Hampshire, she had penned this to a son-in-law she loved, to the father of a delicate, sensitive, favourite grandchild, to the husband of the daughter who must be, whatever her strange predicament, close and dear. All these things were present in Medwin's mind. Her respect for the writer, the mother of a large, now scattered family, had been won when first she heard of her. She was the moving spirit of that musical household which had been to Robert as a boy and young man, his envied and chosen world. She had been, in Robert's eyes, her daughter's dowry. He esteemed her greatly, and anything she said and felt must weigh with him, though through awkward and painful circumstances they had not for some time corresponded. And here was her message, between her hands, with its already almost audible appeal.

"My dear son:

"I am writing to you because I know that Sybil cannot. She is like a bird so caught in a net by every claw and feather that she cannot move. You know how deeply I have longed for a happy outcome to the sad and complex dilemma you have both had to resolve. I am sure you know, too, though I have never actually spoken of it to you, how little I have liked and trusted Hugo, and how unable I was to understand Sibyl's infatuation for him, for infatuation I believe it was. But I am old, and naturally I cannot see in him what she sees. I have prayed that she might cast off this hateful spell, but that she seemed pathetically unable to do. What she has gone through during these past months I hardly like to think. Like other people caught in the same net, she has talked, often enough, of suicide as the only way out, but that is simply a symptom of her malady, and I have discounted it as such. I have no doubt at all that she still loves you, and I know that she deeply loves her son, but this man had come between her and the light.

"About ten days ago he had to fly to Washington, and as I have asked that he should not come here, Sibyl went elsewhere to meet him to say good-bye. On her return she seemed more composed, more certain of her own mind than at any other time. I asked her no questions, but she told me, voluntarily, that she was now certain of his need for her; in fact, that he needed her far more than you had ever needed her, and now that she was sure of this all-important fact, she would waver no longer. I hesitate to tell you this, but I feel I must, as it explains so much. This need she always felt in him was connected with his unfortunate habit of drinking to excess. Here she had helped him enormously; so much so that she believed she had practically cured him, and I do not doubt that this was so.

"When she expressed her determination—and I could see it plainly in her face—to throw in her lot with his, completely and finally, I said:

" 'Then you must at once tell Robert.' She meant to, I know, but before she had time to do so—a friend of hers inopportunely arrived and asked to spend a night or two—a cable came from

Hugo, which said, 'Take no action whatever till my letter arrives.' This startled her a little, but she put some harmless interpretation on it and waited for the letter. It came yesterday. It could scarcely have been crueller had it contained some poison for her to take. He said in it that the long uncertainty had been too much for him, it had worn him out. He now intended putting himself out of her reach by marrying—and at once—a girl he had met in Washington during the war. He said he hoped she would return to you and forget, if she could, the whole episode.

"She does not know I am writing. She sits like a stone; everything seems to have come to a stop and I do not know what to do. She seems incapable of rousing herself, and I am fearful for her health and her reason. She will not reply to the doctor's questions nor obey his orders, and she looks at me as if I were an interloper. You must come to her, Robert, and you must bring John. I say 'must'—forgive me for it—because I think there is no other way of saving her. Will you help me, my son?

"Always yours devotedly,

"Cecilia Wharton."

He had got up now and was walking about the room. He stopped in front of the mantel and she saw him glance at himself in the mirror as if he had spied a stranger. She regarded that compact and sturdy back with a kind of blankness. Indeed, he was a stranger. Who was he? What was he doing there? He had a wife who if ever a woman needed her husband, needed him now. This tremendous, imperative duty made him remote. Or she could think so, while he did not look at her. She laid the letter down and sat folded up in a stillness she could not break. What he was thinking she could not guess. An hour ago, she was certain she would have known. His elbows were on the mantel, and his head was in his hands. At last he turned and when their eyes met there seemed to her to be a silent cry from both their hearts; a cry of grief and protest and anguish. Then she saw tears in his eyes, and looked away. He forced himself to say:

"As a writer, I feel I ought to pay tribute to the ingenuity of fate. This is something I never even thought of. Never."

Outside, the light drizzle that had come on while they were on their way to London, had ceased, and now the sun came out, at first experimentally then brightly, and the sky cleared. The thought passed through her mind, If you're doing this for us, don't trouble.

Neither seemed to know what to say. Words would not come, and those she thought of, she discarded. He glanced out of the window at the scarlet salvias in the garden, then looked back at her.

"We must try to talk about it," he said, and he made his voice matter-of-fact. "We must try to see our way. You noted, of course, what Mrs. Wharton said: that Sibyl had made up her mind to go to him. I hope you will think that fact as important to us as I do."

He eyed her, but got no reply. She did not feel capable of answering. She felt that anything she said she would at once wish unsaid. She felt, too, that she had not the skill to pick her way, verbally, through this tangle.

"My darling," he said, "say something. Anything. Tell me your thoughts, even if what you say now isn't what you would say tomorrow."

"If you want me to comment on what you said just now," she answered, with an effort, "I can only say that I would no more expect you to take advantage of a distracted old woman's honesty than I would expect you to rob my purse."

"And that," he said, with a mere hint of a smile, "is exactly what I knew you would say."

She covered her eyes with her hand for a moment, then looked up.

"Robert," she said, "I love you and I trust you. You must leave me out of this entirely. I want you not to think of me, or consider me. And when I say me, I mean us. You must do whatever you have to do, and you will know best what that is. I shan't presume to advise you, or argue with you, or try to influence you. I'm utterly outside all this."

The late sun was colouring the backs of the houses, and the leaves of the small elm tree, the tips of whose branches she could just see from the window, were glistening with wet. A sparrow alighted on a slender branch and left it again, scattering rain-drops. The sun glanced obliquely in, showing up the four-day dust on the table, and she touched it with her finger.

"You trust me enough, then," he said, "to let me deal with this as I think best."

She looked back at him, and his look was steady and assured.

"I'm not beaten yet," he said. "When I am, you shall hear."

She could not answer. For purposes of talk, there now seemed a barrier between them, and her words were not high enough to leap it. Then at that moment the front doorbell rang, and their eyes quickly came together in a startled inquiry. But as quickly she relaxed.

"It's only the baker," she said. "He comes at about this time. I'll have to go down."

"Let him ring," he said.

She shook her head.

"I'd better go down. We've no bread in the house, and I want to pay him too."

She picked up her bag, and as she left the room she saw Robert take out a cigarette. The first he had felt like smoking since their return. She went down the stairs and along the hall, and opened the door.

Miss Lyddon stood there, and she brusquely pushed her way in. She was hatless, and as Robert had said, in black. It was a black silk suit Medwin knew well, and it had a white ruffle at the neck. She remembered afterwards having noted that the ruffle was edged with narrow real lace, and that above it was a diamond pin that had belonged to her mother. If she looked at these it was because she did not want to see Miss Lyddon's face. If she had been stretched on the rack, it could hardly have worn a more dreadful look.

CHAPTER 17

"I WANT TO SEE YOU," MISS LYDDON SAID, AND HER VOICE AND her face matched each other. "I want to talk to you. Let me in."

Medwin stood there blocking the way with her body, unable, in the chaos of her mind, to think of any other way of averting or delaying disaster. She knew that Robert would never even consider hiding himself; that if fifty Miss Lyddons were on their way up the stairs he would remain precisely where he was. But she felt bound to protect him and herself if she could, and at last she stammered out:

"I'm sorry, Miss Lyddon, but I'm not alone."

Miss Lyddon struck her hand sharply away from the door

she was holding to, and turned and shut it herself, and the sound was final.

"The classic phrase," she said, amusement horridly present, as though the victim of the rack had tried to respond to the torturer's jest. " 'I am not alone.' Well, I expect he won't bite me, whoever he is. I must see you at once, upstairs. This is the first time I have ever paid you a visit, and I find you inhospitable. I see I'll have to invite myself up." And she pushed past Medwin in the narrow hall and started up the stairs.

Events were now in Miss Lyddon's hands. She could not be held back, and what was to come would come. Medwin followed her, but was no longer frightened. She had lost too much to care if she lost what remained. There was nothing now she need cling to; Miss Lyddon, in her hurricane course, was welcome to make a clean sweep of every tree left standing until the landscape was bare. And as she went into the sitting-room ahead of her, Medwin heard her say in clear, harsh, triumphant tones:

"I thought so. I knew I couldn't be mistaken."

As she followed her into the room, Medwin's eyes went at once to Robert's face. He looked perfectly composed, even, she thought, a little amused. As Miss Lyddon spoke he politely stubbed out his cigarette on an ashtray. Then he raised his head and looked at her as if she were any caller to whom he felt it his duty to be polite.

"Yes, I'm afraid we resemble each other too much," he said. "You could have no doubt who I am, nor I who you are. But then, of course, I've sometimes seen you from the window when Gwen Jones was here."

"What are you, then?" she demanded violently. "A hanger-on? A picker-up of crumbs? A sponger upon the women I employ? It doesn't surprise me. I would have expected it of your father's son. Have you been to the kitchen door, too, and the scullery?"

She was looking at him with a quite dreadful concentration. It was more than a stare, it was a devouring with the eyes. She seemed to see more than the man who stood there so composedly, smiling a little now, at what she had just said. She seemed to be looking through him, using him as a glass through which to see back into the past. Her face was a ghastly colour, and the rouge seemed to float upon her cheekbones, as if it had lost contact with the skin below.

"I think," he said, "it would be better if we talked rationally, like human beings, not characters in a stage melodrama. Don't you agree?"

She had looked her fill at him for the moment. She turned to Medwin without answering him.

"And you," she said, in a voice like a whip-lash, "could have thought of nothing else quite as infamous as this. Infamous, base and vile." And she gave every word its full value and meaning. "You deliberately took for your lover the one man I would never have allowed inside my door, the son of the man I most loathe and despise. And you have done this while you were in my employ, knowing what you knew, and so betraying my trust and my confidence. You and this person have dared to make this place into what I believe is called a love-nest. You, so 'nice,' in your conduct, so scrupulous! I tell you you are utterly vile. Pack and leave this place tonight."

"Come, come," Robert said calmly, "all this is quite absurd." He moved unhurriedly to Medwin's side and put an arm about her shoulders, while Medwin stood as still as if some shaft had numbed her. "I met Medwin by chance. I expected to find Gwen Jones still here. Having met her, you can hardly blame me for loving her. You love her too."

"I?" cried Miss Lyddon, shaking. "I, love her? I never want to see or hear of her again. This emotion I can't help feeling is fury that I have been so deceived in her. Fury, and shame. I feel degraded to have had her in my house. Yes," she cried, turning back to Medwin, "you've lied and cheated and deceived me." She brushed past them, and strode towards the two suitcases and pointed down at them. "Don't imagine I care about that! The he and she of it does not concern me. You have a right to your private life and your private loves. Nature will have its way, I suppose. But every minute that you have been with *him* you have vilely betrayed me. Oh!" she cried, and beat her hands together, "It's unbearable, unbearable!"

Medwin looked at her with fear. Not for herself, but for her, and her eyes were filled with pity and an anxious concern. She thought she had never seen anyone so like a dreadful travesty of death. She might have been playing the part of Death itself in some medieval play. She tried to move away from Robert's arm, but he held her back.

"The things you've been saying," he answered quietly, "are so wildly untrue that I won't even trouble to refute them.

Your quarrel with my father was your private affair. This was our private affair."

"Ha!" cried Miss Lyddon, wildly, "how well you put it! Certainly private, and certainly an affair. Well, continue it somewhere else. Take your suitcases and go, both of you! This place is polluted by you."

And she went to the window and flung it open, and stood panting in the air, holding the curtains apart with both hands.

"Miss Lyddon," Medwin said, "Miss Lyddon, you're ill! Let me do something for you! Please, oh, please sit down! Just until you feel better."

This was all nightmare to her, but the worst part of it was Miss Lyddon's ravaged, totally uncontrolled face. Seeing it, she did not care what she said. Miss Lyddon's words scarcely touched her. She freed herself from Robert's arm and went to her. But Miss Lyddon turned on her fiercely, pushed her aside and cried out:

"Don't touch me! I hate and despise you! And I loved you! I loved you! I gave you the best I had to give, and you betrayed me!" And she leaned against the curtains and tears fell down her bitter, tortured face, falling slowly at first and then faster, and she brushed them away with her wrists and the backs of her hands, but they continued to come. She struggled with herself, biting her lips, and they watched her helplessly and in shame and pain.

"Don't you understand?" she cried, looking from one to the other. "Do you imagine there's no love worthy of the name but the sort you feel? The sort every animal feels? Don't you understand that love is love, that betrayal is betrayal? I loved this girl," she cried out, turning towards Robert. "Don't you understand? Do you think it comic that you've slain me between you? Do you think it a joke that I suffer as I do? Little by little I grew to love her, more and more. I would have given her anything, yes, anything. And I swear I didn't love her altogether selfishly, I swear it. Even if she had told me this, I believe I could have understood; I believe I could have forgiven her. It might even have moved me to kindness, for both of you. I don't know. But this stabbing in the dark—do I deserve it?" she cried. "Tell me, do I deserve it? This trickery and deception, this shameless, heartless betrayal! And you are the last," she said, looking at Medwin with her wild grey, eyes, "the last human being I shall ever love. The last I have time to love, now. It's over. It's the end. And I believed in you, I trusted you, utterly. The very sight of you has buoyed me up to bear what I have to bear."

"Miss Lyddon!" Medwin cried out. "Miss Lyddon!"

"Oh, don't pretend to me now that you have a heart! It's too late for that. I know you've looked upon me as a spoilt, absurd woman, trying to buy my way here and there with money. I know you felt contempt for what you considered my poses and pretensions, that you believed my charities a sham and despised them. But I believed you saw, through all that—and God knows I told you the truth about myself—something in me to like, even something to love. And now I come upon this cold betrayal, and it stabs me to the heart."

She dropped her hands, swayed and caught the curtains again. Medwin threw Robert a quick look and he went into the kitchen. She moved to Miss Lyddon's side and put her arm about her waist, firmly, and drew her to the sofa.

"You're ill," she said, "that's all that matters. You're ill. Tell me. Tell me what it is."

At her touch, firm and kind, Miss Lyddon relaxed. She drooped and staggered and clutched the arm of the sofa and then slowly sank into it. She's dying, thought Medwin, and her heart was ice-cold with fear. As if the thought had passed to Miss Lyddon's brain she turned her head and said with a ghastly half-smile, the sweat glistening on her forehead:

"I'm not going to die. It may be months, still, in spite of this. I wish it could be now. But I'm not so lucky."

Robert came back with whisky and put the glass into Medwin's outstretched hand; Medwin put it to Miss Lyddon's lips.

"I'm forbidden to drink it," she said. "How good it is!" And she smiled a little, and let her head sink back against the sofa. Robert turned to go back to the kitchen, and she said, faintly, opening her eyes, "Don't go. Anything I have to say you had better hear." He turned back and sat down again. His look was gentle and dispassionate, full of restrained pity, but impersonal. Between himself and Medwin, occasional quick glances were exchanged, and seeing how anxious she looked he gave her a reassuring shake of the head. Miss Lyddon, he wanted to tell her, was not dying; she had merely spent herself in an emotional outburst of extreme violence. She was now recuperating her forces. She had relaxed, and looked like a long-limbed rag doll thrown upon the sofa. Medwin sat beside her, watching her with strained attention.

What was stirring in Miss Lyddon's brain, neither of the onlookers could tell, but Medwin had the impression that it was intensely active. Head fallen back, eyes closed in exhaustion, she was probably assessing the situation with her customary shrewdness. Whatever the frailties of her body, and these were only too apparent, the working of her mind, now that her fury had spent itself, would be along accustomed lines.

Medwin could picture her standing below in the garage after they had entered the flat and closed the door, racked and torn by a frenzy of jealous hate, heightened and brought to eruption by the shock of complete surprise. What she must have gone through during that quarter of an hour or more, while summoning up her forces to ring the bell and confront them, she could hardly bear to think of. She was quick to realize that the cause of this tumult of feeling, while insufficient and bizarre in her own eyes, was not so in Miss Lyddon's. And no matter what excuses she might find for herself, it was true that she had deceived a woman who, whatever her failings, had only wished to be her friend. She herself had perhaps been guilty of nothing worse than cold-heartedness, but that surely was enough. She had never ceased to judge Miss Lyddon, never ceased to half-depise, half-like her, and to shrug off all that she had offered her in the way of friendship. She looked back upon her own conduct with nothing but disgust and distaste.

Miss Lyddon opened her eyes and then she raised her head slowly to drink the last few sips of whiskey that remained. Medwin took the empty glass from her and put it down, and Miss Lyddon thanked her.

"I'm feeling a little better," she said, "and I want to talk to you. I shall probably be dead in six months' time. It is the usual thing, and inoperable, and there has been no response to treatment. Please say nothing about it. That is one reason I wanted to end my association with Mrs. Gresham—I want to die alone and in peace. She doesn't know, and she will be the last person I will tell. She has been hard to live with. She would be impossible to die with. Well, that is enough about that. I suppose I should have understood why you kept all this from me. One doesn't inform the owner of the house before robbing it, or an intended victim before using the dagger." She addressed herself now to Robert. "I knew, of course, of Miss Jones's relationship with your mother. I asked her one or two questions, which she answered. She told me you were married. It would interest me to hear how you and Medwin met."

If it had to be told, Robert must be the one to tell it, and Medwin's eyes signalled him to this effect. He stated the facts, briefly and without emphasis. It seemed, as he told it, not the thing that, next to their being born, was now the most vital and important happening in their lives; it sounded more like the bare, skeletal outline of some story in book or play. Miss Lyddon may have dressed it in flesh and blood; that they had no means of knowing.

"So," she said, when he had said what he considered enough, "you love each other. You have felt and are feeling now the most exalted, commendable and necessary of all the human emotions, and yet you had no pity or sympathy for me. No understanding, no insight. For you both knew, of course, how I felt about this girl, how important she had become to me. No doubt, you laughed about it together, or treated it as a tiresome and absurd vagary. You didn't know, of course, that she would be the last creature upon earth I would ever care for, and so was trebly dear to me. She came when my horizon was as featureless and bare as the Sahara. When I found that I was once more going to experience that out-going of the spirit we call love, I thanked heaven for it. I thanked heaven as one thanks heaven for the spring after an endless winter. I shall not see another spring, but she has made that thought endurable to me. She has all the charm of youth without its inexperience and folly." She turned her head towards Medwin, and now her face looked less death-like. "I saw, of course how you weighed us both—oh yes, and found us both wanting, but I understand that. We are an odd pair. Sometimes you would lean towards me, sometimes towards her. I have watched all this, sometimes with amusement, often with pain. When Edith told me you had gone to her and asked her help for your father, I could have killed her. I was really afraid of the violence of my own feelings."

Seeing Robert open his cigarette case and then shut it again she broke off to say, "Oh, smoke if you like. I'll have a cigarette too. Perhaps it will help to soothe my nerves. Since they told me it was hopeless, I have been smoking, and eating and drinking what I pleased. If I can hasten the end that way, so much the better."

"I would do the same precisely," said Robert.

"Are you still in the Navy?" she asked him. "I think you were."

"I was," he said, "I'm not now. I am with a shipping firm, and writing in my spare time."

"Writing?" she asked. "Writing what?"

"I've written one novel, and have begun another."

She looked at him with a heightened interest.

"That's something new in our family." Then she gave her short, ironic laugh. "You'd better write the story of Hartsdown. I suppose you know all about it."

"That's just what I intended to do," he told her. "I've written two chapters. But I shall not of course go on with it now."

"Why not?"

"Need you really ask that?" he asked.

"Oh, come!" she said, "why be squeamish? I shall be dead before it's in print."

He got up and moved to the window and back again.

"I wouldn't dream of writing it now," he said. "Before, you were a tale that had been told, a legendary creature whom I made alive by thinking about, over a good many years. But the basis of my whole conception of your character was, as I realize now, a sort of fascinated revulsion. You have blown that to bits. I find I like you. Whether that is chiefly because of your affection for Medwin, I don't know, but the fact remains. I never hated you, but I thought you an entirely detestable character. Now I see that you are nothing of the sort. You are very human and very honest. What you may have been at the time of the trouble, I can't say. But what you are now, I confess, astonishes me. Only, why did you treat poor Gwen so badly? Why were you so cruel to her?"

"I was never cruel to her," Miss Lyddon answered, with a touch of her old impatience. "She chose to make me the object of her adoration, which I found unsuitable and tiresome. And she was not a very good secretary. If her adoration made her unhappy, at least she lived a little. That's apt to be painful, as we both know." And she added, "What else have you got against me?"

"You're colossally selfish," he said, "but I fancy you are rather franker about it than most people are."

"I can't think," she said, ironically, "that all this whitewashing can be good for me. What is your object?"

"In case you should think," he said smiling, "that I hope to benefit after your death, let me hasten to assure you that I would never accept one penny from you. Not a single penny.

She smiled back at him, and there was a little malice in her smile.

"I confess that until you spoke of it," she said, "the idea of making you my heir had not occurred to me. I have made my will and I don't propose to alter it in your favour. What I leave will go to charities—chiefly The Crippled Boys' Home. However, I see that I have missed a great deal by not knowing you sooner, but I could never have forgiven your father, never. I feel no forgiveness now, and I never shall." She paused a moment and said, "As for you, I doubt if you've missed much by not knowing me, or your Uncle James. He is highly intelligent but extremely self-centred. He completely lacks his father's charm. Luke you might like, but he has Americanized himself now, and I doubt if he will ever come home, though if James should die, he might. He loves Hartsdown too. Well, we're a curious family, and all the best and happiest was when we were young. Do you know what heaven would be for me? To wake up at Hartsdown again, in the nursery there, and grow up as I did before, and then, at a certain point, change the course of my life. I think you both know at what point. Someone has said, 'Who has not found the heaven below will fail of it above.' Well, I found it below. It's there, timeless, at Hartsdown. All I ask is to live it over again, but I should pick my way more carefully another time."

She paused, and then said:

"I've talked enough. I gather you both understand that when I came in here I was beside myself. What an odd expression! I was *out* of myself, rather. The anger has gone now. Some of the pain remains." She turned to Medwin. "I need you. Will you stay with me? Until they take me to a nursing home?"

"You know I will," Medwin answered.

"It's time I went," Miss Lyddon said, and got up from the sofa with Medwin's help. She moved slowly and a little feebly towards the door, pencil-thin, a moving black column. Medwin thought how blind she had been, how engrossed in herself and Robert not to have seen how swift the deterioration had been.

"I can go down alone," Miss Lyddon said, but Robert went with her. They went down the stairs together, and he accompanied her as far as the door of the house. Then Medwin heard him come up the stairs again. He came in and sat beside her, and as if words were both too inadequate and at the same time too dangerous, he took her into his arms and said nothing. They had had their four days of extravagant emotional spending; they had had the letter, with the unresolved problems it presented, and now they had had this, and there was little they could say. They had not the will nor the wish to pick their way through the forest of things that could be said. They held each other for a long time in an overburdened silence, and at last he spoke, quietly, and his words seemed to come to her from a distance.

"I'll have to spend tomorrow at the office," he said, "but I'll come here soon after six to say—no, not good-bye, my love—to see you before I go. I'll catch the eight o'clock train to Petersfield. Now listen to what I have to say. She shall have the boy. I do not see how I can ever live with her again as her husband, but she shall have him. Time will soften this thing for her, and I shall not hurry her. I will be as kind as I can. And remember this; even if I give up my son—and I hope not to give him up entirely—I shall have a little daughter. Her name is Sarah."

He kissed her very gently. She did not speak. He presently went on, seeing that she could say nothing:

"I must send a telegram to Mrs. Wharton, and there are other things I ought to do. And now I must go. I'll put the kettle on first so that you can make yourself some tea. Then go to bed. It will be best for you."

He freed her very gently and got up from the sofa, and then stood looking down at her. She sat motionless, her eyes closed.

"Are you all right?" he asked. She gave a little nod of the head in answer, and he bent down and kissed her hair and forehead. Then he picked up his suitcase and went out of the room and down the stairs. She gathered herself up tensely and put her hands over her ears to shut out the sound of the closing of the front door.

CHAPTER 18

MRS. GRESHAM SEEMED TO BE QUITE HER OLD SELF THE next day. She had been up and about, she said, since Friday, and now she felt she was able to take up her normal life again. She said that Dr. Radnytz understood her as no one else did.

"Although I ought to admit that it wasn't entirely Dr. Radnytz's doing," she said to Medwin. "It was partly your saying that you wouldn't leave us, and partly Marietta's coming to me and apologizing for all the cruel things she'd said. She wasn't well, and I ought to have seen it. She still looks very much below par. I wish she'd take a holiday. Anyway, I feel a different woman now. I can't bear living in an unhappy atmosphere. And I feel fairly certain that Marietta doesn't really mean, in the end, to break this up. Though she says she does. Anyway, I'm not going to do anything more about the house for the present. If it is sold, it will have to be an Embassy. No private family could afford to live in it. Or I suppose it could be turned into flats," She sighed heavily. "However, sufficient unto the day, and I feel very much happier than I did." Then she asked, "Tell me, how is your father getting on? Do you think he's made any progress at all?"

"I'm afraid not," Medwin answered. "He would have told me if he had any good news."

Mrs. Gresham stroked herself in a thoughtful way and said, "Poor man I'm sorry for him Well, I did what I could. Oh, I forgot to ask you if you enjoyed your little holiday."

"Yes, I did," Medwin told her. "It was only too short."

"Perhaps later in the summer you can go away again for a while." And then she said, "We must arrange another dinner party, before everyone goes out of town. It's a long time since we had one. And we must try to collect some younger people for you, especially some younger men."

"Oh," Medwin said, "please don't worry about that. I'm not thinking of matrimony just at the moment." And she smiled.

"You should," Mrs. Gresham said. "You really should, you know. Well, now to work. I've decided to buy new matresses for the Holiday Home after all, instead of having the old ones cleaned again. I'll just dictate a letter to Mrs. Thorogood now."

Miss Lyddon spent the morning in bed, but in the afternoon she insisted on dressing and coming down to her sitting-room. She was carefully made up, and her hair had all been beautifully arranged by Antonia. If one did not look too closely, she seemed the Miss Lyddon of five months ago. She stretched herself out on the sofa and said:

"How fatiguing emotions are! They're a luxury I'll have to deny myself, that's quite plain. But can you imagine, can you possibly picture to yourself what I felt when I saw him and recognized him, and then saw you both go into the flat together?"

"Must we speak of that?" Medwin cried. And she thought, will she spare me nothing? But why should she spare me anything?

"Is this remorse?" Miss Lyddon said, looking closely at her. "It's hardly worth that. No, remorse is too costly a thing to spend on me. I know how costly it can be. I absolve you from it, entirely." And then she said, "I have a favour to ask. I asked so much of you once—now I only ask you this—for the moment. Will you drop the Miss Lyddon, for the duration, and call me Marietta? I should like it so much." She gave her wry little smile and added, "It will involve your calling Edith Edith, of course, but perhaps even that isn't too much to ask."

Medwin forced a little smile and said, "It's good to hear the old Marietta once more."

"Oh," Miss Lyddon said, "don't look for any improvement in me. I don't intend to change my spots. The Authorities, if such there be, can take me as I am or not at all. However," she said, "I want to talk about more immediate and important matters. First of all, Sarah, I don't see why you shouldn't have her here. If she has to return to your sister later, well, at least you will have had her for a few months. We can put a small bed in your room, and when you're busy here, she can perfectly well be taken care of by Antonia or Davis. Or, if you prefer, I'll engage a nurse, but I think they will be adequate and they will have ample time to look after her. I don't propose to do any more entertaining. Edith may, if she likes, but when she finds she has to do it alone, she'll soon lose interest in it. Well, what do you say?"

It flashed through Medwin's mind, has she a motive for this, other than kindness? But she dismissed it as quickly.

"I'd love to have her here," she said. "Thank you for suggesting it. I'd love it."

"Good. She can play in the garden. It's a pity it's never used. The next thing I want to ask you is this. Is that contraption of your father's any good? What do you really think about it?"

"I'm not quite sure," Medwin said. "It seems to me as good as a lot of other things on the market. I don't see why it shouldn't be saleable."

"That's all I wanted to know," Miss Lyddon said. "Hand me the telephone, will you?"

Wondering a little, but determined to ask no questions, Medwin passed the telephone over to her, and Miss Lyddon balanced it on her knee. She dialled a number and then said, "Mr. Fullerton please, Miss Lyddon speaking. If he's engaged, ask him to ring me." She waited a moment, then said, "Is that you, Archie? I'm very well indeed, thank you. Archie, you know all about patents, don't you? At least, you're supposed to. Medwin's father, Mr. Fosdick, is at present at the Tennyson Hotel, Bloomsbury. He has an invention—it's for scrubbing floors—that I believe to be perfectly practicable and saleable, but so far he has not been in touch with the right sort of people. I want you to look into it all in a perfectly business-like way and find out what chance it has of being put on the market. I believe Mr. Fosdick has taken out a preliminary patent, but get him to tell you about it. You'll inform him, please, that you are my solicitor and an old friend of Mrs. Gresham's. I want you to make it clear to him that if you do decide to take an interest in this thing, you will expect him to leave the whole matter entirely in your hands. You don't need any advice from me as to how to handle it, but tell him his invention will be well and faithfully dealt with, and that if it's worth putting money into, money will be found. And tell him that he will of course get whatever it is right that he should get out of it. Is that perfectly clear? Good. What? Now, Archie, don't fuss. I'm perfectly all right. Well, no one but you thinks I'm looking ill. Yes, she's promised to stay with us, I'm thankful to say. We both insisted on it. We can't do without her. Come to dinner next week. Just ourselves. Good-bye."

She hung up, but gave Medwin no time to speak.

"Edith's idea of giving him money was quite ridiculous," she said. "She ought to have consulted me. You'd better write to your father, or see him, and tell him that if he'll go home and stay with your mother and keep hens again, he may wake up one fine morning and find himself receiving a modest income. I suppose it's quite possible. Don't you agree that this is the sensible course?"

"I think it's the only sensible course," said Medwin, "and I'm deeply grateful."

"Twice now," Miss Lyddon said, "you have failed to throw a suggestion of mine straight back in my face. We are really getting on."

Medwin smiled at her.

"There's another thing," Miss Lyddon said. "You needn't worry for fear I shall leave you money when I die. I promise you I won't, because I know you'd hate it. Though why you feel like that, you strange girl, I don't know."

The reasons were too complex and too difficult to explain, but there was one thing that Medwin thought she could make clear.

"I don't want my life diverted from its normal course," she said. "I have a feeling that it mustn't be. I believe it has a natural course, that everyone's has, and that it's a sacred thing. It's *my* life. Does this make sense to you?"

"In a way," Miss Lyddon said. "You may be right. Though I should like you to have at least a small cushion against disaster." Medwin made no reply, and she went on:

"And my nephew. Are you and he going to be able to marry one day?"

Medwin quickly looked down at her hands and tightened their clasp. Then she answered in a low voice:

"I would tell you if I could. You have a right to ask. He thinks it will be possible, but I think he has too much heart. I don't know. I don't know."

Miss Lyddon lay very still on the sofa; and a deep silence fell on the room. Then she stirred and said:

"What do you advise me to do about the autumn appeal for the West Hacking Playing Fields for Children? Mrs. Debenham suggests a big film première. I'm inclined to think that people's minds turn rather to dancing in the winter. What do you think?"

"For once," Medwin said, "I find myself in agreement with Mrs. Debenham."

Miss Lyddon laughed.

"You've already agreed with me three times in one afternoon. I could hardly expect you to agree with me a fourth time."

Medwin went back to her flat early. There was not very much work to do, and no reason at all for her to stay later than half-past five. She brushed her hair and quickly put everything she would need for a night into a small bag. Then she went into the sitting-room and taking some paper and an envelope out of her desk began to write a letter, glancing now and then over her shoulder at the clock.

"I cannot say good-bye, my darling," she wrote. "I cannot even see you again, for fear it may be for the last time. And if yesterday's parting was for ever, I shall understand. Oh, how entirely I shall understand! I cannot let you do violence to your feeling of what is just and right. That is the sin of sins; and I do not know what, in the end, you may feel is just and right. You must be free to decide, and you are free. But oh, Robert, don't tell me anything, not a word, until you finally know. Then let the joy come or the blow fall, quickly. I shall continue to make myself ready for either as I have these many weeks past. Then it was *her* choice, now it is yours, and I would rather take my joy or sorrow from your hands than from hers. That is all the difference there is.

"Meanwhile, Sarah will come here to be with me as long as I stay. That will be a great happiness for me. I am going to Charlotte's tonight to tell them.

"My love for you is what it was and always will be. I cannot find any words for it.

"Medwin."

She put the letter into the envelope and throwing on a coat, left the flat. It was raining. The summer had deteriorated, and rain fell more often, but tonight she welcomed it. There was a scarf in the pocket of her coat, and she tied it over her hair. Then she closed the front door and pushed the letter under it until only the smallest corner showed. She had done this before when she expected to be late, and once when she had been summoned unexpectedly to the house. She walked the length of the mews quickly, and then stood on the corner of the street waiting for a taxi. If one came soon she could catch a train that would get her to Charlotte's house before Sarah was in bed. She could be back early the next morning. She saw a taxi, hailed it and got in. She remembered the day she had gone to Reading to see Louise, and her life, since then, seemed to have made a circle. But that was purely imaginary; she was not back where she had started from and never would be. There was no return; there was only a half-blind groping forward, sometimes with the ability to see and sometimes without. It was the moments of seeing that mattered.

WHISKY MADE ME DO IT

WHISKY MADE ME DO IT

60 WONDERFUL WHISKY AND BOURBON COCKTAILS

LANCE J. MAYHEW
ILLUSTRATED BY RUBY TAYLOR

HarperCollins*Publishers*

HarperCollins*Publishers*
1 London Bridge Street
London SE1 9GF
www.harpercollins.co.uk

First published by HarperCollins*Publishers* in 2018

10 9 8 7 6 5 4 3 2 1

Written by Lance J. Mayhew
Illustrated by Ruby Taylor
Designed by Gareth Butterworth

A catalogue record for this book is available from the British Library.

ISBN 978-0-00-831370-8

Printed and bound in Latvia

DISCLAIMER:
This book features recipes that include the optional use of raw eggs. Consuming raw eggs may increase the risk of food-borne illness. Individuals who are immunocompromised, pregnant, or elderly should use caution. Ensure eggs are fresh and meet local food-standard requirements.

Please drink responsibly.

MIX
Paper from responsible sources
FSC™ C007454

This book is produced from independently certified FSC™ paper to ensure responsible forest management.

For more information visit: www.harpercollins.co.uk/green

CONTENTS

INTRODUCTION

'I like whisky and bourbon and Scotch.'

I can't tell you how often I hear that statement, but in reality, bourbon and Scotch are both types of whisky. Just as the word 'beer' is a broad-based word – including ales and lagers – whisky is a catch-all for spirits made from cereal grains that have (usually) been matured in a wooden container.

The world of whisky can be a little confusing, but this book should help you to understand its many forms and production methods. A good place to start is to imagine whisky as beer that has made a leap for immortality. Grain, water and yeast are the backbones of both beer and whisky, the difference being that beer uses hops, while whisky is distilled to concentrate the flavours and alcohol.

Whisky has a long history, particularly in Scotland and Ireland, its veritable homes. So, which country invented whisky? It's an argument that you'll hear in bars around the world, but the best advice is to credit the Irish when in Ireland and the Scots when in Scotland. While distillation is much older than whisky, distilling technology reached both Scotland and Ireland around the 15th century. The first distilling would have been done by monks, who, having tasted distilled spirits, or *aquae vitae* (Latin for 'water of life'), in Europe, would have filled their stills with beer brewed at the monasteries to produce the first iterations of whisky. These efforts were called *uscae beatha* (pronounced 'OO-SKAY BAY-Tha') in Gaelic, meaning water of life. The whiskies produced then would have been unrecognisable to modern consumers; they would have been harsh and unaged, for drinking in the near future rather than allowed to quietly age. *Uscae beatha* slowly became *usquebaugh* in the 1600s, before being shortened to *usque*, which has a pronunciation similar to our modern 'whisky'.

A quick aside on *whiskey* or *whisky* – the correct spelling depends (usually) on the country in which it is made. The Scots spell it whisky, and the Canadians and Japanese follow that custom. The Irish use the 'ey' spelling, as does the United States, but exceptions exist, such as the Tennessee Whiskey, George Dickel whisky – spelled the Scottish way, as Mr Dickel was convinced his whisky was as good as anything produced in Scotland. You'll find both spellings in this book, to respect the naming traditions of each whisk(e)y-producing country.

Tasting and nosing spirits is a challenge for most people. Of course, there are times when one can simply enjoy a whisky without doing an *organoleptic analysis* of the spirit (yes, nosing and tasting has a proper name – you can win bar bets with this knowledge).

Pour yourself a small dram of whisky (there is specialised glassware such as the Glencairn glass that is great for making the aromas and flavours more apparent, or just use a wine glass or Cognac snifter). Note its colour – it can be a clue as to what kind of barrel it was matured in – a red tint can indicate a Scotch whisky matured in a sherry butt, while a more golden colour is often indicative of an ex-bourbon barrel. Slowly tilt the glass and run the liquid along the inside, watching how it moves. If the spirit appears to cling and looks a bit viscous, the remnants that slowly move back down (called the 'legs') indicate an older whisky, whereas young whiskies will run right back down the glass. Keeping your nose above the glass (a couple of centimetres above the rim), inhale through your nostrils and breathe out through your open mouth. This is where the first aromas and clues about the whisky present themselves – the influence of the cereal grains, the type of wood and the environment in which it was matured. If you detect aromas of burnt plastic or cat piss (a real defect in poorly distilled whisky), brace your palate for the assault to come. Feel free to download a whisky aroma wheel from the internet to help you identify flavour notes.

Next is the first sip. This isn't a real sip, this is a small amount taken into the mouth so as not to shock the palate with a big hit of alcohol. Slowly move this around, through your teeth and gums and over your tongue, to get your palate ready for the second sip. Think about the flavours this sip presents when it hits your tongue. Often the entry, as we call it, is more fruit forward, followed by cereal grains, before wood notes start to show up. Each whisky is unique, so let it reveal itself to you on its terms, not yours. The best part of tasting whisky comes at the finish. In order to experience this, you must swallow the whisky. After swallowing, breathe out and note the various flavours and how long these sit on your palate. Some whiskies have very quick and light finishes, whereas others can linger pleasantly on the tongue, revealing more layers and complexity even after they are long gone.

WHISKY BASICS

Cereal grains are used to make whisky. These make up the primary source of flavour before maturation. Some whiskies, like single malt Scotch whisky, are made from 100% of a single grain – in this case, barley – while others, like bourbon, use a mash bill (a blend of grains). A bourbon mash bill has to be 51% corn by law, with other grains, notably malted barley (barley that has been allowed to just germinate before being stopped immediately to take advantage of the extra sugars present), rye and wheat. Even some less-common grains, such as millet or rice, can be distilled into whisky. The bottom line is all whisky is made from cereal grains, and how they are used (malted versus unmalted, and a single variety versus a blend of multiple grains) affects the flavours in the finished product.

Yeast is a very important part of every whisky and a number of major distillers have a proprietary yeast that they use exclusively. (They often keep freeze-dried samples offsite in multiple locations in case a

disaster affects the distillery.) Other producers purchase freeze-dried yeasts and some distillers are experimenting with a variety of unusual yeasts such as Belgian Ale yeast. Yeast is used in one of the first steps of whisky production, as the grain and warm water and yeast are combined to begin fermenting, when the yeast turns the sugars in the cereal grains into alcohol.

Water is also a very important part of whisky production and almost every great distillery is located on or near a pristine water source – a spring, a lake or a river. The great bourbon whiskey producers are renowned for the quality of the limestone water that trickles up through springs in Kentucky. In Japan, the Ministry of Environment has designated the water sources for Suntory Whisky's brand as being among the 'most precious' in the country. The distilleries in Scotland, Ireland and Canada are no different. The unique pH for each water source brings out certain flavour profiles in each whisky.

Maturation occurs primarily through oak barrels, but the size of the barrel, whether it is new oak or has been used before, what kind of oak and how long it is used for aging all affect the final flavours of a whisky. Some distillers use more unusual techniques for maturation, from sending their barrels to sea on ships, to playing music to it as it rests, but it's the magic that happens in the barrel that allows the whisky to mature. Many attempts have been made to speed up the maturation process, including using high pressure, ultrasound or other techniques to fake the effects of barrel aging. None have successfully replicated the correct flavour profile.

Climate plays a major role in whisky maturation. In hot Kentucky, where new oak barrels are stored in tin-sided 'rick houses', the heat creates an angel's share (evaporation of liquid in the barrel) that can reach 10% in year one as the liquid seeps into the porous wood staves, and can average 4% per year for the remainder of its maturation. In contrast, Scotland, which experiences a much lower average summer temperature, allows distillers to write off 2% per year to the angel's share. Other factors are affected by the climate; in an environment with warm temperatures and high humidity, more alcohol will evaporate out of the barrel than water, lowering the abv as it matures, while in a lower-humidity environment water evaporates, which raises the abv.

The kind of still used and how many times a product is distilled affect the final whiskies. There are essentially two types of still:

The **pot still** is the older, less-efficient method of distillation. Modern pot stills are steam heated or occasionally heated by fire. The shape of the still is a good indicator of the type of whisky it is producing – a short, round still with a short neck will produce a fatter, more full-flavoured whisky, while a taller, thinner still with a long neck produces a milder, gentler whisky. A pot still works in batches, and one distillation can achieve an abv maximum of 40–80%. Pot-still whiskies are generally distilled twice, and sometimes three times. A mixture called 'distiller's beer' or 'wash' is put into the still, which is a cloudy liquid that remains after fermentation. The first distillation yields what are known as **low wines**, usually around 20% abv. The resulting liquid is then put into a second pot still (or the first still is reused), and second distillation with heads and tails cut (known as feints and fore shots) has to be made to ensure that only the heart of the run is captured. Any liquid left behind in the still (sometimes called pot ale) is discarded or turned into animal feed.

The **column still**, also known as the continuous still or Coffey still, consists of two columns that continuously distill the spirit. The first column has the wash pumped in from the top while steam comes up from below. A series of either bubble plate or a packing material inside helps the fractional distillation. The second still, the rectifier, condenses the alcohol vapours into liquid form. A column still is much more efficient, being able to distill to a 96% abv, or as close as can be achieved without the use of chemicals or specialised lab equipment. While this still can be run constantly, and extract a purer base alcohol, it does mean less flavour comes through.

STYLES OF WHISKY

As France is to wine, Scotland is to whisky. No true connoisseur can ignore the variety and depth of the whisky produced there. **Scotch whisky** comes in five different styles but around 90% of all that is produced in Scotland is blended. To be labelled as Scotch whisky, it must be distilled in Scotland from water and malted barley and may include other cereal grains. It can be distilled to no more than 94.8% abv. The whisky must be matured for a minimum of three years in oak casks not larger than 700 litres, then bottled at a minimum alcoholic strength of 40% abv. Scotch whisky allows the addition of caramel colouring for colour correcting.

This is a good moment for a note on **barrels**. The majority of casks used for maturation of Scotch whisky (about 97% of Scotch maturing at any time) are ex-bourbon barrels made from American oak (*Quercus alba*). By American law, bourbon barrels can only be used once, so the majority are broken down and the staves shipped to Scotland. The staves are then rebuilt into barrels, with new ends added, and the staves are re-charred to release more wood sugars. This can be done many times during the useful life of a barrel (30-plus years), but the first time it is used to hold Scotch whisky is referred to as a First Fill Barrel (the most esteemed by whisky enthusiasts). This has the greatest bourbon influence, which depletes as the barrel is reused. Sherry butts represent the majority of the other casks used to mature Scotch whisky and are much larger, at 600 litres. Other barrels are often used to 'finish' a whisky for 30–90 days at the end of its maturation, when the whisky is transferred to a new barrel for a short time to pick up some of its characteristics. This will be labelled 'Rum Cask Finished' or 'Gaja Barolo Barrel Finished'.

Peat is one of the most divisive flavour compounds in Scotch whisky. Many people adore it for the smoke and phenol compounds with which it can imbue malted barley, but some find it an acquired taste. I come down firmly in the 'adore' category.

So why is peat in whisky? Simply put, peat is an accumulation of decayed vegetation that forms in bogs. In older times, malted barley would have dried on screens set over burning peat, for the smoke to add its distinctive flavour. Peat is also close to the concept of terroir (flavours that reflect the unique environment of each wine), because various areas have different types of peat based on what grew there thousands of years ago.

BLENDED SCOTCH WHISKY makes up the large majority of Scotch whisky sold worldwide. This style was created when whisky merchants and grocers in the 19th century realised that by mixing single malts, which were rougher and more inconsistent, with relatively new grain whiskies (made from corn or wheat) produced on column stills, they could create a consistent house style that was generally lighter and sweeter, and more marketable to a broader range of consumers. Today, Master Blenders still strive to recreate the same flavour profile of a particular whisky year in and year out. If an age statement is listed on the label of a blended Scotch whisky, it must reflect the age of the youngest whisky in it. The average ratio of grain whisky to single malts runs from 60–85% grain whisky to 15–40% single malts.

SINGLE MALT SCOTCH WHISKY is the second-largest category of Scotch sold worldwide. A single malt must be made from malted barley and distilled in a pot still, usually twice. It has to be made at a single distillery, where it is blended to create a harmonious whole to reflect that distillery's style. There are five official regions for single malt whisky in Scotland, although a sixth, the 'Islands', is unofficially argued by many whisky enthusiasts:

The Lowlands – The whiskies produced in the southernmost area of Scotland are gentle and sweet. Some have been affectionately referred to as 'breakfast whisky' because of the regional tradition of triple distilling, which results in a lighter style.

The Highlands – Physically the largest whisky-producing region in Scotland, its size allows for a variety of styles, from peaty and large to light and floral.

Speyside – This area features the most densely concentrated number of distilleries within its small borders. With production centred on eight locations – Strathisla, Livet, Findhorn, Rothes, Dufftown, Deveron, Lossie and Speyside Central – the whiskies are generally light and fruity with some grassy characteristics, with a greater influence of sherry casks than in other regions.

Campbelltown – This is the only town to be its own whisky region. At its peak, the area featured 30-plus distilleries, all producing powerful whiskies known for their smoke and salinity balanced by fruit and chocolate notes. Now only three remain.

Islay (pronounced *EYE-luh*) – The southernmost island in the Inner Hebrides is home to eight distilleries that produce some of Scotland's most iconic whiskies. As a general rule, these are big, peaty, smoky drams, with sea spray and an underlying sweetness. Geographically, the distilleries on the northern part of the island produce less peaty malts without the salinity of their southern counterparts.

The Islands – Included within the Highlands and not yet recognised as a separate region, the Islands deserve their own category, as their whiskies are unique – ranging from big, briny and peaty to soft and floral, all with their own characters influenced by their location.

BLENDED MALT SCOTCH WHISKY is a newer style, which was known as vatted malt prior to 2009. Essentially a blend of only single malts (no grain whisky), these aren't common but many are excellent.

SINGLE GRAIN SCOTCH WHISKY is made from either corn or wheat and barley (it must include barley) in a column still in Scotland. These don't appear on the market very often but many are quite good. The single grain designation refers to one distiller producing it – grain indicates a mix beyond barley has been used.

BLENDED GRAIN SCOTCH WHISKY is similar to single grain Scotch whisky, except that it contains whiskies from at least two different distilleries blended together.

IRISH WHISKEY is experiencing a Renaissance not seen since the early 20th century, with 18 distilleries now operating in Ireland, and at least a dozen more in the planning. Irish whiskey is the only country-specific whiskey that is actually made in two countries within one island – the Republic of Ireland and Northern Ireland (part of the United Kingdom). Irish whiskey is made from malted barley (other cereal grains can be added), must be distilled to no more than 94.8% abv, be aged in oak casks not larger than 700 litres for a minimum of three years and be matured in Ireland and bottled at not less than 40% abv. It is usually triple-distilled, which results in a light, fruity and sweet style. The use of peat in Ireland is rare, although these whiskies do exist. Like Scotch whisky, the age stated on the label must indicate the youngest age of the whiskes included. The majority of barrels used for maturation are ex-bourbon barrels, with sherry butts and wine casks sometimes used. Irish whiskey allows for the use of caramel colouring for colour correction.

There are four types of Irish whiskey:

Irish Malt Whiskey – This is made using 100% malted barley and triple-distilled in pot stills. An Irish malt whiskey from one distillery can be labelled as an Irish single malt.

Irish Pot Still Whiskey – This is a blend of malted and unmalted (also known as green) barley. A minimum of 30% of each type of barley must be used and up to 5% of other cereal grains. Traditionally triple-distilled, this used to be the most popular style of whiskey in the world during the 19th century. If distilled at one distiller, the term single Irish pot still whiskey can be used.

Irish Grain Whiskey – This is made with no more than 30% malted barley, along with other unmalted cereals such as barley, corn or wheat, and distilled in column stills. Those produced at one distillery can be labelled single grain whiskey.

Irish Blended Whiskey – These make up the vast majority of Irish whiskies sold. Confusingly, any combination of two or more styles of malt, pot still and grain whiskies qualifies as an Irish blended whiskey, but the majority feature a dominant combination of grain and pot still whiskies.

JAPANESE WHISKY traces its roots back to 1870 but really began in its modern form in the 1920s. It is said to model itself on Scotch whisky, although some rice whiskies are produced too. In Japan, if a distillery wants to produce a blend, they make many different styles in-house or under the umbrella of a company, usually grain whiskies from column stills and pot still-based single malts, then blend these disparate whiskies into a house style. Japanese single malt whiskies are 100% malted barley (often imported from Scotland) and double-distilled in pot stills. Occasionally, Japanese oak barrels (called *mizunara* oak) are used, but they are very expensive and tend to leak; however, they do add a complex cedar spice component.

CANADIAN WHISKY can be made from any cereal grain or grain products (wheat, rye and corn being the most common) and are aged in 'small wood' of not more than 700-litre casks for a minimum of three years. The product must be distilled and matured in Canada and not bottled at less than 40% abv. Many styles of Canadian whisky allow caramel colouring for colour correcting, but they also allow up to 9.09% of flavouring to be added as long as it is a spirit aged at least 24 months or a wine. Generally, Canadian whiskies are a blend of base whiskies produced in column stills to a high proof then matured in used barrels, blended with flavouring whiskies. They are generally distilled to a lower abv on column stills, then possibly in a pot still, before being matured in ex-bourbon, ex-rye or virgin-wood barrels. Both styles are generally distilled and matured from one grain at a time, then blended to create a house style. Barrels may be new or used, charred or uncharred. Canadian whisky is often referred to as 'rye' because it traditionally contains rye in the blend (dating back to German and Dutch immigrants adding rye to the wheat mash), but wheat is most widely used. Now Canada is home to eight major distilleries and a number of small micro-distilleries.

AMERICAN WHISKIES include several styles that are distinctive to the United States, including bourbon and Tennessee whiskey, although it was rye whiskey that was distilled by German and Scottish immigrants in Maryland and Pennsylvania. Settlers then moved into Kentucky and Tennessee, where corn grows well and water filters up through a natural limestone shelf, and where the majority of American whiskey production still occurs.

The 'rules' for American whiskies (a catch-all name for all whiskies distilled in the US) are that they must be distilled to no more than 95% abv from cereal grains and stored in oak barrels. Mash bill is the most common recipe for American whiskies, which must then be bottled at no less than 40% abv. To be labelled as a straight whiskey, it must be aged for a minimum of two years and have no additives.

These are very broad regulations, so let's take a look at American whiskey categories.

American Blended Whiskey – This is very popular, due in part to its use in cocktails like the 7&7 (Seagram's 7 Blended American Whiskey and 7up). It has to contain at least 20% straight whiskey, with the rest as neutral spirits (think vodka) or whiskey that doesn't qualify as straight whiskey, or a mix of both.

American Spirit Whiskey – This type is so-named as a ghost of most whiskies, containing only 5% of the real stuff with the remaining 95% being neutral spirits. Rarely seen.

American Light Whiskey – An outlier among whiskey regulations, this specifies that it must be distilled over 80% abv and can be stored in either used or uncharred oak barrels. Rarely seen.

American Bourbon Whiskey – This was declared the United States' native spirit by an Act of Congress in 1964. While widely assumed to be made only in Kentucky (the majority is produced there), it can be made anywhere in the US. Bourbon has to be made with a minimum of 51% corn, although mash bills usually include 70–80% corn with the remainder a combination of malted barley and rye or wheat. Four-grain mash bills containing both wheat and rye along with corn and malted barley are rare. Wheated bourbons are sweeter and gentler whiskies, while rye-heavy bourbons are spicier with a cinnamon note. Bourbon must be distilled to no more than 80% abv using either a column or pot still, or a combination of both. Many bourbon stills start with column distillation and then go into a 'doubler' or 'thumper', a variation of a pot still. Once bourbon comes off the still, the new-make spirit, called 'white dog', must go into a new American charred oak barrel. Barrels cannot be reused for bourbon, but there is a loophole as no period of time is specified – any contact with wood, even for as little as 15 seconds, transforms white dog into bourbon. Most bourbons are aged from 2–6 years – some longer – and to be labelled as straight bourbon whiskey, it must be at least two years old, any less than four years must state its age. White dog must go into the barrel at no more than 62.5% abv and the finished product must be bottled at not less than 40% abv.

One subcategory that is increasingly popular among bourbon aficionados is **Bottled-in-Bond Bourbon**. The Bottled-in-Bond Act of 1897 requires whiskies thus labelled to be produced in a single distilling season (there are two recognised distilling seasons: spring – January to the end of June, and autumn – July to the end of December). It must be made at a single distillery and matured in a US Government bonded warehouse for at least four years and be a minimum 50% abv. If the whiskey is bottled anywhere other than the distillery of origin, it must be noted on the label. The act also covers other American whiskies, notably rye and corn whiskies, as well as apple brandy.

Tennessee Whiskey – This must be made in Tennessee according to state law. It follows the same rules for bourbon with one additional step known as the Lincoln County Process, which involves dripping the new-make spirit over a vat packed with sugar maple charcoal before going into a barrel. This process smoothes out the whiskey and mellows it. Only one small Tennessee whiskey distiller is exempt.

American Rye Whiskey – This has the same requirements as bourbon, minus the mash bill, when made in the US. Rye is the most expensive grain to distill, and the most dangerous in inexperienced hands, as it can stick to the inside of stills, causing a catastrophic failure of the still and potentially explosions or fires. Many distillery operators opt not to produce rye whiskey, instead sourcing it from a distillery in Indiana.

American Malt Whiskey – This style is increasingly seen from small distillers in the United States. While US regulations only require 51% malted barley in the mash bill versus 100% for single malt Scotch whisky, there has been a growing movement to both up the requirement for barley to 100% and push for a similar designation for single malt. All other regulations here are similar to bourbon.

America Corn Whiskey – This seems a close cousin to bourbon, and its mash bill requirements and abv off the still and strength going into the barrel are the same as

bourbon, but it's the maturation (or lack thereof) that separates the two. Corn whiskey can be released unaged – there is no requirement for it to touch a barrel, and if it does, it must be matured in either a used or uncharred barrel. Corn whiskey is really about the grain itself.

American Wheat Whiskey – This is another style of whiskey with the same requirements as bourbon, except that the mash bill must be at least 51% wheat.

Now that we've covered the basics, history and process of making whisky, let's get to the good stuff. In the next section, we're going to explore some great ways to enjoy whisky in 60 creative cocktails – some old, some new, and even one with a completely fraudulent history. What all these drinks have in common, though, is that they are delicious. My suggestion is to try them as written first, then play around with the type of whisky you prefer in each drink. I've offered a couple of caveats where you shouldn't make substitutions, but for the most part, be bold and experiment! Have fun and enjoy yourself. Cheers!

SYRUPS

SIMPLE SYRUP

Add 200g (7oz) of sugar to a small pan. Pour 240ml (8fl oz) of water into the pan. Heat this over medium heat, stirring occasionally until the sugar dissolves. Remove from the heat and let it cool. Store the syrup in an airtight container in the refrigerator for up to one week.

BROWN SUGAR SIMPLE SYRUP

Add 200g (7oz) of brown sugar to a small pan. Pour 240ml (8fl oz) of water into the pan. Heat this over medium heat, stirring occasionally until the sugar dissolves. Remove from the heat and let it cool. Store the syrup in an airtight container in the refrigerator for up to one week.

GINGER SYRUP

Add 200g (7oz) of sugar to a small pan. Add 1 thumb-sized piece of peeled and sliced ginger to the pan. Pour 240ml (8fl oz) of water into the pan. Heat this over medium heat, stirring occasionally until the sugar dissolves. Remove from the heat and let the ginger steep for 20 minutes. Strain out the ginger with a mesh strainer. Store the syrup in an airtight container in the refrigerator for up to one week.

HONEY-GINGER SYRUP

Add 240ml (8fl oz) honey to a small pan. Add 1 thumb-sized piece of peeled and sliced ginger to the pan. Pour 240ml (8fl oz) of water into the pan. Cook over high heat, stirring occasionally until the mixture boils. Reduce the heat to medium and simmer for 5 minutes. Remove from the heat and let the ginger steep for 20 minutes. Strain out the ginger with a mesh strainer. Store the syrup in an airtight container in the refrigerator for up to one week.

MAPLE-SPICED SIMPLE SYRUP

In a small pan, combine 120ml (4fl oz) of maple syrup, 2 cinnamon sticks, 2 star anise, 5 whole cloves and 120ml (4fl oz) of water. Bring to a boil and then turn off the heat. Cover and let stand for at least 30 minutes (or up to overnight), then strain into an airtight, sterilised container. This can be stored in the refrigerator for up to one week.

THE RECIPES

OLD FASHIONED

OLD FASHIONED

This drink is just that, old-fashioned. When celebrity bartender 'Professor' Jerry Thomas wrote the world's first bartenders' guide, *How to Mix Drinks or The Bon Vivant's Companion*, in 1862, his Old Fashioned recipe called for Holland Gin. By the 1880s, a bartender in Louisville, Kentucky, at the famed Pendennis Club, is believed to have popularised a bourbon version, taking it to New York's Waldorf Astoria Hotel, from where it spread to the rest of the world. Whatever its history, this is one of the most important whisky drinks around. We offer it both ways - the traditional recipe, and the modern, post-Prohibition version with muddled fruit. Both have their adherents, so why not try them both?

Ingredients

CLASSIC

60ml (2fl oz) good bourbon or rye whiskey
15ml (½fl oz) Simple Syrup (see page 20)
4 dashes of Angostura bitters
a large orange twist and an amarena cherry, to garnish

MODERN

1 sugar cube
6 dashes of Angostura bitters
a large orange twist and an amarena cherry
60ml (2fl oz) whiskey
60ml (2fl oz) soda water

Instructions

For the Classic, pour the whiskey into a glass named, appropriately enough, an old fashioned. Add the Simple Syrup and bitters. Add ice - preferably a single large cube or rock, but the larger the lumps the better. Cut a large orange twist, being careful to only get the skin and not the bitter pith, and express it over the drink with a twisting motion. Drop it in. Garnish with the orange twist and an amarena cherry. For the modern take, place a sugar cube in the glass and sprinkle it with the bitters. Add the orange twist and an amarena cherry and muddle the fruit and sugar cube. Pour in the whiskey and add ice, then top up with soda water. Serve.

MANHATTAN

Not only one of the finest cocktails ever served, this is also one of the most famous. Like many cocktails, the origins of the Manhattan are murky, although some say that it was created in the 1880s at the Manhattan Club for Winston Churchill's mother, Lady Randolph Churchill. This classic combination of whiskey, vermouth and bitters makes it a foundational cocktail for all bartenders, and a great drink for experimenting with different whiskies. Originally rye would have been used, but now bourbon and other whiskies appear in this drink in bars across the globe. Take it a step further and substitute dry vermouth for sweet for a 'Dry Manhattan', or use equal parts sweet and dry vermouth for a 'Perfect Manhattan'. One variation pays tribute to the legendary group of entertainers who put Las Vegas on the map. The 'Rat Pack Manhattan' has one ingredient for each member of the group, so in addition to the whiskey, use equal parts sweet and dry vermouth, a dash of Grand Marnier and 2 or 3 dashes of Angostura bitters. Stir over ice to the sounds of Sammy Davis Jr. and garnish with a cherry, and even an orange twist.

Ingredients

60ml (2fl oz) whiskey (bourbon or rye are most frequently used, or use Canadian whisky or a blended whisky)
30ml (1fl oz) good sweet vermouth
2 dashes of Angostura bitters
an amarena cherry, to garnish

Instructions

Into a cocktail mixing glass, pour the whiskey, sweet vermouth and bitters. Add some ice and stir with a barspoon until chilled – about 1 minute. Strain into a chilled martini glass and garnish with an amarena cherry.

WELCOME TO

Manhattan

Ballantine's
FINEST
BLENDED SCOTCH WHISKY
GEORGE BALLANTINE AND SON
DUMBARTON, G82 2SS, SCOTLAND
PRODUCT OF SCOTLAND
70cl e
40% vol

ROB ROY

Also occasionally referred to as a 'Scotch whisky Manhattan', this is the Manhattan's close relative in the cocktail world. It is reputed to have been originally created in 1894 at the Waldorf Astoria Hotel, in New York City, for the premiere of an operetta called, obviously enough, *Rob Roy*, which was based on the Scottish outlaw and folk hero. This cocktail works best with a blended Scotch whisky that has a smoky character, but don't be afraid to play around with your favourite single malt here, too.

Ingredients

60ml (2fl oz) blended Scotch whisky
30ml (1fl oz) good sweet vermouth
2 dashes of Angostura bitters
an amarena cherry, to garnish

Instructions

Pour the whisky, sweet vermouth and bitters into a cocktail mixing glass. Add some ice and stir with a barspoon until chilled – about 1 minute. Strain into a chilled martini glass and garnish with an amarena cherry.

CINNAMANHATTAN

This was created by San Francisco bartender Sierra Zimei in 2008. By adding Grand Marnier and bitters to a high-rye bourbon, it showcases some delicious cinnamon and spice notes in a drink that is also very easy to prepare. The Cinnamanhattan is a riff on the classic Manhattan and provides a good example for home mixologists on how a minor substitution to a cocktail can create something entirely new and different.

Ingredients

75ml (2½fl oz) high-rye bourbon
15ml (½fl oz) Grand Marnier
5 dashes of Angostura bitters
a cinnamon stick and dried cherries on a cocktail pick, to garnish

Instructions

Add the bourbon, Grand Marnier and Angostura bitters to a mixing glass. Add some ice and stir for 1 minute, then strain into a martini glass. Garnish with a cinnamon stick and dried cherries on a cocktail pick.

CORDON ROUGE
Maison Fondée en 1827
Grand Marnier
LIQUEUR
ORANGE & COGNAC
PARIS-FRANCE

BROOKLYN

BROOKLYN

While this cocktail may be less well known than the more uptown Manhattan, just because it has fallen into a bit of post-Prohibition obscurity doesn't mean it should be ignored. If you enjoy cocktails that are brown, bitter and stirred, then this is the drink for you. You may occasionally spot this cocktail on the menu at a mixology-focused bar, as it is adored by many bartenders in that world – but don't order one of these at a local tavern and expect anything more than a blank stare from the barkeep. That said, the best way to enjoy the Brooklyn is prepared by your own hands.

Ingredients

60ml (2fl oz) rye whiskey
30ml (1fl oz) dry vermouth
15ml (½fl oz) Picon Amer (substitute Ramazotti Amaro liqueur if need be)
15ml (½fl oz) maraschino liqueur
4 dashes of orange bitters
a large orange twist, to garnish

Instructions

Pour the rye whiskey, dry vermouth, Picon Amer, maraschino liqueur and orange bitters into a mixing glass. Add some ice and stir for 1 minute. Strain into a chilled coupe or martini glass and garnish with a large orange twist.

JOHN COLLINS

Most likely descended from the late 19th-century punch style of cocktail, this drink would have originally included water, a spirit, fruit, sugar and spices. At that time, punches would have been made in large punch bowls, but the John Collins offers a more manageable individual serving. Light and refreshing, this is the whisky-based cousin to the better-known, gin-based Tom Collins. The John Collins is a perfect vehicle for experimenting with different whiskies; bourbon, Canadian whisky and Irish whiskey are all ideal choices, but feel free to find your own perfect match.

Ingredients

45ml (1½fl oz) whisky (bourbon is traditional)
22ml (¾fl oz) freshly squeezed lemon juice
22ml (¾fl oz) Simple Syrup (see page 20)
120ml (4fl oz) soda water
a lemon slice and cherry, to garnish

Instructions

Half fill a cocktail shaker with ice. Pour in the whisky, lemon juice and Simple Syrup, then shake vigorously for 1 minute. Strain into a highball glass filled with fresh ice cubes. Top with soda water and garnish with a lemon slice and cherry.

LONDON
J.C'S
CLUB
SODA
SPECIAL
FIZZY · FIZZY

Nº: 04-6379
OLD FASHIONED IN 1891
EDWARD & MACKIE
FOUNDERS
CRAIGELLACHIE
SPEYSIDE
SINGLE MALT SCOTCH WHISKY
OUR DISTILLERY
BUILT ON A ROCKY BLUFF SITUATED ABOVE
THE CONFLUENCE OF THE RIVER FIDDICE
AND
THE RIVER SPEY
CRAIGELLACHIE LIES IN THE HEART OF SPEY
13
AGED YEARS

WHISKY HIGHBALL

This cocktail is making a comeback, which certainly isn't surprising. A refreshing combination of whisky, ice and soda water or ginger ale, this one is easy to make and easy to drink. It's the perfect cocktail for a Monday evening after a rough day at work when you want something both simple and delicious. For a more exacting take on the Highball, we go to Japan, where the Mizuwari (meaning 'mixed with water') has a ritual all its own. Fill a glass with whisky (Japanese whisky preferred) and ice, then stir 13½ times (slowly). Top up the drink with ice again and add sparkling water. Now stir 3½ more times to incorporate everything, and serve. Just don't forget what your count is on the stirs or you'll ruin not only your Mizuwari but also lose face for being unable to count to seventeen whilst making a drink.

Ingredients

60ml (2fl oz) whisky
120ml (4fl oz) soda water or ginger ale

Instructions

Pour the whisky into a highball glass. Add some fresh ice cubes and top with soda water or ginger ale.

LOMO

Modern highball-style drinks are a trend right now, and James Ault from Dig-A-Pony in Portland, Oregon is on point with the Lomo, a cocktail highball mixing bourbon with ginger drinking vinegar, yellow chartreuse, orange bitters and soda water. The trendy drinking vinegar adds a bit of Asian flair to this drink and the result is a complex highball that is eminently quaffable. Add the complex herbal notes of the yellow chartreuse, which contributes just enough sweetness to mellow the bite of the drinking vinegar and enhances the bourbon, and this is a cocktail you won't soon forget.

Ingredients

45ml (1½fl oz) bourbon
15ml (½fl oz) yellow chartreuse
22ml (¾fl oz) ginger drinking vinegar
2 dashes of orange bitters
soda water, to top up
fresh basil leaves and a flamed orange peel (see page 60), to garnish

Instructions

Combine the bourbon, yellow charteuse, drinking vinegar and orange bitters in a highball glass. Add some fresh ice cubes and top up with the soda water. Stir gently to incorporate and garnish with fresh basil leaves and a flamed orange peel.

Since 1821
ANGOSTURA
ORANGE
bitters
200ml

Blanton's
THE ORIGINAL
SINGLE BARREL
BOURBON WHISKEY

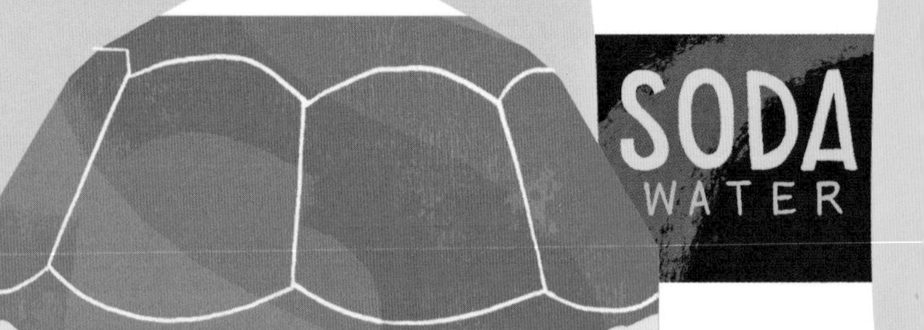
SODA
WATER
Bourbon Whiskey dumped on 4-2009 from Barrel No 300
Stored in Warehouse H on Rick No 38
Traditionally selected filtered and bottled by hand at 93 Proof
RAIGHT BOURBON WHISKEY
46% ALC/VOL (93 PROOF)

WHISKEY RICKEY

This is a refreshing long drink that eschews sugar for a tart combination of whiskey, lime and soda water. This drink was originally created by a bartender named George A. Williamson at Shoomaker's Bar in Washington, D.C., in the 1880s. The original recipe calls for bourbon, although any whisky (or preferably whiskey) will work well in this drink. Ironically, it wasn't until gin was substituted for bourbon about 10 years after this drink's creation that the Rickey took off in popularity. The large majority of Rickeys are still ordered with gin, but try this with your favourite whiskey and enjoy a tipple that 19th-century US Congressmen would have sipped during the warm-weather months in the US capital.

Ingredients

60ml (2fl oz) bourbon or whiskey of choice
soda water, to top up
½ lime, for squeezing and garnish

Instructions

Fill a highball glass with ice, add the whiskey and top up with soda water. Squeeze the ½ lime into the drink and drop in the lime shell as a garnish.

BOBBY BURNS

Named after the great Scottish poet Robert Burns, whose poem *Address to a Haggis* is one of his best-known pieces of writing and a staple at Burns Night (25 January) whisky celebrations the world over, this three-ingredient cocktail combines Scotch whisky with sweet vermouth and Benedictine liqueur. While it may seem simple, the end result is a cocktail with a depth and complexity far beyond these three separate ingredients. Don't wait until Burns Night to discover this one, though; the Bobby Burns also makes a great accompaniment to a steak dinner.

Ingredients

30ml (1fl oz) blended Scotch whisky
15ml (½fl oz) Benedictine liqueur
30ml (1fl oz) sweet vermouth
a lemon twist, to garnish

Instructions

Pour the blended Scotch, Benedictine and sweet vermouth into a mixing glass. Add ice and stir for 1 minute. Strain into a chilled coupe or martini glass and garnish with a lemon twist.

J&B
RARE
A BLEND OF THE PUREST
OLD SCOTCH WHISKIES
J&B
JUSTERINI & BROOKS
St James's Street London S.W.
KING GEORGE III
PRODUCED AND BOTTLED IN SCOTLAND
70cl e
40%vol

BULLEIT
BOURBON
FRONTIER
WHISKEY
—AGED 10 YEARS—
BULLEIT BOURBON
FRONTIER WHISKEY
10
KENTUCKY STRAIGHT BOURBON WHISKEY

BOURBON DAISY

This is one of the Daisy category of cocktails that has expanded beyond its original grouping to become a bit of an amorphous drink. This particular version is a nod to the 19th-century, classic Daisy style, although you'll often find modern versions of this drink to be little more than a Whisky Sour with added soda water. You could easily make this version a long drink by doing just that, but the real charm of this cocktail is the interplay between whisky and yellow chartreuse, a herbal liqueur made by Carthusian monks in France. Just about any non-peated whisky will work well here – the question is simply which one works best for your palate.

Ingredients

60ml (2fl oz) whisky
22ml (¾fl oz) freshly squeezed lemon juice
15ml (½fl oz) grenadine
15ml (½fl oz) yellow chartreuse

Instructions

Pour the whisky, lemon juice and grenadine into a mixing glass. Add some ice and stir for 1 minute. Strain into a chilled coupe or martini glass. Float the yellow chartreuse on top of the drink by pouring it over the back of a barspoon onto the surface of the cocktail and serve.

SCOFFLAW

This drink wins the award for 'Best Name for a Cocktail', as it was developed during Prohibition and the name literally means 'a person who drinks illegally'. Debuting at the famous Harry's New York Bar in Paris in 1924, which would have been filled with American celebrities travelling overseas for cocktails and fun, this mixture of lemon, whiskey and vermouth appears in a number of drinks from this time. Harry's Bar is still open in Paris, and it remains a throwback to those glory days. The Scofflaw works best with rye or bourbon. A word of warning: be careful of choosing another style of whiskey for this drink; substitutes generally don't work well in this cocktail. Some bartenders prefer to substitute lime juice for lemon, but that is up to individual tastes.

Ingredients

60ml (2fl oz) rye whiskey or bourbon
30ml (1fl oz) dry vermouth
8ml (¼fl oz) freshly squeezed lemon juice
15ml (½fl oz) grenadine
2 dashes of orange bitters

Instructions

Half fill a cocktail shaker with ice. Pour in the whiskey, vermouth, lemon juice, grenadine and bitters and shake vigorously for 60 seconds. Strain into a coupe or martini glass and serve.

IN COMPLIANCE
WITH THE
8th AMENDMENT
NO
INTOXICATING
LIQUOR
ALLOWED ON
HE PREMISES

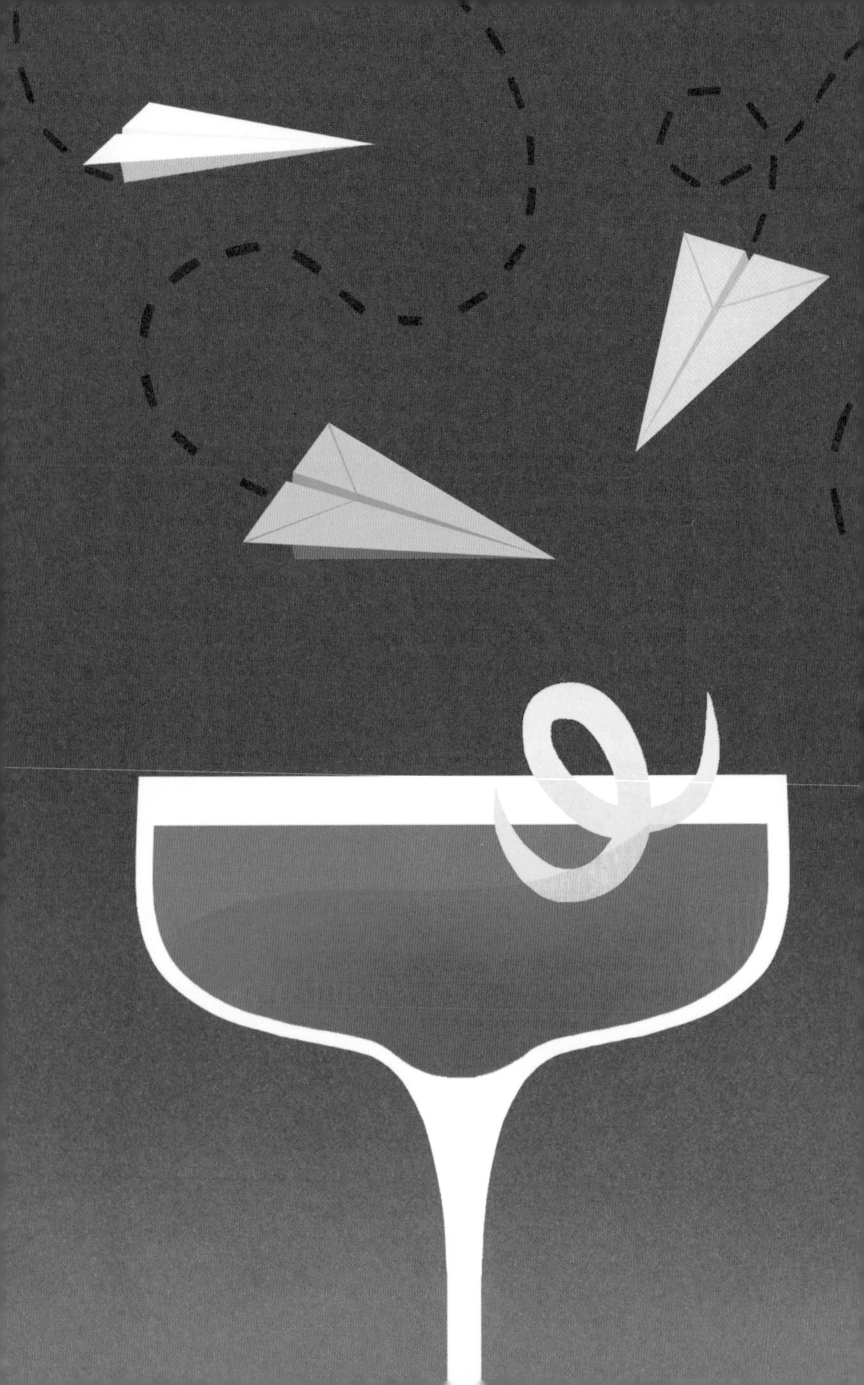

PAPER PLANE

Created by New York bartender Sam Ross, this modern cocktail classic is both stunningly beautiful and refreshing and complex, making it the perfect aperitif. It is easy to make, simply being equal parts of each ingredient combined and can be pre-batched for cocktail parties – just increase the ingredients to make how ever many drinks you need, then pour the cocktail into a shaker, one batch at a time, with some ice, shake and strain. This classic drink works best with bourbon.

Ingredients

22ml (¾fl oz) bourbon
22ml (¾fl oz) Aperol
22ml (¾fl oz) Amaro Nonino
22ml (¾fl oz) freshly squeezed lemon juice
a lemon twist, to garnish

Instructions

Half fill a cocktail shaker with ice. Pour in the bourbon, Aperol, Amaro Nonino and lemon juice, then shake vigorously for 1 minute. Strain into a martini glass or coupe. Garnish with a lemon twist.

BLOOD AND SAND

This cocktail gets its name from the eponymous 1922 bullfighting film starring Rudolph Valentino. The recipe for this drink first appeared in print in *The Savoy Cocktail Book* in 1930. Originally, it would have been made with blood orange juice (much more common in Europe than in the United States). The red colour of the juice was supposed to call to mind the blood of the bulls in the movie, and while this is considered one of Valentino's finest performances, the movie itself opened to less than enthusiastic reviews. This is also one of the few classic cocktails to use Cherry Heering, a Danish cherry brandy that is matured for three years before being bottled.

Ingredients

22ml (¾fl oz) blended Scotch whisky
22ml (¾fl oz) Cherry Heering liqueur
22ml (¾fl oz) sweet vermouth
22ml (¾fl oz) freshly squeezed orange juice (blood orange, if possible)
a large orange twist, to garnish

Instructions

Half fill a cocktail shaker with ice. Pour in the whisky, Cherry Heering, sweet vermouth and orange juice and shake vigorously for 1 minute. Strain into a coupe or martini glass, garnish with a large orange twist expressed over the drink.

BOULEVARDIER
PUBLISHED MONTHLY IN PARIS
JUNE 1928
COCKTAILS of
PARIS
SIRS, A DRINK?
oui! FOR ME A ROB ROY.

NO, NO, NO! IT SHOULD BE A BOULEVARDIER!
• WINES OF BURGUNDY • AMERICAN STYLE •
• HARRY'S NEW YORK BAR • WITH A TWIST? •

BOULEVARDIER

If you haven't heard of the Boulevardier, it is the cousin of the better-known gin-based cocktail, the Negroni. Originally appearing in American-expat and celebrity bartender Harry McElhone's 1927 cocktail book *Barflies and Cocktails*, it is mentioned as the signature drink of one Erskine Gwynne, socialite and editor of the Paris-based journal, *The Boulevardier*. A deceptively simple drink, many recipes for the Boulevardier will merely call for equal parts whisky, Campari and sweet vermouth for simplicity, but increasing the proportion of whisky results in a better-balanced cocktail. Stick to rye whiskey or a high rye-content bourbon for best results.

Ingredients

45ml (1½fl oz) rye whiskey or bourbon
30ml (1fl oz) sweet vermouth
30ml (1fl oz) Campari
an orange twist, to garnish

Instructions

Pour the whiskey or bourbon, sweet vermouth and Campari into a mixing glass. Add some ice and stir with a barspoon until chilled – about 1 minute. Strain into a chilled martini glass and garnish with an orange twist expressed over the surface of the drink.

OLD PAL

Today this cocktail is made with rye whiskey, but the original version would have used Canadian whisky. The Old Pal is constructed in a similar way to the gin-based Negroni, but dry vermouth is substituted for sweet and the rye for gin. This classic drink also dates back to Harry McElhone's 1927 book, *Barflies and Cocktails*, and it makes a drier and smoother change of pace from the usual Manhattans and Boulevardiers.

Ingredients
30ml (1fl oz) rye whiskey
30ml (1fl oz) dry vermouth
30ml (1fl oz) Campari
a lemon or orange twist, to garnish

Instructions
Pour the rye whiskey, dry vermouth and Campari into a mixing glass. Add some ice and stir for 1 minute. Strain into a chilled coupe or martini glass and garnish with a lemon or orange twist.

• BIRTHPLACE OF THE BLOODYMARY •
5 rue Danou
75002
HARRY'S
N.Y.
BAR
ESTD 1911
PARIS
93%
CALL
OLD PAL
HEY BUDDY!
OLD PAL!?
FANCY A DRINK?
WHISKEY!
CAMPARI...
AND MARTINI.
HARRY'S BAR, 9 PM.

PENICILLIN
CONTAINS:
BLENDED SCOTCH
HONEY & GINGER SYRUP
LEMON JUICE
ISLAY SINGLE MALT

PENICILLIN

The aptly named Penicillin is a modern classic crafted by bartender Sam Ross. Created in 2005, the Penicillin mixes Scotch whisky with honey, ginger and lemon to create one of the best and most popular Scotch-based drinks of modern times. Walk into a mixology bar in Hong Kong, London, Seattle or anywhere in between, sidle up to the bar and order a Penicillin and enjoy the drink that has gone viral.

Ingredients

60ml (2fl oz) blended Scotch whisky
22ml (¾fl oz) Honey-Ginger Syrup (see page 20)
22ml (¾fl oz) freshly squeezed lemon juice
8ml (¼fl oz) Islay single malt Scotch whisky
grated candied ginger, to garnish

Instructions

Pour the blended Scotch whisky, Honey-Ginger Syrup, lemon juice and Islay whisky into a mixing glass. Add some ice and stir for 1 minute. Strain into a chilled coupe glass and garnish with a little candied ginger on a cocktail pick.

SUFFERING BASTARD

The Suffering Bastard is perhaps the strangest cocktail in this book. Created in the 1940s by Joe Scialom at the Long Bar at the Shepheard Hotel in Cairo, Egypt (not exactly a hotbed of mixology), this potent mixture of bourbon, gin, lime juice, bitters and ginger ale was originally designed as a hangover cure. The hotel was a hangout for British Army officers during World War II, and enough of them had such bad hangovers that they would decide to drink them off (not recommended except in war zones). Thus this cocktail became the signature drink.

Ingredients

30ml (1fl oz) bourbon
30ml (1fl oz) gin
30ml (1fl oz) freshly squeezed lime juice
1 dash of Angostura bitters
120ml (4fl oz) ginger ale
an orange slice and a sprig of fresh mint, to garnish

Instructions

Pour the bourbon, gin, lime juice and Angostura bitters into a mixing glass. Add some ice and stir for 1 minute. Strain into an old fashioned glass filled with fresh ice cubes, top with ginger ale and garnish with an orange slice and a sprig of mint.

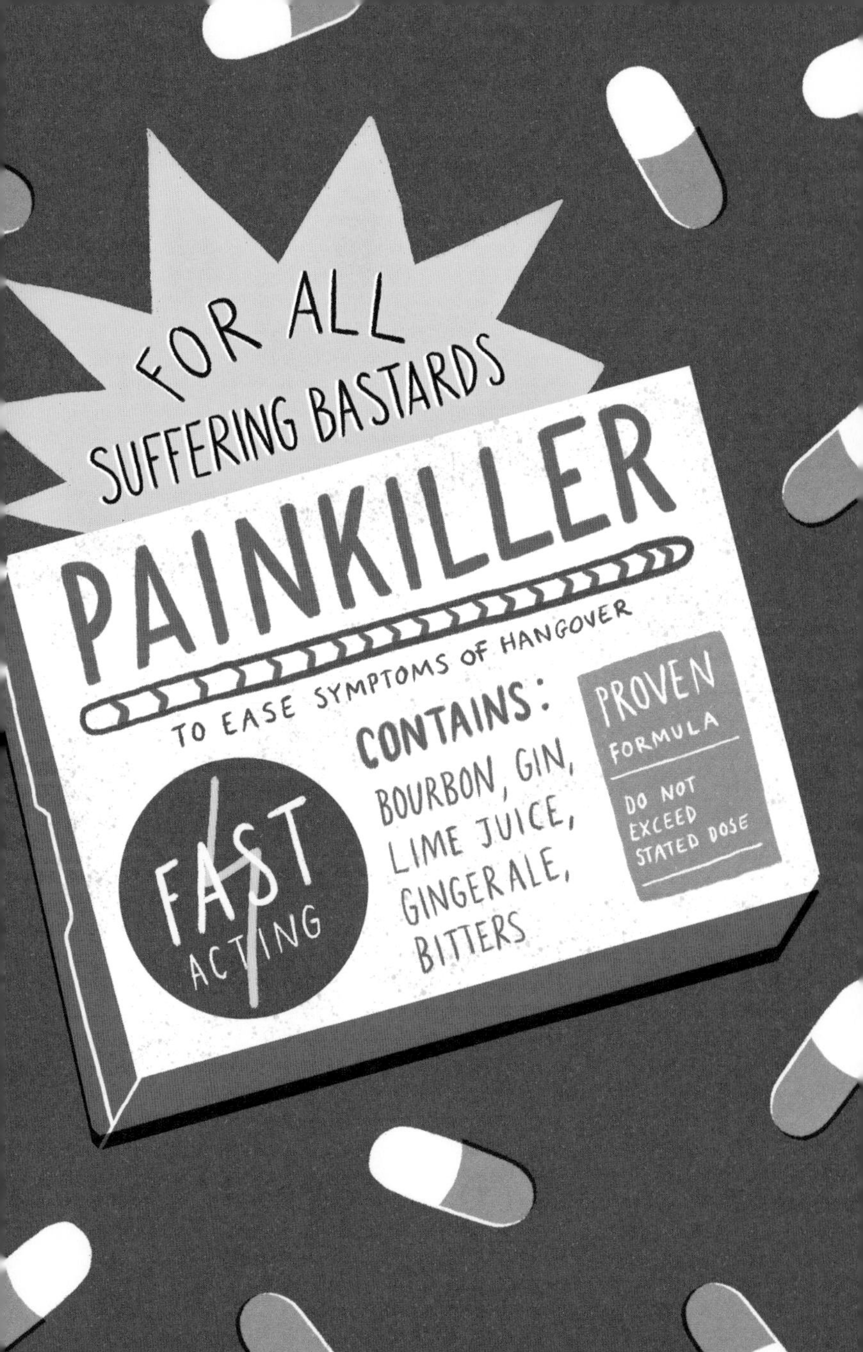
FOR ALL
SUFFERING BASTARDS
PAINKILLER
TO EASE SYMPTOMS OF HANGOVER
CONTAINS:
BOURBON, GIN,
LIME JUICE,
GINGER ALE,
BITTERS
PROVEN
FORMULA
DO NOT
EXCEED
STATED DOSE
FAST
ACTING

BOYLAN
EST. 1988
GINGER ALE
CANE SUGAR
330ML
BOTTLING CO

PRESBYTERIAN

Otherwise known as 'Press' for short, this cocktail is a bar staple – both for its simplicity and its refreshing taste. It is a close cousin of the Highball for its combination of whisky, soda water and ginger ale. Originally created in the 1890s, this drink is actually named after the Presbyterian Church, which originated primarily in Scotland, and the original recipe for this drink called for Scotch whisky – hence the name. Today, any whisky is acceptable, so feel free to experiment.

Ingredients

45ml (1½fl oz) whisky
60ml (2fl oz) soda water
60ml (2fl oz) ginger ale
a lemon wedge, to garnish

Instructions

Fill a highball glass with fresh ice cubes and pour in the whisky. Top with soda and ginger ale and garnish with a lemon wedge.

JOHN JONES

This cocktail, created by Jacob Grier – Portland, Oregon's magic enthusiast and bartender – falls into the bitter and stirred style of whisky drinks, by featuring both sweet vermouth and an Italian amaro to play with the spice notes in the rye whiskey base. The flamed orange peel adds just enough brightness to the drink, and let's be frank – flaming an orange peel adds a certain showmanship that can't fail to impress your guests.

Ingredients

60ml (2fl oz) 100% proof rye whiskey
22ml (¾fl oz) Carpano Antica Formula
22ml (¾fl oz) Amaro Ramazzotti
a flamed orange twist, to garnish (see below)

Instructions

Combine the rye whiskey, Carpano Antica and Amaro Ramazzotti in a cocktail shaker. Add some ice and shake vigorously. Strain over fresh ice cubes and garnish with a flamed orange twist. Serve immediately.

How to flame an orange twist: First cut a wide piece of peel without any pith (a Y-shaped vegetable peeler helps). Keeping the skin between your thumb and forefinger, begin to heat the peel with a lighter. After a few seconds of warming, squeeze the zest above the surface of the drink to create a large flame.

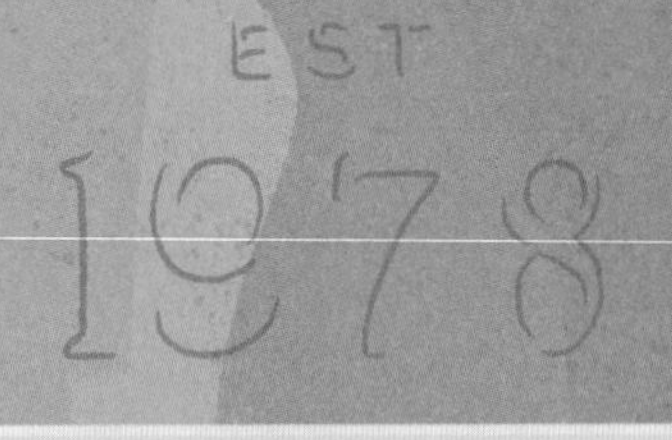
EST
1978
ESTº 1978
RUSTY'S
BLENDED SCOTCH WHISKY
PRODUCT OF SCOTLAND
ORIGINAL

RUSTY NAIL

That classic mix of Scotch whisky and Drambuie (a Scotch whisky-based liqueur flavoured with honey and herbs and associated with Bonnie Prince Charlie) has also lent its name to an entire category of drink preparation: Nail-style drinks. While the origins of the Rusty Nail are a bit murky, the best theory is that it was created at New York's Club 21, where bartenders could take the edge off rougher spirits often found during Prohibition by adding the sweetness of Drambuie. No matter its origin, the Rusty Nail continues to have legions of fans and is a delightful Scotch cocktail. No substitutions either on Scotch whisky or the Drambuie, please.

Ingredients

30ml (1fl oz) blended Scotch whisky
30ml (1fl oz) Drambuie

Instructions

Pour the whisky and Drambuie into a rocks glass, add a little fresh ice, then stir gently to incorporate.

THE GODFATHER

A mixture of Scotch whisky and amaretto in what bartenders refer to as a Nail-style drink - into which any combination of a base spirit (in this case, Scotch) and sweetener (amaretto) fall. This recipe calls for a 1-1 ratio of Scotch to amaretto, but feel free to play with the proportions as you like. This is a drink where a big, bold whisky works best, as the sweetness of the amaretto takes things down a notch and civilizes even the most uncouth of whiskies in your cabinet. Master this drink, then take this general idea and apply it to a number of different liqueurs and create all kinds of 'nails' of your own.

Ingredients

45ml (1 ½fl oz) Scotch whisky
45ml (1 ½fl oz) amaretto

Instructions

Add the whisky and amaretto to a rocks glass. Add some fresh ice cubes and stir gently to incorporate. Serve.

DISARONNO

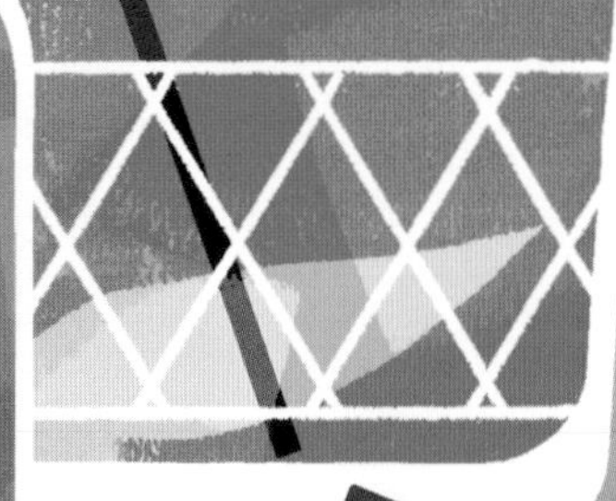

DISARONNO
ORIGINALE
SINCE 1525
THE WORLD'S FAVORITE
ITALIAN LIQUEUR
A LIQUEUR PRODUCED BY
ILLVA · SARONNO · ITALY
28% ALC. BY VOL. 750 ML
VINTAGE

ESTABLISHED 1831.
SAZERAC
COFFEE HOUSE
NEW ORLEANS.
MENU

SAZERAC

One of New Orleans' many contributions to cocktail culture, the Sazerac was originally made with French cognac in the 1850s. Named after Sazerac de Forge et Fils, a then-popular cognac brand, it used a local bitters produced by Antoine Amédée Peychaud - Peychaud's bitters. By the 1870s, due to cognac shortages after the phylloxera infestation in France's vineyards, rye whiskey was substituted and has since become the drink's base ingredient. The Sazerac has been the official cocktail of New Orleans since 2008. While it's a great drink to sip in the Big Easy, you can also easily replicate it at home. Stick with rye whiskey here, as other whiskies make poor substitutes. If you are feeling experimental, try the original recipe with a VSOP-level cognac instead of rye whiskey.

Ingredients

1 sugar cube
4 dashes of Peychaud's bitters
8ml (¼fl oz) water
45ml (1½fl oz) rye whiskey
8ml (¼fl oz) absinthe
a large lemon twist, to garnish

Instructions

Take two old fashioned glasses. Fill the first with ice and set it aside to chill. In the second, combine a sugar cube with the bitters and water, and gently muddle to dissolve the sugar. Pour in the rye whiskey, add some ice and stir for 30 seconds. Next, dump the ice from the first glass and pour in the absinthe, swirling it to coat the inside of the glass. Discard any extra absinthe in the bottom of the glass. Strain the whiskey mixture into the absinthe-rinsed glass. Express a large lemon twist over the top of the drink, rubbing it around the inside rim of the glass to maximise the flavour, then discard it. Serve.

TORONTO

This is not a drink for amateurs. Originally, Canadian whisky was used (although rye is more common today) and combined with Fernet (a very bitter type of Italian amaro), bitters and just a touch of sugar. This cocktail originally appeared in the 1922 cocktail book *Cocktails: How to Mix Them*, by London barman Robert Vermeire, who noted that this drink was 'much appreciated' by Canadians from Toronto. Given that the province of Ontario had a prohibition on alcohol from 1916 until 1927, it is safe to assume that this drink was most likely created in London and favoured by travelling Canadians.

Ingredients

60ml (2fl oz) rye whiskey (or Canadian whisky, to be authentic)
8ml (¼fl oz) Fernet Branca
8ml (¼fl oz) Simple Syrup (see page 20)
2 dashes of Angostura bitters
a large orange twist, to garnish

Instructions

Pour the rye whiskey, Fernet Branca, Simple Syrup and Angostura bitters into a mixing glass. Add some ice and stir for 1 minute. Strain into a chilled martini or old fashioned glass and garnish with a large orange twist.

TORONTO

COOPER'S COCKTAIL

A bartender in Seattle by way of Canada, Jamie Boudreau, proprietor of Canon in the Emerald City, is the creator of the this drink. While the Toronto (see page 68) is an older style of a whisky-and-Fernet cocktail, with the Cooper's, Boudreau has tempered the bitterness inherent in the amaro with elderflower liqueur and allowed both the Fernet and the elderflower to complement the spice notes in the rye whiskey. The result is a modern classic and one that's worth creating at home.

Ingredients

60ml (2fl oz) rye whiskey
22ml (¾fl oz) elderflower liqueur
8ml (¼fl oz) Fernet Branca
an orange twist, to garnish

Instructions

Pour the rye whiskey, elderflower liqueur and Fernet Branca into a mixing glass. Add some ice and stir for 1 minute. Strain into a chilled coupe or martini glass and garnish with an orange twist.

OLD BAY RIDGE

This creation comes from modern cocktail historian David Wondrich, but it tastes like a cocktail that would have originated in the 1920s. Rye whiskey shares the stage with aquavit, a Scandinavian spirit similar to vodka that is spiced with caraway or dill. This recipe calls for Linie Aquavit, which is matured at sea, making a transequatorial trip from Norway to Australia and back, before being bottled. It is notoriously tough to mix cocktails with aquavit, but this is an amazing cocktail and one worth investing in this unique spirit.

Ingredients

1 sugar cube
2 dashes of Angostura bitters
30ml (1fl oz) rye whiskey
30ml (1fl oz) Linie Aquavit

Instructions

Start by muddling the sugar cube, Angostura bitters, rye whiskey and aquavit in a mixing glass. Next add some ice and stir to combine the flavours. Strain into an old fashioned glass filled with fresh ice cubes.

LINIE AQUAVIT
LYSHOLM
FABRIK MÆRKE
LINIE
AQUAVIT

aromatic bitters
ANGOSTURA
200ml

Welcome to
KENTUCKY

KENTUCKY MULE

This cocktail is a member of the family of drinks known as mules or bucks, of which the most famous is the vodka-based Moscow Mule, created in the 1940s at Hollywood's famous Cock 'n' Bull. However, mules and bucks have been around for much longer. While the origin of these drinks is unclear, legend has it that adding a spirit such as whisky to ginger beer gave the drink a 'kick', hence the name. Obviously, bourbon is the classic call here, but rye whiskey will up the spiciness factor a bit, while an American blended whiskey is a perfectly fine choice for a lighter, smoother option. The choice is yours.

Ingredients

60ml (2fl oz) bourbon
120ml (4fl oz) ginger beer
a lime wedge, to garnish

Instructions

Pour the bourbon into a copper mug. Add fresh ice cubes, then fill to the brim with ginger beer. Garnish with a lime wedge.

REMEMBER THE MAINE

'Remember the Maine' was a rallying cry for the Spanish-American War in 1898 that led to Cuban independence. While few people remember the sinking of the *USS Maine* in Havana harbour, the drink is a reminder of that historic time, and it uses good American rye whiskey in a patriotic nod to the US. The drink first appeared in Charles Baker's 1939 cocktail book, *The Gentleman's Companion: Being an Exotic Drinking Book Or, Around the World with Jigger, Beaker and Flask*. Think of this as a Manhattan cocktail modified with a bit of Cherry Heering and absinthe. The key to this drink is using rye whiskey only (no substitutions, please!) and going easy on the absinthe. A little absinthe goes a long way, and too much will quickly tip this cocktail from delicious to unpleasant.

Ingredients

60ml (2fl oz) rye whiskey
22ml (¾fl oz) sweet vermouth
¼ tsp absinthe
2 tsp Cherry Heering liqueur
a cherry, to garnish

Instructions

Pour the rye whiskey, sweet vermouth, absinthe and Cherry Heering into a mixing glass. Add ice and mix for 6 seconds. Strain into a chilled coupe glass and garnish with a cherry.

RST PUBLISHING
1939
THE GENTLEMAN'S COMPANION
VOL.1
BEING AN EXOTIC COOKERY BOOK
VOL.2
BEING AN EXOTIC DRINKING BOOK
CHARLES H. BAKER, JR.

JIM BEAM.

RSt
ESTD 1888
WHITE
SUGAR
100% NATURAL
FAIRTRADE

THE WORLD'S NO.1 BOURBON
JIM BEAM
BOURBON
KENTUCKY STRAIGHT
BOURBON WHISKEY
JAMES B. BEAM DISTILLING CO.

CHATHAM ARTILLERY PUNCH

(Serves 45 120-ml/4-oz servings)

This is a throwback to the 1800s, and while many drinks from that era just don't hold up for modern palates, the Chatham Artillery Punch remains as relevant as ever. Essentially just a simple combination of whisky, cognac, rum and sparkling wine with a bit of sugar and lemon thrown in for good measure, this punch will serve an entire military regiment and then some, between the volume of drinks and the sheer strength of each serving. This drink is best served in small portions.

Ingredients

12 lemons
450g (16oz) caster sugar
1 bottle cognac
1 bottle bourbon
1 bottle dark rum
3 bottles sparkling wine

Instructions

Using a Y-shaped vegetable peeler, peel all the lemons, leaving the white pith behind. Combine the peels and sugar in a bowl and muddle together to combine, then set aside to rest for 2 hours.

Juice enough lemons to obtain 450ml (16fl oz) of lemon juice, then pour this over the peels and sugar mixture. Add 120ml (4fl oz) water, strain off the peels and reserve the lemon juice/sugar mixture. Fill a punch bowl with cracked ice and pour in all the bottles of whisky, rum and wine, plus the sugar and lemon mixture. Stir to combine and serve in small punch glasses.

FEZ MEDINA

Denver Colorado's Ky Belk is one of the most talented bartenders in America today. A winner of numerous awards for his bartending, Belk juggles running multiple beverage programmes at some of Denver's top restaurants and bars. With the Fez Medina, rye whiskey is combined with Aperol, amaro and orange bitters to highlight the spice notes and orange undertones in the rye whiskey. This is a deceptively simple drink that delivers layer upon layer of flavour.

Ingredients

45ml (1 ½fl oz) rye whiskey
22ml (¾fl oz) Amaro CioCiaro
15ml (½fl oz) Aperol
3 dashes of orange bitters
a dehydrated orange slice, to garnish

Instructions

Add the rye whiskey, amaro, Aperol and orange bitters to a mixing glass. Add some ice and stir for 1 minute. Strain into an old fashioned glass and garnish with a dehydrated orange slice.

ORANGE
bitters
200ml

APER
Aperi
LIQU
ITAL
A
BARBI

PEROL
APE

JACK DANIEL'S
RYE
JACK DANIEL'S
BARRELL AGED
RYE
WHISKEY
Tennessee
STRAIGHT
RYE WHISKEY
DISTILLED AND BOTTLED BY
JACK DANIEL DISTILLERY
LYNCHBURG, TENN. USA
45% ALC/VOL (90 PROOF)
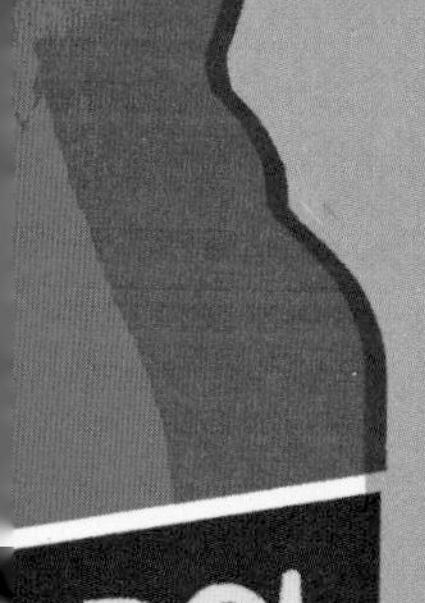
EROL
peritivo
LIQUEUR
ITALY
A
ARBIERI

Since 1821
ANGOSTURA
ORANGE
bitters

JACK DANIEL'S
RYE

WDG

W.D.G ORIGINAL
RUM
• SMALL BATCH •
Dark
70cle
40%vol
AGED IN OAK BARRELS
DISTILLED FROM SUGAR CANE MOLASSES

M.E
OK

PORTO
Niepoort
SINCE 1848

RUBY
DUM

SUBURBAN

This drink dates from the golden age of 19th-century cocktails. This heady mix of rye whiskey, rum and port wine is a veritable greatest hits compilation of favoured beverages from that era, so it makes sense that someone decided to combine all three. This drink was originally created by bartenders at the Waldorf Astoria Hotel in New York City for a racehorse owner who had a horse running in the Suburban Handicap at Brooklyn's Sheepshead Bay Race Track.

Ingredients

45ml (1½fl oz) rye whiskey
15ml (½fl oz) dark rum
15ml (½fl oz) ruby port
1 dash of Angostura bitters
1 dash of orange bitters
an orange twist, to garnish

Instructions

Pour the rye whiskey, dark rum, ruby port and both bitters into a mixing glass. Add some ice and stir for 1 minute. Strain into a chilled coupe and garnish with an orange twist.

WHISKEY BRAMBLE

This is a variation on a gin-based drink created in 1980 by legendary London barkeep Dick Bradsell at Fred's Club, in London's Soho district. While gin is wonderful here, whisky (Irish *whiskey* in particular) is a natural pairing with both lemon and crème de mûre (or blackberry brandy), and the results for this version may be even better than the original. Bradsell said that childhood berry-picking trips on the Isle of Wight inspired this drink, and the name is a nod to those blackberry bushes, otherwise known as brambles.

Ingredients

60ml (2fl oz) bourbon or Irish whiskey
22ml (¾fl oz) freshly squeezed lemon juice
8ml (¼fl oz) Simple Syrup (see page 20)
15ml (½fl oz) crème de mûre (blackberry brandy)
a few blackberries and a lemon wheel, to garnish

Instructions

Half fill a cocktail shaker with ice. Pour in the bourbon or whiskey, lemon juice and Simple Syrup, shake vigorously and strain into an old fashioned glass filled with crushed ice. Drizzle crème de mûre over the top of the drink, then garnish with blackberries and a lemon wheel.

MINT JULEP

A symbol of the American South, the Mint Julep is inextricably linked to the Kentucky Derby horse race, where it has been the official drink since 1938. Amazingly, up to 120,000 juleps are consumed at Churchill Downs over Derby weekend every year. The word 'julep' is descended from the Arabic drink 'julab', which is made with water and rose petals. The modern julep dates back to the 1700s, and the silver or pewter julep cup is key to this drink. Glass is an insulator, so a proper julep cup will get icy on the outside while it sits. Spearmint is the go-to mint in the South, although peppermint will also work in a pinch. The julep is a rare drink that actually gets better as it sits, so try your hand at one of these on a warm summer day, then sit back and relax, sipping slowly as the world whizzes by.

Ingredients

a large bunch of mint sprigs
15ml (½fl oz) Simple Syrup (see page 20)
60ml (2fl oz) bourbon

Instructions

In the bottom of a julep cup, add 8–10 mint leaves, stripped from the bunch, and half the Simple Syrup. Gently muddle the mint in the Simple Syrup, being careful not to bruise the leaves. Fill the julep cup with crushed ice, mounding it over the top and creating a look reminiscent of a snow cone. Slowly pour the bourbon over the top of the ice, followed by the remaining Simple Syrup. Next, take the remaining bunch of mint sprigs and give them a good spank between your hands to release the essential oils. Place these into the ice as a garnish, along with a short (paper) straw so that the aromas of the drink can be better enjoyed.

BOURBON SMASH

A close cousin of the Mint Julep, the Bourbon Smash is enhanced with a slightly different preparation and the addition of lemon juice. The resulting cocktail combines the mint of a julep with the lemon of a sour, creating a happy medium of both. This cocktail takes well to freshly muddled fruit (think berries in particular) as an additional alternative. The smash is a drink that deserves more attention than it currently gets and is perfect as a warm-weather cocktail.

Ingredients

8–10 mint leaves, plus a sprig to garnish
15ml (½fl oz) Simple Syrup (see page 20)
60ml (2fl oz) bourbon
22ml (¾fl oz) freshly squeezed lemon juice

Instructions

Place the mint leaves at the bottom of a cocktail shaker. Add the Simple Syrup and gently muddle the mint leaves. Add some ice cubes, and pour in the bourbon and lemon juice. Shake vigorously and strain into an old fashioned glass filled with fresh ice cubes. Garnish with a sprig of freshly spanked mint.

SPECIAL
BOURBON
MATURED IN OAK CASKS
CRAFTED WITH
STRAIGHT BOURBON
43%ALC/VOL
Vol.700ml

DERBY

The Derby cocktail is served by bartenders in a couple of variations, but this version with sweet vermouth, orange curaçao and lime juice is the real classic. Originally created by tiki legend 'Trader Vic' Bergeron, this version of the Derby produces a drink with herbal overtones offset by the tartness of the lime. Tiki fans beware: despite the link with Trader Vic, this isn't a tiki drink. Instead it is a serious whisky drink that showcases Trader Vic's ability to go 'off brand' and create classic cocktails without an island vibe.

Ingredients

30ml (1fl oz) whisky
15ml (½fl oz) sweet vermouth
15ml (½fl oz) orange curaçao
22ml (¾fl oz) freshly squeezed lime juice
a lime wedge and mint leaves, to garnish

Instructions

Pour the whisky, sweet vermouth, orange curaçao and lime juice into a cocktail shaker along with some ice. Shake vigorously and strain into a martini glass. Garnish with a lime wedge and mint leaves.

FROZEN THAI WHISKEY COKE

This cocktail contains both Thai whiskey and bourbon, but only one of those ingredients is actually whisky . . . Thai whiskey is actually closer to a rum, as it is made from 95% sugar or molasses and 5% rice, which is then flavoured with local herbs and spices for a spirit that is uniquely Thai. This delicious drink from mixologist Ky Belk is a great excuse to break out your blender on a warm day and whip up this refreshing frozen drink.

Ingredients

30ml (1fl oz) Mekhong Thai whiskey
30ml (1fl oz) bottled-in-bond bourbon
8ml (¼fl oz) freshly squeezed lime juice
1 barspoon ginger juice (shop-bought or home-juiced – alternatively, swap for ginger beer)
120ml (4fl oz) cola

Instructions

If juicing your own ginger, peel it first. Pour both whiskies, the lime juice, ginger juice and cola into a blender along with one giant scoop of ice. Blend until combined, then pour into whatever glass you may have on hand that looks like it might fit!

PRODUCT OF THAILAND
ESTD 1941 THAILAND
Mekhong
THE SPIRIT
OF THAILAND
IMPORTED
Distilled Blended & Bottled by
BANGYIKHAN DISTILLERY
Product of Thailand
700ml e
35%vol.

SEELBACH
SPARKLING WINE

SEELBACH

This cocktail hails from Louisville, Kentucky, where it was created at the Seelbach Hotel in the 1800s. Oh wait, no, forget that . . . It was actually a Kentucky bartender who created it in the 1990s and then lied about the origins of the drink for 20 years, before eventually confessing. The bartender claimed that the drink was discovered on an old menu at the hotel, but he finally admitted that he concocted the story because it sounded better. (The bar world isn't known for letting truth stand in the way of a good story.) Regardless, the Seelbach is a great drink with echoes back to the classics. Make one of these and raise a toast to one of the greatest frauds the cocktail world has ever seen.

Ingredients

30ml (1fl oz) bourbon
15ml (½fl oz) Cointreau
6 dashes each of Angostura and Peychaud's bitters
sparkling wine, to top up
a lemon twist, to garnish

Instructions

Pour the bourbon, Cointreau and bitters into a mixing glass. Add some ice and stir for 1 minute. Strain into a champagne flute and top up with sparkling wine. Garnish with a lemon twist.

DUCK FART

No cocktail book is complete without a reference to flatulence, and the Duck Fart is the only whisky drink that meets the criteria, so here it is. It was created at the Peanut Farm in Anchorage, Alaska, in the 1990s during a time when all the good names for cocktails were taken. Great drink, lousy name. To pay homage to the era that spawned this unfortunately titled drink, some bartenders don't even bother layering this pousse-café-style drink with a barspoon and instead just use a maraschino cherry to build up the spirits. Why not try this yourself?

Ingredients

15ml (½fl oz) coffee liqueur
15ml (½fl oz) Irish cream liqueur, such as Bailey's
15ml (½fl oz) whisky

Instructions

Using the back of a barspoon to pour over, layer the drink into a shot glass. Start with the coffee liqueur, followed by the Irish cream, and then finish with the whisky on top.

IRISH
SHOT
DROP

GUINNESS

IRISH DROP SHOT

This is a simple, tasty and very, very Irish cocktail. It is a drink for socialising and partying, not for putting into a snifter to discuss its many qualities. One word of warning, though - because this drink goes down so easily, some people won't pay attention to their consumption and can overdo it quickly. Pace yourself with a full glass of water or other nonalcoholic beverage in between rounds, and be aware that this one can sneak up on you pretty quickly.

St. Patrick's Day is the most famous day to consume this drink in the US, but it's an appropriate order any time one wants to get the party started!

Ingredients

22ml (¾fl oz) Irish whiskey
22ml (¾fl oz) Bailey's Irish Cream
240ml (8fl oz) Guinness Irish Stout

Instructions

In a shot glass, combine the Irish whiskey and Irish Cream. Pour the Guinness into a pint glass, then drop the shot glass into the beer and consume immediately.

BOILERMAKER

This is the kind of drink one expects dockworkers and other salt-of-the-earth types to drink in the morning for breakfast right after a tough night's work. However, any combination of a beer and a shot of whisky is actually a Boilermaker – it's up to you how you drink it.

A classic light lager is the traditional choice for the Boilermaker.

Ingredients
60ml (2fl oz) whisky
450ml (16fl oz) beer (a classic light lager)

Instructions
There are two options here.
Option 1: drop a shot of whisky into a glass of beer and drink immediately; or option 2: pour the whisky and beer into separate glasses and alternate sips of each.

SIP?

DROP?

TOMATO
Juice

C SAUCE O.
SAUCE CO.
PREMIUM SAUCES SINCE
1938
WORCESTERSHIRE
SAUCE

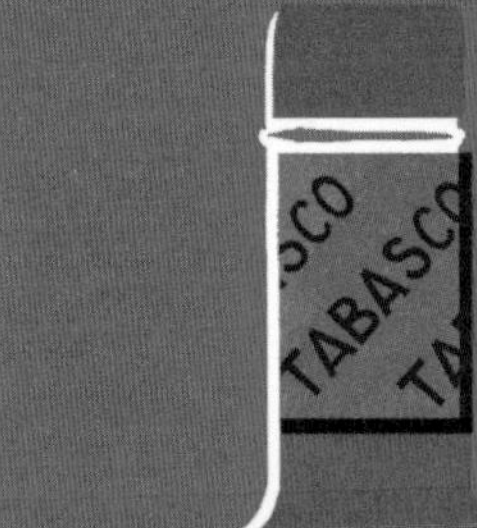
TABASCO

MC ILHENNY CO.
AVERY ISLAND
L.A
TABASCO
BRAND
PEPPER SAUCE

CELERY
SALT

SCOTCH BLOODY MARY

While this might sound like the kind of a drink concocted by a bartender after a cocktail too many, the combination works surprisingly well. Choose a blended Scotch with a bit of smoke to complement the tomato juice and spices, and you'll be rewarded with a very balanced flavour combination - perhaps even more so than the traditional vodka version, which adds little to no character. This is also a fun drink to order at the bar, as you are sure to get a second look from the bartender (whether from intrigue or a sense of dread). However, once the barkeep overcomes any apprehension, they will usually promise to enjoy one the next time they are on your side of the bar, so spread the gospel of this underrated cocktail far and wide.

Ingredients

a lime wedge and 2 dashes of celery salt, for the glass
60ml (2fl oz) blended Scotch whisky
8ml (¼fl oz) freshly squeezed lemon juice
1 pinch of black pepper
1 tsp grated horseradish
1 tsp soy sauce
6 dashes of Worcestershire sauce
2 dashes of hot sauce
120ml (4fl oz) tomato juice
a celery stalk, green olive and lemon wedge, to garnish

Instructions

Take a pint glass and rub a lime wedge around the rim, then dip it in the celery salt. Next, add the whisky, lemon juice, pepper, horseradish and the sauces. Stir briefly. Add ice to the glass, top with tomato juice and stir briefly to combine. Garnish with a celery stalk, green olive and lemon wedge.

SHIFT DRINK

Jacob Grier's other contribution to this book, the Shift Drink was inspired by the two things bartenders often reach for at the end of their shift: whisky and Fernet Branca. A 'shift drink' is the free drink that bartenders and other restaurant and bar staff often receive at the end of their shift as a thank you from the house for their hard work. This cocktail marries these two popular choices for shift drinks and complements them with ginger and lemon to create something that is truly memorable.

Ingredients

45ml (1 ½fl oz) rye whiskey
22ml (¾fl oz) Ginger Syrup (see page 20)
22ml (¾fl oz) freshly squeezed lemon juice
15ml (½fl oz) Fernet Branca
a lemon twist, to garnish

Instructions

Half fill a cocktail shaker with ice. Pour in the rye whiskey, Ginger Syrup, lemon juice and Fernet Branca and shake until chilled. Strain over fresh ice cubes into an old fashioned glass and garnish with lemon twist.

FERNET-BRANCA
BRANCA
CASA FONDATA NEL 1845
FERNET-BRANCA
FRATTELLI BRANCA-DISTILLERIE
del famoso
FERNET BRANCA
PRODOTTOENITALIA

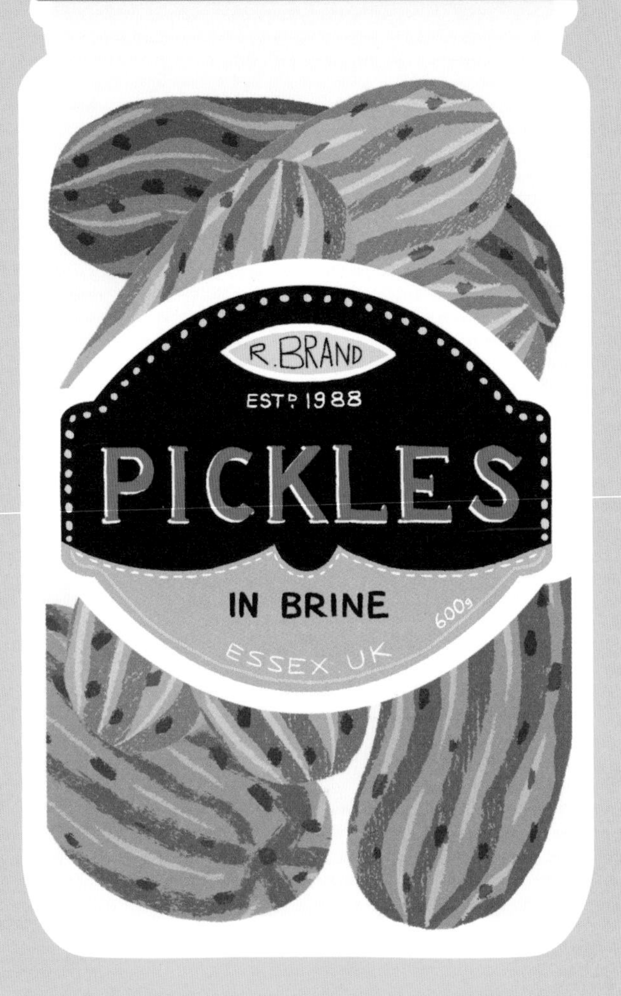
R. BRAND
ESTD 1988
PICKLES
IN BRINE
600g
ESSEX UK

PICKLEBACK

This is one of those drinks that serves as an unofficial 'bartender's handshake', as it is a very popular choice at the end of a shift. Essentially a shot of whisky (originally it would have been Irish whiskey, but use what you enjoy) followed by a chaser of pickle brine, the Pickleback has evolved into some unusual whisky-and-brine pairings. The combination is a classic, and cocktails don't get much easier to make than this. Even better, go into your local bar right before closing time and order one from the bartender. You'll likely get a knowing smile and a few questions about where you might bartend.

Ingredients

60ml (2fl oz) whisky
60ml (2fl oz) pickle brine

Instructions

Pour some whisky into a shot glass and a shot of brine into a second shot glass. Drink the whisky, then chase it with the brine.

SWAFFORD COCKTAIL

Tom Swafford is a legend in the restaurant circles of Portland, Oregon, and the Swafford cocktail was named in his honour. Spicy rye whiskey combines with Applejack brandy to form the base spirits of the cocktail, while green chartreuse and maraschino liqueur work together to create a drink as elegantly sophisticated and timeless as the man himself. Put on some old jazz records, open a good book and warm yourself next to a crackling fire on a cold night while you sip. Rumour has it, that's how Mr Swafford himself enjoys this drink.

Ingredients

30ml (1fl oz) rye whiskey
30ml (1fl oz) Applejack
15ml (½fl oz) green chartreuse
15ml (½fl oz) maraschino liqueur
an orange twist, to garnish

Instructions

Pour the rye whiskey, Applejack, green chartreuse and maraschino liqueur into a mixing glass. Add some ice and stir for 1 minute. Strain into a chilled coupe or martini glass and garnish with an orange twist.

RTREUSE

CHARTREUSE
LIQUEUR FABRIQUÉE
PAR LES PERES CHARTREUX
1605
L. Garnier
Product of France
ALC 40% BY VOL. 750 ML
CHARTREUSE DIFFUSION

IMPROVED WHISKEY COCKTAIL

'Professor' Jerry Thomas included this Improved Whiskey Cocktail in his original bartender's book back in 1862. You may ask yourself, 'What is being improved?' Well, the answer is simple. This drink takes the classic Old Fashioned and 'improves' it with the addition of a liqueur – in this case, maraschino. The result is a cocktail that tastes great. However, unless you have a barkeep in the know, you may have to walk them through this drink. Option two, of course, is to perfect it yourself and enjoy making it at home.

Ingredients

1 sugar cube
1 dash of Angostura bitters
1 dash of Peychaud's bitters
1 dash of absinthe
1 tsp maraschino liqueur
60ml (2fl oz) bourbon
a lemon twist, to garnish

Instructions

Muddle the sugar cube with both bitters, the absinthe and the maraschino liqueur in an old fashioned glass. Pour in the bourbon and stir until the sugar is completely dissolved. Add some fresh ice cubes and garnish with a lemon twist.

STONE FENCE

If you only make one cocktail from this book, let this be the one. This version is from the era of the US Civil War, featuring bourbon and nonalcoholic cloudy apple cider. In Colonial times this drink would have been made with rum and hard apple cider, which would have naturally fermented as it aged. The original Colonial form is a rough, 'any-port-in-a-storm' kind of a drink, while this take on it is simple, elegant and tastes like autumn. Even better, you can let your guests make this for themselves during holiday cocktail parties. The proportions offered here are merely a guideline - pour a little more bourbon or get a bit heavy on the bitters, and this drink still tastes great. Even the most inexperienced hands can create this cocktail.

Ingredients

60ml (2fl oz) bourbon or rye whiskey
6 dashes of Angostura bitters
120ml (4fl oz) cloudy apple cider
a cinnamon stick and grated nutmeg, to garnish

Instructions

Pour the bourbon or whiskey into an old fashioned glass. Add fresh ice cubes and the Angostura bitters, then top up with cloudy apple cider. Garnish with a cinnamon stick and grated nutmeg.

WHISKY SOUR

This is a simple but delectable combination of whisky, lemon juice, sugar and, optionally, egg white. The egg white gives a richer mouthfeel, but either way this drink is a classic not to be missed. The Whisky Sour is another foundational drink that allows the mixer to create some fun variations (see New York Sour on page 116). Why not try adding a barspoon of good British orange marmalade to the cocktail shaker for an interesting twist? Traditionally, this drink would be made with bourbon, but feel free to use whatever whisky you prefer. Irish whiskey and Canadian whisky would be great choices here, and a Japanese blended whisky could work well.

Ingredients

45ml (1 ½fl oz) whisky
22ml (¾fl oz) freshly squeezed lemon juice
22ml (¾fl oz) Simple Syrup (see page 20)
1 egg white (optional)
a lemon wheel and an amarena cherry, to garnish

Instructions

Pour the whisky, lemon juice, Simple Syrup and separated egg white, if using, into a cocktail shaker. Add some ice and shake vigorously for 1 minute. Strain into an old fashioned glass filled with fresh ice cubes. Garnish with a lemon wheel and an amarena cherry.

NEW YORK SOUR

This aptly named drink is the uber-sophisticated cousin of the more down-to-earth Whisky Sour (see page 114). Now, you may be asking yourself, 'Red wine in a Whisky Sour?' and that is a fair question. But the result is delicious, and the drink looks great when served to friends - plus, it's fairly simple to make.

Ingredients

60ml (2fl oz) bourbon
30ml (1fl oz) freshly squeezed lemon juice
30ml (1fl oz) Simple Syrup (see page 20)
1 egg white (optional)
15ml (½fl oz) red wine

Instructions

Half fill a cocktail shaker with ice. Pour in the bourbon, lemon juice, Simple Syrup and separated egg white (optional) and shake vigorously for 1 minute. Strain into an old fashioned glass filled with fresh ice cubes. To float the red wine, just place a barspoon over the surface of the drink and pour the wine onto the back of the spoon, allowing it roll off it and stay on top of the drink. This drink does not require a garnish but feel free to add.

TAXI

BRUICHLA

PROGRESSIVE HEBRIDEAN
DISTILLERS
BRUICHLADDICH

BRUICHLADDICH
ISLAY SINGLE MALT
THE
CLASSIC
LADDIE
SCOTTISH BARLEY
IT IS OUR MISSION TO PURSUE THE ULTIMATE PEDIGREE, PROVENANCE AND TRACEABILITY OF OUR RAW MATERIALS. CHIEF OF WHICH IS OUR BARLEY AND TO PUSH THE BOUNDARIES OF THE CONCEPT OF TERROIR IN ARTISANAL SINGLE MALT WHISKY.
UNPEATED
ISLAY SINGLE MALT
SCOTCH WHISKY
DISTILLED, MATURED AND BOTTLED
UN-CHILL FILTERED AND COLOURING-FREE
AT BRUICHLADDICH DISTILLERY,
ISLE OF ISLAY, SCOTLAND.
PRODUCT OF SCOTLAND.
750 ML
50% ALC/VOL.

WHISKY FLIP

This is about as old school as cocktails get. Whisky, egg and sugar, shaken together into a froth that is far more than the sum of its parts. The flip is a great drink to have in your repertoire, as it's anything but run of the mill, has a long history and, most importantly, tastes great. In 1695, 'flip' was originally used for a mixture of rum, beer and sugar that was heated with a red-hot iron, or loggerhead. The intense heat of the iron caused the drink to froth up or 'flip', hence the name. Over time, beer was replaced with whisky, more sugar was added, an egg found its way into the mix, and the drink stopped being served hot. This recipe is for the 1800s-era version of the 'flip', and is easily the most suited for a modern palate.

Ingredients

60ml (2fl oz) whisky
30ml (1fl oz) Simple Syrup (see page 20)
1 whole egg
1 nutmeg, for grating, to garnish

Instructions

Put the whisky and Simple Syrup into a cocktail shaker, then crack in the whole egg. Add some ice and shake hard for 60 seconds. Strain into a wine glass and grate some nutmeg over the top.

IRISH FLIP

John Lermayer from Miami's Sweet Liberty created the Irish Flip in 2016. It isn't the type of drink one would expect to come from a bartender in a warm, tropical location, but this combination of Irish whiskey, chocolate bitters, Licor 43, Irish stout and an entire egg is a very modern interpretation of the classic flip. The key to this drink is to shake it long enough and hard enough to ensure that the ingredients are well combined.

Ingredients

30ml (1fl oz) Irish whiskey
30ml (1fl oz) Licor 43
45ml (1½fl oz) Irish stout
1 dash of chocolate bitters
1 whole egg
1 nutmeg, for grating, to garnish

Instructions

Half fill a cocktail shaker with ice. Pour in the Irish whiskey, Licor 43, stout, chocolate bitters and crack in the whole egg. Shake very vigorously for 90 seconds to incorporate the egg into the drink. Strain into a martini glass and garnish with freshly grated nutmeg.

1864
CHOCOLATE
BITTERS

IRISH
STOUT
O'HARAS
IRISH
STOUT
EST 1801
IRISH
STOUT
BREWED IN
IRELAND

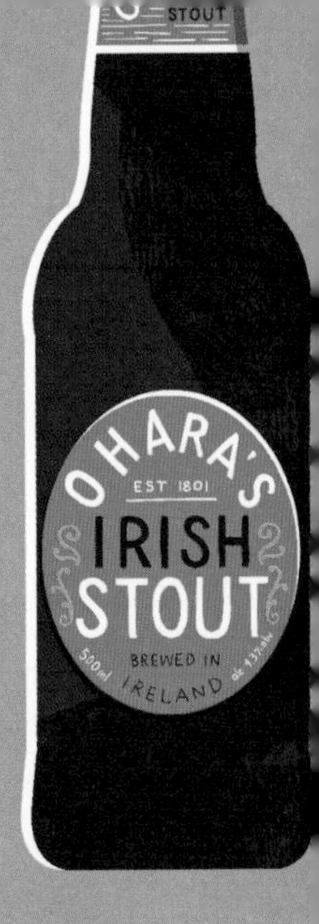
O'HARA'S
EST 1801
IRISH
STOUT
BREWED IN
IRELAND
500ml

1864
CHOCOLATE
BITTERS

IRISH
STOUT
O'HARAS
IRISH
STOUT
O'HARA'S
EST 1801
IRISH
STOUT
BREWED IN
IRELAND
500ml

IRISH
STOUT
O'HARAS
IRISH
STOUT

1864

1864
CHOCOLATE
BITTERS

EXQUISITE
COFFEE
LIQUEUR
BATCH NO : 3
BOTTLE NO 2301
25% ABV
70cl e

REVOLVER

The Revolver was created in the early 2000s by legendary San Francisco bartender Jon Santer, now owner of the renowned cocktail bar Prizefighter in Emeryville, California. Santer's original recipe called for a rye-heavy bourbon, but a rye whiskey also works well in this drink, adding a touch of spice that cuts through the dark coffee and orange notes. However, avoid whiskies that are too light-bodied, as the other ingredients will overwhelm the flavour.

Ingredients

60ml (2fl oz) rye-based bourbon
15ml (½fl oz) coffee liqueur
2 dashes of orange bitters
a large orange twist, to garnish

Instructions

Pour the bourbon, coffee liqueur and orange bitters into a mixing glass. Add some ice and stir for 1 minute. Strain into a chilled coupe or martini glass and garnish with a large orange twist.

TONKA COCKTAIL

Created in 2010 at Schumann's Bar in Munich, Germany by Klaus St Ranier, the Tonka Cocktail is an inventive Japanese whisky-based drink. Pairing the blended Japanese whisky with sweet vermouth and chocolate vodka creates a rich, complex drink that shows just how mixable Japanese whisky can be. Notes of chocolate and orange are dominant flavours in this drink, but it is interesting to taste the secondary flavours of vanilla and caramel from the whisky, and marvel at so many layers in one drink.

Ingredients

60ml (2fl oz) Japanese blended whisky
30ml (1fl oz) sweet vermouth
15ml (½fl oz) chocolate vodka
2 dashes of Angostura bitters
a flamed orange peel (see page 60), to garnish

Instructions

Combine the Japanese blended whisky, sweet vermouth, chocolate vodka and Angostura bitters in a mixing glass. Add some ice and stir for 60 seconds. Strain into a chilled martini glass and garnish with a flamed orange peel.

SUNTORY WHISKY
響
HIBIKI
SUNTORY WHISKY
JAPANESE HARMONY

MEZCAL
Espadin
100%
PURE
CANADIAN
MAPLE
SYRUP

SMOKY ROBINSON

Not to be confused with the legendary R&B and soul singer Smokey Robinson, this drink combines whisky with the smoke of mezcal, tequila's bad-boy cousin. Add in some Maple-Spiced Simple Syrup and there is a lot going on in this drink. This is one to sit and savour on a crisp autumn night, perhaps with a little Smokey Robinson playing in the background.

Ingredients

45ml (1½fl oz) Tennessee whiskey (such as George Dickel)
15ml (½fl oz) mezcal
22ml (¾fl oz) Maple-Spiced Simple Syrup (see page 20)
22ml (¾fl oz) freshly squeezed lemon juice
a lemon twist, to garnish

Instructions

First make the Maple-Spiced Simple Syrup (see page 20).

In a cocktail shaker, combine the Tennessee whiskey, mezcal, Maple-Spiced Simple Syrup and lemon juice. Add some ice and shake. Strain into an ice-filled rocks glass and garnish with a lemon twist.

MILK PUNCH

(Serves 40 120-ml/4-oz servings)

This is a classic drink from New Orleans, where there is no wrong time to order one but the majority are consumed over brunch. And it really is a perfect brunch cocktail; the addition of some milk and sweetener makes it a great pairing with traditional beignets, waffles or a nice stack of pancakes. Start your weekend right like a true New Orleanian – with a Milk Punch in one hand and a cup of chicory coffee in the other.

Ingredients

60ml (2fl oz) bourbon
15ml (½fl oz) Simple Syrup (see page 20)
120ml (4fl oz) whole milk
1–2 drops of vanilla extract
1 nutmeg, for grating, to garnish

Instructions

Add the bourbon, Simple Syrup, milk and vanilla extract to a cocktail shaker. Add some ice and shake for 1 minute. Strain into a chilled coupe or martini glass and garnish with grated nutmeg.

Milk
FRESH

PURE
VANILLA
EXTRACT

CLARIFIED MILK PUNCH

(Serves 40 90-ml/3-oz servings)

While the Milk Punch hearkens back to yesteryear, the Clarified Milk Punch is a modern interpretation that is definitely worth the work. Probably the most complex preparation in this book, this recipe is also the most rewarding, as it offers a peek behind the curtain at one of the techniques that many avant-garde bartenders use with molecular mixology – milk washing. While it may sound absurd, this technique works well, creating a drink that is both visually stunning and delicious. There is no way you can fail to impress your guests with this cocktail.

Ingredients

11 lemons
700ml (24fl oz) bourbon
700ml (24fl oz) blended Scotch whisky
450ml (16fl oz) freshly squeezed lemon juice
900ml (32fl oz) water
340g (12oz) caster sugar
1 whole nutmeg
2 cinnamon sticks
1 star anise
700ml (24fl oz) whole milk

Instructions

Day one: Peel the lemons with a Y-shaped vegetable peeler, avoiding the bitter white pith. Combine the peels with the whiskies in a jar or bowl, cover and let it rest in the refrigerator for 24 hours.

Day two: Strain the peels out of the whisky mixture, add the lemon juice, sugar and water and stir until the sugar is dissolved. Grate the nutmeg and break up the cinnamon sticks and star anise into the mix. Bring the milk to a boil in a large pan, and as soon as it is boiling, add the spirits and lemon juice mixture. Stir a bit to dissolve any remaining sugar, then turn off the heat and let the milk curdle. Let it sit with a cover on the pan for a couple of hours. Using lots of cheesecloth, strain the milk solids out of the punch. Working in small batches, run the punch through the cheesecloth, regularly rinsing the cloth as needed. Cover and refrigerate the punch until any remaining sediment settles (about 2 hours). Ladle the punch into a clean bottle or serving container and keep refrigerated. To serve, pour over a large ice cube or drink neat in an old fashioned glass.

EGGNOG

(Serves 8 120-ml/4-oz servings)

Originally a British tradition, this drink eventually found its way to the United States. Usually consumed around Christmas, Eggnog is descended from 'posset'- a hot drink made with ale. The origin of the name 'Eggnog' remains elusive; some think 'nog' was a style of beer brewed in England, while others believe it is descended from 'noggin' – a small wooden mug used for consuming ale in the 1800s. Whatever the lineage, Eggnog is a holiday staple and one worth mastering. This recipe will yield an Eggnog far superior to any commercial varieties and is sure to impress your friends and neighbours. This drink is best made a few days before serving, so that the flavours have a chance to get to know each other. The extra time and effort are worth it.

Ingredients

4 large eggs
170g (6oz) granulated sugar
1 tsp freshly grated nutmeg
⅛ tsp ground allspice
⅛ tsp ground cloves
½ tsp ground cinnamon
60ml (2fl oz) Hennessy VSOP cognac
60ml (2fl oz) Grand Marnier
120ml (4fl oz) Bulleit bourbon
340ml (12fl oz) whole milk
225ml (8fl oz) double cream

Instructions

Crack the eggs into a large blender and pulse until blended. Then slowly work your way down the ingredients list (in order), adding each item until they are all incorporated, for a total blending time of about 5 minutes. Serve immediately in punch cups or glass mugs with grated nutmeg.

OPEN HERE
FESTIVE & DELICIOUS
EGG NOG
WITH BOURBON,
HENNESSY & GRAND MARNIER

FINE ★ MALT
LAPHROAIG
OLD ISLAY WHISKY
JOHN ANDERSON & Co
101. High Street.
ELGIN.
TRADE
MARK

ISLAY HOT CHOCOLATE

This drink is an easy gem that is perfect for a very cold night. Choose any Islay Scotch whisky that you like (note for any non-Scots: Islay is pronounced 'Eye-luh' not 'iss-lay'!), and combine with good-quality hot chocolate. It's simple, easy and delicious, and the sweetness of the chocolate tempers the bold smoke and peat that Islay Scotch is famous for. Rumour has it that this is Santa's favourite tipple after a hard night of delivering presents, so don't be afraid to substitute this for his usual glass of milk.

Ingredients

60ml (2fl oz) Islay single malt Scotch whisky
120ml (4fl oz) good-quality brewed hot chocolate
whipped cream, to garnish

Instructions

Pour the Islay Scotch into a coffee mug and top with the hot chocolate prepared according to packet instructions or personal preference. Garnish with whipped cream just before serving.

IRISH COFFEE

This cocktail can trace its origin back to Shannon Airport in the 1950s, where it was first created by Joe Sheridan to warm up a group of cold and travel-weary American travellers. Back home, two San Franciscans, writer Stanton Delaplane and Jack Koeppler – the owner of a local bar, called the Buena Vista – set out to recreate the drink they had first tasted back in Shannon. Eventually, the two men hit on the perfect combination of coffee, sugar, Irish whiskey (no substitutions, please!) and whipped cream. The drink became such a hit at the Buena Vista (which serves up to 2,000 Irish coffees a day) that this increase in demand eventually helped to revive the flagging fortunes of the Irish whiskey industry. All from one little drink. So while you sip, take a moment to reflect on how two friends half a world away may have inadvertently saved the Irish whiskey industry and raise a toast to Misters Delaplane and Koeppler.

Ingredients

45ml (1 ½fl oz) Irish whiskey
15ml (½fl oz) Brown Sugar Simple Syrup (see page 20)
120ml (4fl oz) freshly brewed black coffee
whipped cream, to garnish

Instructions

Into a heatproof mug, pour the Irish whiskey and Simple Syrup. Top with the freshly brewed coffee. Then, using a barspoon, carefully pour whipped cream off the back of the spoon onto the surface of the coffee so that the cream floats. Serve hot.

IRISH COFFEE

KENTUCKY STRAIGHT
BOURBON
WHISKEY
AGED 20 YEARS
700ml 90.2 PROOF

ARTISAN
HONEY

HOT TODDY

This is a drink that has been used to take the chill off one's bones and to cure what ails since perhaps the very creation of whisky itself. It is the kind of drink that would have been served in 18th-century taverns and inns across Scotland, with the mugful of water heated by a large piece of iron called a loggerhead, which was kept in the fireplace just for the purpose. But don't let its simplicity fool you – this drink is far more than the single ingredients. Once you've mastered the toddy, feel free to play around with variations. You can easily substitute the hot water for your favourite tea (I recommend Earl Grey) or switch the honey for another sweetener.

Ingredients

30ml (1fl oz) honey
15ml (½fl oz) freshly squeezed lemon juice
45ml (1½fl oz) whisky
60ml (2fl oz) hot water
a cinnamon stick, to garnish
½ lemon wheel studded with cloves, to garnish

Instructions

Into a heatproof glass mug, pour the honey, lemon juice and whisky. Add the hot water and stir to combine. Garnish with a cinnamon stick and the half lemon wheel studded with cloves. Serve hot.

LONDON FOG

(Serves 24 120-ml/4-oz servings)

This classic yet simple ice-cream-based drink is perfect for parties. All you need is a punch bowl, some vanilla ice cream and coffee (cold-brew works best, but don't let it prevent you from making this if you don't have any around), decent whiskey and a ladle. Questions about the origin of this drink abound, but many credit computer programmer Ward Cunningham, developer of the world's first wiki, for popularising the drink by serving it as his signature cocktail at holiday gatherings. No matter how it came about, this is a great party drink that is certain to impress a crowd.

Ingredients

2 litres (½ gallon) drippy vanilla ice cream (leave out of the freezer for at least 35 minutes)
475ml (16fl oz) bourbon
475ml (16fl oz) cold-brewed coffee

Instructions

Combine the ice cream, bourbon and coffee in a punch bowl. Stir occasionally as the ice cream melts. Serve in punch cups. This cocktail is to be drunk, but a spoon can also be used.

WHISKEY

90
BOURBON
WHISKE
6% ALCOHOL 373
LONDON
FOG
LONDON
FOG
DELICIOUS
Ice Cream
VANILLA

INDEX

CREDITS

Lance J. Mayhew would like to thank:
For Amelia, Samuel and Charlotte, my pride and joy. Chase your dreams. Raena, my rock, I love you like a tomato. Mom, Dad, Wayne and Denise, thank you for all that you have done and continue to do. Richard DellaPenna, Joseph 'Moose' Morante, Dave Cupps and Chris Curtis – the bartenders who inspired and mentored me. Jacob Grier and Ky Belk, great bartenders and even better people. Father Mike Biewend and the entire Madeleine Parish and School for their unceasing support and love. John Zimmer and Jennifer Moore, Paul and Manda Hardy, Steve Mendiola and Jason and Grace Thornton. If the measure of a person is the friends one has, then I am a very lucky man. Takesuke Naito and Mike Dunne, thanks for putting up with me. Terry Boyd and Matt Wilcox, who make radio seem far easier than it really is and gave me the chance to make cocktails on air and tell embarrassing stories about myself. Caitlin Doyle, the best editor I've ever had the pleasure to work with; thank you for your patience and kindness. And lastly, thank you dear reader, without whom this book would just be words on paper. *'You miss 100% of the shots you don't take.'— Wayne Gretzky*

Ruby Taylor would like to thank:
For all the love, support (and drinks) always; Katie Price, Nancy Edmondson, Billie Alder, Ella Antebi, Roxanne Simmonds, Pema Seely, Ellie Yates, Anita Kershaw.

The publisher would like to toast:
Gareth and Jacqui for the excellent design. Lance for being such an ease to work with. And Ruby for her boundless creativity. Tim Doyle for his Rat Pack Manhattan. Stewart 'It's pronounced *Oh-Bin'* Rassier. Jason Gresalfi and Danny Trenz, for early lessons in bourbon. And cheers from Meghan to Howe's Bayou for the ultimate Sazerac.